P9-ASJ-645

# BSCS PUBLICATIONS

## HIGH SCHOOL BIOLOGY: BSCS Green Version
RAND MᶜNALLY & COMPANY, Chicago

BIOLOGICAL SCIENCE: AN INQUIRY INTO LIFE (BSCS Yellow Version), Harcourt, Brace and World, Inc., New York

BIOLOGICAL SCIENCE: MOLECULES TO MAN (BSCS Blue Version), Houghton Mifflin Company, Boston

BSCS QUARTERLY TESTS
available from the version publishers

BSCS COMPREHENSIVE FINAL EXAMINATION (two alternate forms), available from the version publishers

PROCESSES OF SCIENCE TEST (for all versions), The Psychological Corporation, New York

BIOLOGICAL SCIENCE: PATTERNS AND PROCESSES (BSCS Special Materials), Holt, Rinehart & Winston, Inc., New York

BSCS UNIT TESTS AND FINAL EXAMINATION FOR BIOLOGICAL SCIENCE: PATTERNS AND PROCESSES, The Psychological Corporation, New York

BIOLOGICAL SCIENCE: INTERACTION OF EXPERIMENTS AND IDEAS (BSCS Second Course), Prentice-Hall, Inc., Englewood Cliffs, N.J.

BSCS LABORATORY BLOCKS (12 titles), D. C. Heath & Company, Boston

RESEARCH PROBLEMS IN BIOLOGY: INVESTIGATIONS FOR STUDENTS (Series 1–4), Doubleday & Company, Inc., Garden City, N.Y.

INNOVATIONS IN EQUIPMENT AND TECHNIQUES FOR THE BIOLOGY TEACHING LABORATORY, D. C. Heath & Company, Boston

BSCS TECHNIQUES FILMS (10 titles), Thorne Films, Boulder, Colo.

BSCS SINGLE TOPIC FILMS, Rand McNally & Company, Chicago; Harcourt, Brace and World, Inc., New York; Houghton Mifflin Company, Boston

STORY OF THE BSCS (information film), BSCS, Boulder, Colo.

BIOLOGY TEACHERS' HANDBOOK, John Wiley & Sons, Inc., New York

BSCS PAMPHLET SERIES (24 titles), D. C. Heath & Company, Boston

BSCS PATTERNS OF LIFE SERIES, Rand McNally & Company, Chicago

BSCS BULLETIN SERIES (Nos. 1–3), BSCS, Boulder, Colo.

BSCS SPECIAL PUBLICATIONS (Nos. 1–5), BSCS, Boulder, Colo.

BSCS NEWSLETTER, BSCS, Boulder, Colo.

BSCS INTERNATIONAL NEWS NOTES, BSCS, Boulder, Colo.

BIOLOGICAL SCIENCES CURRICULUM STUDY • *University of Colorado, Boulder*
P. O. Box 930
Boulder, Colorado

*Revision Team:*
   HAVEN KOLB, Hereford High School, Parkton, Maryland, *Supervisor*
   NORRIS A. ANDERSON, Burlingame High School, Burlingame, California
   RICHARD G. BEIDLEMAN, Colorado College, Colorado Springs, Colorado
   CHARLES BUTTERFIELD, Brattleboro Union High School, Brattleboro, Vermont*
   DONALD S. FARNER, University of Washington, Seattle, Washington
   VICTOR LARSEN, Adelphi University, Garden City, New York
   WILLIAM V. MAYER, Biological Sciences Curriculum Study, Boulder, Colorado
   ELRA M. PALMER, Baltimore City Public Schools, Baltimore, Maryland
   ELIZABETH PERROTT, University of Stirling, Stirling, Scotland
   PAUL G. PEARSON, Rutgers, The State University, New Brunswick, New Jersey
   PRESTON WHITE, Brattleboro Union High School, Brattleboro, Vermont*

   *Mr. Butterfield and Mr. White joined the teacher's guide revision team in 1968.*

*Editors:*   WILLIAM B. MILLER and CAROL LETH
         Rand McNally & Company, Chicago, Illinois

**BSCS GREEN VERSION**

# HIGH SCHOOL BIOLOGY

SECOND EDITION

# *Teacher's Guide*

RAND McNALLY & COMPANY

*Chicago*

*Printed in the United States of America*

Prepared by BSCS

Printed and published by
Rand McNally & Company

For permissions and other rights
under this copyright, please write
the BSCS, P.O. Box 930,
Boulder, Colorado 80302

## THE WRITERS

More than one hundred high school and university teachers participated in writing the experimental forms of this book in 1960 and 1961. Their names are listed in the first commercial edition (1963). That edition was produced by a team consisting of:

HAROLD DURST, Southeast High School, Wichita, Kansas

HAVEN KOLB, Overlea High School, Baltimore County, Maryland (*Supervisor*)

VICTOR LARSEN, Adelphi University, Garden City, New York

WILLIAM MILLER, Rand McNally & Company, Chicago

ELRA M. PALMER, Baltimore City Public Schools, Baltimore, Maryland

JONATHAN WESTFALL, University of Georgia, Athens, Georgia

The members of the revision team for the 1968 edition are listed on the title page.


## THE BSCS STAFF (Current)

ARNOLD B. GROBMAN, *Chairman,* BSCS Steering Committee

WILLIAM V. MAYER, *Director*

MANERT H. KENNEDY, Associate Director

GEORGE M. CLARK, Assistant Director for Fiscal Affairs

KEITH L. BUMSTED, Business Manager

THOMAS J. CLEAVER, Consultant

BERT A. KEMPERS, Consultant

GLEN E. PETERSON, Consultant

## ILLUSTRATIONS STAFF

Robert F. Wilson, *Art Director*
Lawrence Strand, Assistant Art Director
Roy M. Udo
Linda G. Boley*
James E. Bramlett*
Eugene J. Diodato, Jr.*
Margery A. Gardephe*
Eldridge Hardie*
Robert G. Haynes*
Laney Hicks*
Gary J. Keimig*
Robert T. Kusserow*
Jane Larson* (Former Art Director)
Sheng-Hing Lee*
Raymond S. Orosz*
Kent Pendleton*
D. Phillip Willette*
*Formerly on Illustrations Staff

## RAND MCNALLY

William B. Miller and Carol Leth, *Editors*
Roberta McAllister, Copy Editor
Gordon Hartshorne and Elizabeth Riedel, Designers
Karen Olson, Picture Editor

# REVIEWERS

**A.** A number of biological societies appointed reviewers whose comments have been helpful in preparing the revision:

**American Association of Physical Anthropologists:** Dr. Robert Ascher, Cornell University, Ithaca, New York; Dr. William Laughlin, University of Wisconsin, Madison, Wisconsin; Dr. Lawrence Oschinsky (deceased), University of Toronto, Toronto, Canada

**American Physiological Society and Society of General Physiologists:** Dr. Robert D. Allen, Princeton University, Princeton, New Jersey; Dr. Leon Goldstein, Harvard Medical School, Boston, Massachusetts; Dr. Eugene M. Renkin, Duke University Medical Center, Durham, North Carolina; Dr. R. R. Ronkin, University of Delaware, Newark, Delaware; Dr. William G. Van der Kloot, New York University School of Medicine, New York, New York

**American Phytopathological Society:** Dr. E. H. Barnes, Michigan State University, East Lansing, Michigan; Dr. Carl Boothroyd, Cornell University, Ithaca, New York; Dr. R. J. Campana, University of Maine, Orono, Maine; Dr. J. L. Dale, University of Arkansas, Fayetteville, Arkansas; Dr. Ralph J. Green, Jr., Purdue University, Lafayette, Indiana

**American Society of Agronomy:** Dr. Frank Himes, Ohio State University, Columbus, Ohio; Dr. Darrell A. Miller, North Carolina State University, Raleigh, North Carolina

**American Society of Animal Science:** Dr. Duane Acker, Kansas State University, Manhattan, Kansas; Dr. A. W. Burger, University of Illinois, Urbana, Illinois

**American Society for Horticultural Science:** Dr. W. A. Sistrunk, University of Arkansas, Fayetteville, Arkansas

**American Society for Microbiology:** Dr. David E. Contois, University of Hawaii, Honolulu, Hawaii; Dr. Gordon Roberstad, South Dakota State University, Brookings, South Dakota; Dr. Kenneth Temple, Montana State College, Bozeman, Montana

**American Society of Range Management:** Dr. Wayne McCully, Texas A & M University, College Station, Texas

**Botanical Society of America:** Dr. Adolph Hecht, Washington State University, Pullman, Washington; Dr. John Mooring, University of Santa Clara, Santa Clara, California; Dr. Irwin Spear, University of Texas, Austin, Texas

**Central Association of Science and Mathematics Teachers:** Mr. Louis E. Shrode, Oak Park – River Forest High School, Oak Park, Illinois

**Chemical Education Materials Study:** Mr. Robert L. French, Westminster High School, Westminster, California; Dr. Richard Merrill, Albany, California

**Entomological Society of America:** Dr. Robert V. Travis, Mainesburg, Pennsylvania; Dr. Howard Owens, Prince George's County, Maryland

**Mycological Society of America:** Dr. Robert W. Lichtwardt, University of Kansas, Lawrence, Kansas; Dr. Arthur L. Weldon, Tulane University, New Orleans, Louisiana

**National Catholic Educational Association:** Sister Julia Marie Van Denack, O.S.F., Holy Family College, Manitowoc, Wisconsin

**National Science Supervisors Association:** Mr. Richard Kay, Idaho State Department of Education, Boise, Idaho; Mr. John Leake, Jefferson City, Missouri; Mr. LaVar Sorensen, Supervisor of Science, Salt Lake City Public Schools, Utah

**Society of American Foresters:** Mr. Stanley Jepsen, Chevy Chase, Maryland; Dr. Orie L. Loucks, Department of Botany, University of Wisconsin, Madison, Wisconsin; Dr. Harrison H. Payne, State University College of Forestry, Syracuse, New York

**B.** The following individuals reviewed all or part of the 1963 edition:

DR. DAVID AUSUBEL, University of Illinois, Urbana, Illinois

DR. ROBERT M. W. TRAVERS, Western Michigan University, Kalamazoo, Michigan

**C.** The following individuals provided consultant service on aspects of the 1968 revision:

DR. HARRY BRENOWITZ, Adelphi University, Garden City, New York

MISS NINETTE CAMENS, Adelphi University, Garden City, New York

DR. DELAPHINE WYCKOFF, Wellesley College, Wellesley, Massachusetts

**D.** In 1965 and 1966 the following high school teachers attended feedback meetings, where their interaction in criticism of the 1963 edition provided the background for revision:

FOSTER AARON, Burr & Burton Seminary, Manchester, Vermont
VERYL ALLEN, Salida High School, Salida, Colorado
VIRGINIA F. ALLEN, P. K. Yonge School, Gainesville, Florida
GARY G. ALLENSTEIN, Badger High School, Lake Geneva, Wisconsin
JAY ANDERSON, Powell County High School, Deer Lodge, Montana
DONALD B. ASH, Pleasant Grove High School, Pleasant Grove, Utah
LAWRENCE E. BACH, Ithaca High School, Ithaca, New York
JAY M. BERNHISEL, Fort Bragg High School, Fort Bragg, California
PAUL A. BRICKER, Coronado High School, Scottsdale, Arizona
DOROTHY L. BROCK, West Fulton High School, Atlanta, Georgia
GEORGE R. CARMICHAEL, JR., Medill Bair High School, Fairless Hills, Pennsylvania
MARTIN CHRISTIE, Lee High School, Springfield, Virginia
KERMIT DAUM, Derby Senior High School, Derby, Kansas
GEORGE DAWSON, Waggener High School, Louisville, Kentucky
HARRY DAWSON, McMinnville High School, McMinnville, Oregon
ROBERT DeBISHOP, Southington High School, Southington, Connecticut
R. EHLI, Billings Central High School, Billings, Montana
CAROL JOY ERICSON, Middleburg Heights, Ohio
LLOYD G. FARINASH, JR., Parkersburg High School, Parkersburg, West Virginia
DONALD R. GARREN, Sullivan High School, Sullivan, Illinois
BARBARA K. HOPPER, Cleveland High School, Reseda, California
R. DeWITT IVEY, Sandia High School, Albuquerque, New Mexico
VICTOR LaCOURSE, Mount Edgecumbe High School, Mount Edgecumbe, Alaska
ROBERT LYONS, Wheatridge High School, Wheatridge, Colorado
EDNA L. MEADOWS, Stephen Decatur High School, Decatur, Illinois
HENRY E. MELTON, Crisp County High School, Cordele, Georgia
MERLIN MILLPACK, Ogden Senior High School, Ogden, Utah
TY MINTON, Putney School, Putney, Vermont
HILDA B. NEWMAN, Tyner High School, Tyner, Tennessee
ART PAPENFUSS, Golden Senior High School, Golden, Colorado
ELIZABETH PENTON, Holmes County High School, Bonifay, Florida
JERRY PETERSON, Franklin Senior High School, Livonia, Michigan
VERA B. REMSBURG, Herndon High School, Herndon, Virginia
RICHARD W. SCHUETT, North High School, Omaha, Nebraska
KENNETH L. SHIRLEY, Ben Lomond High, Ogden, Utah
ANNAJEAN SLATER, Valley Forge High School, Parma Heights, Ohio
GLEN E. SOULIER, Hillcrest High School, Midvale, Utah
JIMMIE STOTHART, Coushatta High School, Coushatta, Louisiana
ROSEMARY B. STROTHER, Clarke County Jr. High School, Athens, Georgia
GERALD TAGUE, East High School, Wichita, Kansas
SISTER M. TOMAIS, O.P., St. Mary's High School, Cheyenne, Wyoming
EDWARD D. TRINER, Carl Sandburg High School, Orland Park, Illinois
WILLARD L. UNSTADTER, JR., Glen Rock High School, Glen Rock, New Jersey
EDGAR WARREN, South High School, Denver, Colorado
DOROTHY WENDT, Waipahu High School, Honolulu, Hawaii
PRESTON WHITE, Brattleboro Union High School, Brattleboro, Vermont

## ACKNOWLEDGMENT

The revisors are grateful to Mrs. Martha Phillips for her work in preparing the original typescript.

# A FOREWORD

We live in an age of science, and it is essential that students of today, who will occupy positions of leadership in the twenty-first century, have the background of a modern and forward-looking program in science. As biology may be the first, last, and only science to which the majority of students are exposed in their formal education, it must be accurate and modern in biological content and must instill a comprehension of both science and the scientific enterprise.

For years many of our better teachers have been expressing dissatisfaction with the tools with which they have had to work. They wanted to teach modern biology in an imaginative, investigative, and inquiry-oriented fashion, but the texts available to them fostered the rote memorization of lists of names, facts, and dates. This decade has witnessed a spectacular improvement in biological education, and the Biological Sciences Curriculum Study has played an important role in that improvement. The Biological Sciences Curriculum Study was organized to improve biological education at all levels of instruction.

The initial goal of the BSCS was the production of classroom materials for average students in a first course in biology at the secondary school level. The materials were structured around a series of major themes: science as investigation and inquiry; the history of biological concepts; complementarity of structure and function; diversity of type and unity of pattern; change of organisms through time as evolution; genetic continuity; the complementarity of the organism and its environment; regulation and homeostasis; and the biological basis of behavior. These themes were presented through the use of a variety of organisms best illustrating the concept in question. Thus, use of microorganisms, plants, and animals conveys the pervasiveness of these themes in all living things. At the same time, cognizance needs be taken of a balanced consideration of all levels of organization of life—from the molecule through cells, tissues, organs, individuals, populations, species, communities, and the world biome. It is the interweaving of the themes with organisms and levels of organization that gives biology a structure as a science. Recognition of this structure makes possible a series of patterns that tremendously increase the effectiveness of instruction in biology. Each program includes materials selected for their applicability in the latter half of the twentieth century and their ability to illuminate the principles and concepts that underlie biological science. The BSCS program presents a balanced approach to the science of biology without presenting excessive details. Content has been carefully selected by learned biologists and educators as that most contributory to understanding the basics of biological science.

The first experimental editions of three versions of BSCS books were completed in 1960 and were tested in approximately 100 schools throughout the country. From this experience, the three experimental versions were revised in 1961 and subjected to trials in 500 schools during the 1961–62 school year and in 950 schools the following year. After three years of extensive trial and revision, the three experimental versions were reorganized to become the commercially published editions that appeared in 1963.

The present book is a complete revision of one of the 1963 versions and is based upon feedback of the last five years together with the most recent scientific information available. The BSCS deeply appreciates the singularly important contributions to the improvement of biological education made by 1,000 teachers and 150,000 students who used the experimental editions and reported their experiences to us. Over two million pupils have studied from the first editions of these books; to them and their teachers the BSCS is indebted for many constructive suggestions that have been incorporated in the present volumes.

A unique BSCS contribution to the development of teaching materials for high school biology has been a fruitful cooperation between college biologists on the frontiers of research and high school teachers on the frontiers of teaching. This cooperation has continued over a period of years. The procedure of producing text materials, with the active involvement of cooperative teams of writers and extensive classroom testing, has obvious advantages over the work of either a single author or small groups of authors. It could not have been accomplished without the support provided the BSCS by the National Science Foundation.

In addition to the three versions of a first high school biology program (including text materials, integrated laboratory exercises, quarterly tests, a comprehensive examination, and teacher's guides), the BSCS has produced a wide variety of course materials that offer the teacher maximal flexibility in programming—and the student, optimal use of his talents.

The BSCS is a continuing curriculum study concerned with the improvement of biological education. It welcomes observations from interested persons, and such comments may be sent to the Director, at the University of Colorado.

Arnold B. Grobman
*Chairman*, Steering Committee
Biological Sciences Curriculum Study
Rutgers, The State University
New Brunswick, New Jersey 08903

William V. Mayer, *Director*
Biological Sciences Curriculum Study
Post Office Box 930
Boulder, Colorado 80302

# PREFACE

In 1963 we wrote:

For four years the team charged by the Biological Sciences Curriculum Study with the development of the *Green Version* has had the advice and assistance of high school biology teachers, college biology teachers, research biologists, psychologists, and many others. The team hopes that this magnificent example of academic cooperation will be perpetuated. Curriculum evaluation, curriculum development, curriculum revision, can never safely cease. Every student, every teacher, every reviewer of the educational program, is invited to contribute to the obsolescence of these materials.

But the team would like to keep abreast of the tide of change. Criticisms, comments, and calumnies may be addressed either to the Biological Sciences Curriculum Study, University of Colorado, Boulder, or to the publisher.

The invitation extended in those paragraphs was heartily accepted. The result is the edition of 1968. In prefacing this edition, the revision team can do no better than echo those words of our predecessors.

HAVEN KOLB, *Supervisor*

NORRIS A. ANDERSON

RICHARD G. BEIDLEMAN

CHARLES BUTTERFIELD

DONALD S. FARNER

VICTOR LARSEN

WILLIAM V. MAYER

ELRA M. PALMER

PAUL G. PEARSON

ELIZABETH PERROTT

PRESTON WHITE

*Parkton, Maryland*
*October 15, 1968*

# INTRODUCTION

More than a decade has passed since that pattern of change of which the Biological Sciences Curriculum Study has been a part appeared upon the American educational scene. SMSG, PSSC, BSCS, CHEMS, CBA, ESCP—a long and still lengthening line of acronyms stands as an unimaginative facade behind which a revolution in curriculum construction has occurred.

There is no need here to elaborate upon the nature of this revolution. This has been done in part elsewhere (cf. John I. Goodlad, *The Changing School Curriculum.* New York: The Fund for the Advancement of Education, 1966). But it is necessary to point out that *High School Biology: BSCS Green Version* is a product of these times and therefore a special sort of educational tool. The effectiveness of any tool—of all the new hardware and software of expanding educational technology —depends upon the skill of the user, and this skill must be developed independently for each tool. The *Green Version* student's book is no exception. Skill in making study assignments in a textbook is scarcely more relevant to its use than skill in wielding a scythe is relevant to modern wheat harvesting.

The skills required for successful modern science teaching have been under close study by science educators. Here and there the results of these researches are beginning to be applied in teacher-preparation programs. And teacher education is the field in which the next great advance in science education must surely occur. But in the meantime thousands of teachers require all the aid they can get if they are to provide a high-quality science education for their students. This book is one such aid.

The greater part — Part Two — of this guide is made up of comments, advice, and background information on specific teaching problems, taken chapter by chapter and page by page. But a competent teacher demands a rationale. Therefore, Part One begins with a general statement of the philosophy of the Biological Sciences Curriculum Study. Then, against this background, it presents the points of view that are particularly stressed in the *Green Version* and the principal classroom strategies that are necessary for obtaining optimal outcomes.

The content of this guide has been determined largely by the teachers who have used previous editions. Especially helpful have been comments received from users of the 1963 edition, most of whom had had little or no direct instruction in teaching BSCS biology. Many of these comments were received through spontaneous correspondence. In preparation for the 1968 revision, four day-and-a-half conferences were held with selected *Green Version* teachers (listed on a previous page), and from these came many suggestions for the teacher's guide as well as for the student's materials. Further, advice has been received from those who work for the improvement of instruction with teachers and with teachers-in-training.

Such widely sought counsel has inevitably contained conflicts. And limitations of space have prevented the use of every suggestion. It cannot be expected, therefore, that the guide will be found adequate by all teachers. Of course, nothing can substitute for the energy, zeal, and vision of the professional teacher — and no book can make a teacher. But we believe that all teachers can obtain benefits — great or little — from the *Green Version Teacher's Guide*.

# FOR THOSE WHO USED THE 1963 EDITION

Part One of this teacher's guide is addressed primarily to new users of the *BSCS Green Version*. The authors believe that teachers who have had experience with the 1963 edition require initially a short summary of new features in the 1968 edition. They may then glance over the revised Part One when time permits.

*Organization.* Chapter 11 of the 1963 edition has been dropped, but some of its material has been incorporated into Chapter 8. Chapter 12 of the 1963 edition has been divided into two chapters. The new Chapter 11 retains materials on the development of the cell theory, on cell structure, on the movement of substances into cells, and on cell duplication. Chapter 12 is concerned with cell biochemistry, particularly the transfer of energy. It includes the biochemistry of photosynthesis, which was a part of Chapter 13 in 1963. The chapter on behavior (Chapter 18 in 1963) has been added to Section Four as Chapter 15. The chapter on reproduction (Chapter 15 in 1963) has been grouped with the chapters on genetics and on mechanisms of evolution to make a new Section Five (now Chapters 16, 17, and 18) concerned with continuity of the biosphere. This change is largely one of emphasis rather than material.

*Laboratory.* The laboratory manual has been integrated with the textbook. In the single student's book the laboratory investigations are woven into the textual materials. Investigations are considered as essential as the intervening reading matter, and all investigations are considered equally important. Several of the laboratory investigations are new (5.1, 12.1, 12.2, 12.3, 12.5, 13.2, 15.2, 15.3, 18.3), and all have been carefully rewritten in the light of classroom experience. The materials in the introduction of the 1963 manual are found in the Preface and in Appendix I of the 1968 student's book.

*Technical vocabulary.* Some terms have been dropped, some have been added, and better synonyms have been adopted for others. The principal terms dropped are: *alimentation, anaerobic respiration, cytoplasm, deamination, hydrosphere, kinetic energy, lithosphere, mycelium, osmosis, potential energy, protoplasm, symbiosis.* The general term *saprovore* replaces the terms *decomposer* and *scavenger. Dynamic equilibrium* is replaced by *steady state,* and the related term *homeostasis* is added. In accordance with recent biochemical practice, *TPN* becomes *NADP* and the older enzyme nomenclature is revised (e.g., *pepsin* becomes *gastric proteinase; sucrase, maltase,* and *lactase* become *disaccharidases*).

*Style.* A great effort has been made to retain the flowing and reasoning style of the earlier edition, but probably no paragraph and perhaps scarcely a sentence remains exactly as it was in 1963. The revisors have attempted three things. First, they have cut excessive wordiness. Second, they have used the classroom experience of many teachers to reorganize wording of sentences and to reconstruct paragraphs for greater clarity. Third, they have eliminated the definite article where it tended to encourage typological thinking.

*Miscellaneous.* For most chapters the list of "Guide Questions" has been augmented. To the marginal materials have been added a considerable number of questions intended to encourage an investigative and reflective attitude toward study. Suggestions "For Further Investigation" have been increased in number.

# CONTENTS

---

# THE COURSE:
# GENERAL CONSIDERATIONS

# THE BIOLOGICAL SCIENCES CURRICULUM STUDY

Considering the pace at which science and science education have been proceeding, the early development of the BSCS has become almost ancient history in 1968. Yet the conditions that brought about the BSCS's organization and the way in which it developed are still relevant to proper understanding and use of the latest revision of its materials. At this point the teacher unfamiliar with the story should at least read our Foreword, by Drs. Mayer and Grobman. Later, he should consult fuller accounts, for example, Grobman's forthcoming *The Curriculum Study and American Education: The Story of the Biological Sciences Curriculum Study* (publisher to be announced). A concise account of BSCS philosophy and rationale may be found in Cox's *Patterns for the Preparation of BSCS Biology Teachers*, Special Publication #2, BSCS, Boulder, Colorado, 1963.

## OBJECTIVES

The determination of educational objectives is a creative and continuing process. In all fields, objectives need to be continually under scrutiny. In the field of science this is especially true. Not only is science itself changing at an accelerating rate, but its relation to society has been altering rapidly in a period during which educational objectives have only slowly shifted.

In the determination of objectives for science education, biological science plays a crucial role because biology touches more students at the high school level than does any other science. For a large proportion of students, the objectives of science education are the objectives of their high school biology course, since they will receive no further formal instruction in science after they leave their biology classrooms.

Early in its work, therefore, the BSCS Steering Committee directed attention toward the study of objectives in high school biology-teaching. To provide a background, Dr. Paul Hurd studied the history of biology-teaching in the United States. (Hurd, Paul deHart. *Biological Education in American Secondary Schools, 1890 – 1960.* Boulder, Colo.: Biological Sciences Curriculum Study, 1961.)

On the basis of this study, and after deep consideration of the present state of science, society, and the American educational system, a BSCS committee formulated objectives that guided the initial development of the BSCS curricular materials. Through succeeding revisions these objectives have been refined and restated. For the present they may be listed as follows:

1. An understanding of the nature of scientific inquiry: Science is an open-ended intellectual activity, and what is presently "known" or believed is subject to change at any time.

2. An understanding of the limitations of science and of the scientific method: Some problems of great importance cannot be dealt with scientifically.

3. An understanding of the diversity of life and of the interrelations of all organisms.

4. An appreciation of the beauty, drama, and tragedy of the living world.

5. An understanding of the biological bases of problems in medicine, public health, agriculture, and conservation.

6. An understanding of the historical development of biological concepts and their dependence upon the nature of the society and technology of each age.

7. An understanding of man's own place in nature: namely, that he is a living organism, that he has much in common with other organisms, and that he interacts with all organisms in the biological system of the earth.

## CONTENT

The content of biology is vast. The BSCS Steering Committee recognized that the task of selection could be accomplished only after work was begun on a course having some rationale of its own. The only alternative is an encyclopedic treatment which must necessarily be—in the space of a high school book—so telegraphic that it must also be almost meaningless. Therefore the committee chose to state content in the very broad form of themes—leitmotivs—to run through whatever organization of bi-

ological subject matter the authors might determine upon.

Being broadly stated, these themes, though not immutable, are less subject to change than more specific content is. For 1968 they remain much as in the 1963 edition:

1. Science as Inquiry

2. Change of Living Things through Time: Evolution

3. Regulation and Homeostasis: Preservation of Life in the Face of Change

4. Diversity of Type and Unity of Pattern in Living Things

5. The Complementarity of Organisms and Environment

6. The Complementarity of Structure and Function

7. The Genetic Continuity of Life

8. The Biological Roots of Behavior

9. The History of Biological Concepts

Despite differences in approach and sharp divergence in the backgrounds, attitudes, and temperaments of the writers, the content that has been incorporated into the three BSCS versions shows a high degree of overlap.

## SPIRIT

The selection of modern content cannot of itself ensure an approach to the objectives that have been outlined for BSCS biology. Far more important is the proper structuring of what goes on in classrooms.

Among these things, first rank was unanimously accorded by the BSCS Steering Committee to laboratory work. But this was not to be the sterile repetition of activities that excited Agassiz's students a century ago—such repetition serves only to restrict the modern student's views of biological science. Laboratory work for biology-teaching in the second half of the twentieth century must allow the student some insight into the real work of the present-day biologist; it must reflect the investigative, experimental approach of the scientific enterprise.

From this emphasis on investigative laboratory work later arose what has come to be the essence of BSCS biology-teaching: the spirit of inquiry. This involves the constant cultivation of a questioning attitude in both teacher and student. It is not so much a matter of the tools used in the classroom — textbooks, audiovisual aids, laboratory apparatus — as it is a *Weltanschauung*. The tools can aid or hinder it, but only the teacher can establish it and make it pervade the classroom. Perhaps because of this, much of the more recent work of the BSCS has tended to emphasize teacher education. And certainly because of this, the teacher's guides have become an indispensable part of BSCS biology courses.

\* \* \*

In these broad areas of objectives, content, and spirit, the BSCS Steering Committee has functioned. It has been left up to the writers of each version to translate them into courses. A large number of professional biologists and professional teachers have contributed to the shaping of the *BSCS Green Version* (see pages 5 – 8), and we turn now specifically to their work.

# THE *GREEN VERSION*

The word "ecology" was proposed by Ernst Haeckel in 1870 to cover what he called "outer physiology." It is the point of view in biology that takes the individual organism as the primary unit of study, and is concerned with how these individuals are organized into populations, species, and communities; with what organisms do and how they do it.

This contrasts with "inner physiology," the study of how the individual is constructed and how the parts work. Obviously the inside and outside of the organism are completely interdependent, and one cannot be understood without constant reference to the other. The division is arbitrary, but so are all of the ways in which biological subject matter might be split. We stress the outside rather than the inside on the assumption that this is more familiar and more easily understood. We believe, too, that it is more important for the citizen, who must participate in decisions about urban development, flood control, public health, conservation—always as a voter and sometimes as a member of the town council or state legislature.

For disorders of inner physiology the citizen should consult his physician. But there is no specialist for outer physiology, for disorders of the human biological community. Here each citizen shares responsibility, and biological knowledge is greatly needed for some kinds of decisions.

Thus wrote Dr. Marston Bates, the first supervisor of the BSCS team entrusted with the development of the high school biology course that was to become known as the *Green Version*. The statement appeared in the first experimental edition (1960). Sociological, educational, and biological events of the years that followed have given the statement even greater import.

## AIMS

Within the framework of the BSCS, the *Green Version* has been developed on the basis of the following facts: (a) The great majority of high school students take biology. (b) A large number of these students will take no more science in school. (c) Very few will become research biologists, and only a slightly larger proportion will enter the biological professions. (d) All are potential voting citizens.

To the revision team of 1968, these facts mean essentially the same things that they meant to our predecessors: that the high school biology course should encourage a scientific viewpoint in the student; that it should provide him with a background in biology that is as advanced as he is able to assimilate; that subject matter should be selected to increase his effectiveness as a future citizen as well as to help him assert himself in his universe. A course that does these things will serve the interests of all.

Clearly, the writers believe that secondary-school science should be presented as an aspect of the humanities. If, in some cases, a secondary-school course also arouses the student to pursue further biological studies, fine—but this should be an incidental rather than a primary aim. The high school is not the place to begin the training of biological scientists.

These general aims, logically derived from four simple and undeniable facts, are the foundation of the *Green Version*. They explain what is included and what is excluded. They explain the manner as well as the matter. Whoever undertakes to use the *Green Version* in his teaching needs to understand this position.

## SOME POINTS OF VIEW

In addition to the distinctive aims presented above, the successive members of the *Green Version* team have carried out their writing and revising with a number of special viewpoints constantly in mind. In part these derive from attitudes that have pervaded BSCS Steering Committee deliberations, and in part they derive from sources within the team.

**Level.** The course was planned for the middle 60 percent (in interest and ability) of tenth-grade students. For the lower range, the BSCS has developed special materials (*Biological Science: Patterns and Processes.* New York: Holt, Rinehart and Winston, 1966). No classroom course will completely satisfy the needs of the upper range of students. However, by wise use of the "Problems" and "Suggested Readings" appended to each chapter and of the suggestions "For Further Investigation" following many of the investigations, the teacher of the *Green Version* may carry such students beyond the classroom and into other BSCS materials. (See, for example, *Research Problems in Biology: Investigations for Students.*

4 vol. New York: Doubleday & Co., Inc., 1963–1965.)

Experience with previous editions has shown that the level sought has been attained, and careful attention was devoted to maintaining this level in the 1968 revision. In the tenth grade we are not teaching children, and we are not teaching adults. Teachers who regard tenth graders as children may be appalled by the degree of mental sophistication demanded in this course, by the lack of clear-cut definition, by the emphasis on chiaroscuro rather than on the black-and-white thought patterns whose beautiful simplicity we adults find so difficult to shake from our Greco-Hebraic heritage. On the other hand, teachers who ignore the difference between the adolescent and the adult may be scornful of the control of running vocabulary, the attention to development of ideas, the paucity of esoteric detail.

The title of the student's book simply and adequately describes it: one version of a biology course specifically designed for *high school* students.

**Scope.** The *Green Version* is not intended to provide an encyclopedic account of biology. Many topics are omitted; many are treated cursorily. But those topics that have seemed to the authors to best fit the aims discussed above have been developed in depth. For example, the ecological concept of infectious disease seems to be more important to a thinking citizenry than theories concerning the mechanisms of immunity. The ecosystem concept likewise seems more important than the electron microscopy of cells. So also, the concept of speciation against the decipherment of protein structure. In each case topics that are beautiful and exciting to the biological pioneers are slighted in favor of meat for the supporting troops. Yet, room has been left for the imaginative and adept teacher.

**Laboratory.** Paraphrasing an earlier statement by Dr. H. Bentley Glass, Chairman (1959–1966) of the BSCS Steering

Committee, the Preface "For the Student" clearly states the viewpoint of the *Green Version* writers. Laboratory work is *sine qua non* in this course.

A year might be devoted entirely to laboratory work. But the result would be either a myopic view of a narrow segment of biology or an episodic view such as might be obtained by glancing out a car window at a landscape every 50 miles. In the *Green Version* the text is used to provide continuity and perspective. Laboratory investigations are placed at points in the course where firsthand experience is most pertinent, most feasible, and most efficient in the utilization of student time.

"Laboratory" has been interpreted broadly. The laboratory is where the work of the scientist is done; it need not be bounded by four walls. Moreover, some of the investigations involve much reasoning and little or no doing. These also may be legitimately regarded as laboratory work.

**Continuity.** The course intentionally avoids the designation of its sections as "units"—paradoxically, it does so in order to unify. In practice, the unit organization tends to compartmentalize—though such was certainly not the original aim. In practice, the student takes the unit test, breathes a sigh of relief, and murmurs, "Now I can forget all that; tomorrow we start a new unit." And too often he has been quite correct.

The writers of the *Green Version* intend to give the student no relief at any time from the healthy tension of learning. The course is designed to build up ideas from beginning to end. Everywhere an effort is made to relate what is immediately in front of the student with what has preceded. At the end, the course returns to the beginning—like the Chinese dragon with its tail in its mouth—and relates all aspects of the course to a biological world view.

**Mensural units.** Long antedating the Iron Curtain, a "Mensural Screen" has divided the nations of the world into two camps. Even within nations this screen has divided scientist from engineer. For one camp the tide is running out, slowly but inexorably; economics, not science, is the moon in this affair.

In high school science it has been customary to *talk* about the metric system, to spend much time converting units from system to system, to express quantities in metric units during some laboratory procedures. But *consistent* use of the metric system has usually been lacking, and students have gained the impression that it is of ritualistic importance only—on a par with school-dress codes and academic gowns.

In the *Green Version* the metric system is used throughout. For explicatory purposes, equivalents are sometimes given; for designating a few pieces of equipment, sizes are expressed in British units. However, no exercises on conversion of units are offered. In this, a modern principle of language-teaching has been followed: "The word to the object, not to another word." We want the student to use centimeter measurements so frequently that he will have a mental image of 10 centimeters, not a recollection of "about 4 inches."

## THE STUDENT'S BOOK: AN OVERVIEW

Before specific suggestions for teaching can be meaningful, the teacher must be acquainted with the organization of the course, with variations in organization that experience has shown to be feasible, and with the teaching aids supplied to teacher and student. The following sections are intended to provide such general background.

### Organization

In the student's book sections and chapters are of unequal lengths, but the number of pages devoted to a topic is not necessarily an indication of that topic's relative importance or of the amount of time to be spent upon it. In general, the first three sections are discursive, with a rather low density of ideas. The last three are more compact, with an increasing load of ideas per page.

**Section One: THE WORLD OF LIFE: THE BIOSPHERE.** It is whole individual organisms with which the student has had experience. He is one himself. Therefore the course begins with biology at the level of the individual and treats the ways in which such biological units interact.

Chapter 1, "The Web of Life," is designed chiefly to lay some groundwork, to establish the direction of the course. The interdependence of organisms in the transfer of energy and in the cycling of matter, the interdependence of the living system and the physical environment — these things will never be stated again quite so explicitly, but they will persist in the background throughout the course. "Scientific method" is not preached; instead, the laboratory work is relied upon to introduce such basic matters as observation, measurement, experimentation, instrumentation.

The units of ecological study form a series from the individual (the most concrete) to the ecosystem (the most abstract). Chapter 2, "Individuals and Populations," deals with individuals and the various groupings of individuals that can be called populations. The concept of a population keeps turning up: species populations form the basis of classification; populations interact in communities; contemporary genetic and evolutionary theories turn largely on population studies.

The actual field study of a community — even the community in a crack in a city sidewalk — is essential to Chapter 3, "Communities and Ecosystems." Since communities available for study differ greatly among schools, a brief description of a community is provided as a basis for comparison. The kinds of ecological relationships in communities are considered and, finally, the concept of an ecosystem is introduced.

**Section Two: DIVERSITY AMONG LIVING THINGS.** The student should have some idea of the diversity of organisms and of their classification before going further into the patterns of ecological organization. But there is no need for a "type study" of living things. Emphasis is on the variety of forms in which life can occur and on those aspects of form and function that are relevant to a useful and meaningful organization of such diversity.

On the principle of starting with the familiar, Chapter 4, "Animals," begins with mammals. This, of course, makes for difficulties, but at this point there is no basis for a meaningful discussion of phylogeny, anyway. Instead, diversity of form within the animal kingdom is stressed. But this diversity is not endless; patterns are discernible. And evolution is offered as a possible explanation for the apparent order within the general diversity.

The concept of classification does not need repetition in Chapter 5, "Plants," but another abstract idea is developed — that of nomenclature. Historically, nomenclature and classification have developed together, but this is not sufficient pedagogical reason for presenting them to the student together. Experience has suggested that these concepts are better understood when they are presented to the student separately rather than as a single large block of abstract material.

In Chapter 6, "Protists," a third kingdom is introduced. The teacher may not agree with the system of kingdoms that has been used in the text or with the way particular groups have been assigned to these kingdoms. But there is no classification on which all biologists agree. Pointing out the reasons for disagreement ought to give students an idea of the nature of the problems of classification.

**Section Three: PATTERNS IN THE BIOSPHERE.** There are three bases on which patterns of biotic distribution within the biosphere may be constructed: ecological, historical, and biogeographical. Each of these is treated in this section.

A number of laboratory investigations involving microorganisms have been started during the work on Chapter 6. Therefore, to facilitate continuity of laboratory procedures, Chapter 7, "Patterns of Life in the Microscopic World," deals with ecological groupings of microorganisms. Two such groupings, both of great import to man's existence, are treated in some detail: soil organisms and the microorganisms involved in disease.

The theme in Chapter 8, "Patterns of Life on Land," is the distribution of macroscopic terrestrial organisms. The relation of physiological tolerances to the global distribution of abiotic environmental factors leads to the description of biomes. But ecological conditions do not wholly explain distributions. Explanation is then sought in evidence of past distribution and of artificial distribution by man.

Chapter 9, "Patterns of Life in the Water," extends the principles of ecological distribution to aquatic environments. Ponds are probably more easily visualized as ecological systems than any other part of the biosphere. Running waters are treated briefly. Finally it seems desirable that the student obtain some understanding of marine life—which is certain to become increasingly important as a resource for man.

In Chapter 10, "Patterns of Life in the Past," attention is given chiefly to the nature of the evidence in paleontology, to the kinds of work that paleontologists do, and to some principles of paleontological reasoning. Emphasis on ecosystems is maintained, and the temporal continuity of the biosphere is thereby stressed. The principle of evolution is not discussed here but simply assumed as the most reasonable basis for interpreting the evidence.

**Section Four: WITHIN THE INDIVIDUAL ORGANISM.** Having spent nearly half its duration on the supra-individual levels of biological organization, the course now turns to the infra-individual levels. Some acquaintance with "inner physiology" is essential—not only for appreciation of some rapidly developing areas of modern biology but also as background for topics, such as genetics and evolution, that are important parts of the biological understanding required by the functioning citizen.

The objective of Chapter 11, "The Cell," is to provide the student with sufficient understanding of cellular structure, of some cell physiology, and of cell duplication to enable him to interpret subsequent chapters. Only those cell structures that have relevance to later discussion are treated, and the physiology deals principally with the relations of a cell to its environment. Two important topics, differentiation and aging, are presented primarily as problems undergoing current investigation.

Energy-flow in living systems has been a fundamental idea from the beginning of the course. In Chapter 12, "Bioenergetics," attention is focused on energy-storage and energy-release in cells. Here the student is exposed to some of the biochemical aspects of modern biology.

Chapter 13, "The Functioning Plant," chiefly concerns the structure and function of those plants with which the student comes in contact most frequently—the vascular plants.

The theme of Chapter 14, "The Functioning Animal," is the variety of ways in which the necessary functions of an animal body are carried out in different animal groups. In each case, the comparative physiology uses man as a principal example.

In Chapter 15, "Behavior," the reactions of organisms to external environment are considered as stemming from internal mechanisms. From the vast field of behavioral biology, topics have been chosen that are related to other parts of the course and that have proved stimulating and fairly comprehensible to tenth-grade students: learning, periodicity, territoriality, and social behavior.

**Section Five: CONTINUITY OF THE BIOSPHERE.** This may be considered the heart of the course. Perhaps the most fundamental thing that can be said about life is that it goes on. In this section much of the matter from the preceding four sections is directed toward an understanding of this basic idea.

Reproduction is considered as a life process unimportant to an individual's continuity but—because of individual death —essential to the continuity of populations and all higher levels of biological organization. Chapter 16, "Reproduction," continues the comparative method employed in the two previous chapters and again, as in Chapter 14, uses man as a principal example.

It is difficult to overestimate the importance of genetics in contemporary biology, but balance in the biology course demands that genetics not be allowed to get out of hand. In Chapter 17, "Heredity," the topic is developed historically, and from this development some ideas concerning the logic of evidence are derived. Mathematics is not shunned; it can be either minimized or maximized by the teacher.

The entire course—indeed, any modern biology course—can be regarded as a summary of the evidence for evolution. The main objective of Chapter 18, "Evolution," then, is not to give the *evidence* for evolution; that has already been done is several ways, both implicit and explicit. Instead, the chief aim is to give the student some idea of the *mechanism* of evolution. Darwin is presented as one who provided an explanation of how evolution operates, not as the originator of evolution as a concept.

**Section Six: MAN AND THE BIO-SPHERE.** We are human, and biology in the high school can be justified only on humanistic grounds. After putting man in perspective with the rest of nature, the course here, at its end, focuses explicitly on him.

In Chapter 19, "The Human Animal," some ways in which man differs anatomically and physiologically from fellow organisms are discussed. Since much of man's distinctiveness is behavioral rather than physiological or anatomical, the chapter inevitably becomes involved in borderline areas between anthropology and biology. Then the paleontological evidence for the origin of man is examined. Finally, racial variation within the human species is viewed biologically.

The authors hope they have woven the whole course together in Chapter 20, "Man in the Web of Life." The student is confronted with topics that will concern him in the future as a citizen—topics for which biological information has some relevance. These topics, of course, all go beyond biology; the primary aim is to provoke the student into continuing to think about them.

## Organizational Alternatives

The student's book has been organized so that vocabulary and concepts are sequential and accumulative. Full advantage can be taken of this only if the chapters are studied consecutively. Further, if this is done, the teacher is freed from problems of extemporaneous course design—which is expensive of time and which, like all extemporaneous art, has a low probability of success even though the occasional success may be brilliant. More time can then be put into the tasks of actual teaching, especially into the time-consuming organization and supervision of laboratory work. Nevertheless, it is recognized that every wise teacher will look for adaptations to enhance the instructional opportunities available in his own situation or inherent in his own resources.

One of the most pressing problems in biology-teaching is the seasonal availability of materials. Use of greenhouses, aquariums, and refrigerators can do much to circumvent this problem but cannot entirely eliminate it. Locale, weather, class schedules, and other factors may create the need for a change in chapter sequence. For example, in some localities the fieldwork suggested in Chapter 3 may have to be postponed until spring. It can then reintroduce outdoor aspects of biology, perhaps at the end of Section Four or even at the end of Section Five.

For various reasons it may seem desirable to omit or to treat lightly certain portions of the course. If the teacher uses a BSCS laboratory block (published by D. C. Heath & Co., Boston), some omission will certainly be necessary. In this case the portion to be omitted will depend upon the nature of the block that is used. For example, if the *Animal Growth and Development* block is used, Chapter 16 might be omitted or used as collateral reading. If the block *Microbes: Their Growth, Nutrition, and Interaction* is used, Chapters 6 and 7 might be omitted or used as collateral reading.

If the school year is simply too short for study of the entire course, Chapter 9 may be considered the most expendable. For the most part, however, omission of parts of chapters is a better choice: for examples, pages 234–242 from Chapter 7, pages 286–290 from Chapter 8, pages 556–566 from Chapter 15, pages 591–599 from Chapter 16. However, in making omissions care must be taken to see that sequences of thought are not ruptured. For example, it is difficult to make omissions from Chapter 18. In schools where much human anatomy is taught in connection with health courses in earlier grades, much of Chapter 14 might be omitted.

In any case it must be emphasized that Sections One and Six are indispensable to the philosophy of the *Green Version*. If the teacher is disposed to omit them, then he is unconvinced by the arguments presented on pages T5–T7 and would do better to choose some other set of course materials.

It is very easy to allow a course to fray out and expire merely by reason of the arrival of the last day. *This must never happen with the* Green Version. No matter where the class may be in the course, no matter what the route through the course may have been, the teacher *must* reserve a few days at the end of the school year for the last chapter. Here an attempt is made to bring the whole course into focus. Here are discussed those biological problems man must face if he is to continue his existence on this planet. So that the teacher may put his laboratory in order, take his inventories, and close out the laboratory accounts while classes continue to meet, no laboratory activities are proposed for Chapter 20.

## Conspectus of Teaching Resources

Tenth-grade students do not automatically recognize the uses of textual apparatus. Therefore the wise teacher will devote a little time to familiarizing students with the book. But first, of course, he himself must investigate its resources. The following paragraphs discuss the intentions of the authors. No doubt teachers will find many other ways to use the resources of the student's book.

**Preface for the student.** The front matter in textbooks is read by reviewers presumably, by teachers possibly, but by students never. Some sections *are* expendable—it is not necessary that the foreword be read by the student at all, and it is not necessary that the preface for the student be read immediately. But sometime before Investigation 1.1 has been concluded, the material in the Preface should be introduced. It provides a *raison d'etre* for a high school biology course and, specifically, it explains the heavy emphasis upon laboratory work.

**Section introductions.** The several paragraphs introducing each of the six sections are not informational. Rather, they set the stage, present a viewpoint, relate the section to the whole of the course. The accompanying photographs bear no captions, but each has relevance to the theme of the section. Student speculation on this relevance would not be inappropriate as a terminal activity.

**Headings.** One of the principal differences between good and poor students, both in high school and in college, lies in their use of textbook headings. Poor students plod through printed matter, oblivious to organization; good students make full use of the authors' typographical attempts to display the relationships between ideas. Teachers can point at least some poor students toward a higher degree of reading comprehension merely by stressing the utility of headings.

The *Green Version* student's book employs headings in four orders. Boldface capitals set flush to the left margin distinguish major chapter divisions. For example:

## RABBITS AND RASPBERRIES

Second-order headings are set as indented, thinner capitals, thus:

## FOOD WEBS

Boldface type run into the beginning of a paragraph distinguishes the third-order heads:

**Energy pathways.** Energy is continually brought into the system of living things through the producers. All other organisms. . . .

In a few chapters, centered small capitals are employed as headings, thus:

### TROPICAL RAIN FOREST

These are intermediate between second- and third-order headings and are used only where the chapter organization is more complex than usual.

Investigations occur at suitable places within chapter organization (see page T14). They do not consistently occur at any level of chapter subordination. Therefore, they have an internal system of headings paralleling that of the chapter as a whole.

**Italics.** Within paragraphs, italics are used for either of two purposes: (1) they indicate the first occurrence of a technical term, or (2) they indicate an emphasis. They are used for the second purpose quite sparingly.

**Vocabulary.** In any science textbook, vocabulary is of two kinds: technical and running. Technical vocabulary is part of the course content because ideas cannot be divorced from terms. But the learning of terminology is not a proper *aim* of science-teaching; it is a means only.

High school biology has been particularly subject to criticism for its high density of technical terms. In the *Green Version* considerable effort has been made to keep technical vocabulary within reasonable limits. This effort has inevitably resulted in the loss of some terms that may be favorites with teachers. There is, of course, no reason why a teacher cannot increase the load if he wishes. But the authors trust that he will approach each addition as they have—with a penetrating *Why?*

Though each technical term has been carefully considered before being admitted to the text, the load remains large. Several levels of importance can be distinguished. Some terms are of pervasive importance throughout the course—*photosynthesis, environment, evolution,* for example. They must be applied again and again, examined in many contexts, approached from many viewpoints. Others are of less pervasive importance, but fundamental to some major section of biology—*meiosis, predation, natural selection.* Still others are not important in themselves but are essential as steps to larger ideas—*natality, crossing-over, tropism.* At the lowest level of technical vocabulary are names of things—*kinetochore, host, ATP.* Certainly it would be a pedagogical error to treat all technical terms in the same way.

The running vocabulary carries the narrative. In the first part of the text, it is rather simple, though no attempt is made to "write down" to the students. In the latter part of the book, the authors have made less effort to find simple synonyms, and the running vocabulary probably approaches the recognition level of the average tenth grader —with occasional excursions beyond.

**Marginal notes.** The single-column format permits the use of a wide outer margin for a variety of purposes. Principally, it allows the placement of aids to the student's comprehension in a position that makes such material available but optional. Students who have no need for this kind of help are able to read on without interruption, while those who require it have assistance immediately at hand.

The marginal notes provide pronunciations for technical words as a matter of routine. Pronunciations are also given for some running vocabulary—at first rather freely, later somewhat sparingly.

Some definitions are given in the notes. These are never definitions of technical vocabulary. (Technical terms are italicized and explained where they first occur in the body of the text.) They are definitions of words in the running vocabulary that might be unfamiliar to a considerable proportion of tenth-grade students. They become fewer in the latter parts of the book.

Marginal notes call attention to related laboratory exercises, refer the student to appropriate illustrations in other parts of the book, and give brief biographical notes on scientists mentioned in the text.

In addition to these strictly adjuvant services, marginal notes provide the ambitious and thoughtful student with opportunities to expand his understanding. Many notes provide derivations of technical terms. For the most part, these derivations give Latin and Greek roots from which the student can accumulate a stock of word elements that will facilitate the building of scientific vocabulary throughout the course and (hopefully) beyond. Finally, questions that are intended to be thought-provoking are sparingly inserted in the margins.

All marginal notes are printed in an unobtrusive gray. All are to be regarded as *optional* material. Students should be reminded—frequently, at first—that the notes are present to help when help is needed. The notes should never be allowed to become an obstacle to study.

**Illustrations.** In any textbook that stresses the biology of whole individual organisms, constant reference to kinds of organisms is necessary to provide examples of the general principles discussed. But tenth-grade students vary greatly in their previous experience with living things. Therefore, pictures of many organisms are provided in many cases simply to strengthen general discussion with visual images. Like the marginal notes, such illustrations are to be used only as needed and are usually placed in marginal positions.

All other illustrations are teaching materials of an importance coordinate to that of the letterpress. No illustration is printed for decoration alone, though an effort was made to obtain pictures that are as attractive as possible. Captions tie in with the rest of the letterpress and, often, extend it.

The questions that frequently occur in the captions are by no means rhetorical; they are worthy of class discussion.

Wherever the practice might be helpful, an illustration is accompanied by indications of the size of the pictured subject. In all such instances, the ratio of the picture size to life-size is given ($\times$ 1/4 = reduced to one-fourth life-size; $\times$ 1 = life-size; $\times$ 2 = enlarged to twice life-size).

**Laboratory investigations.** The first function of a teaching laboratory is to present from nature the evidence for the basic biological concepts. This *illustrative* function was probably the principal one in Thomas Henry Huxley's mind when he introduced laboratory work into science education. His insight was a simple one: Seeing is believing. In teaching science one must appeal not to the authority of a teacher or a book; one must look squarely at the facts, at the infinitely varied phenomena of nature. Unfortunately, the illustrative function came to be so heavily emphasized that students spent most of the laboratory time watching demonstrations, looking through microscopes, dissecting animals or plants, learning names, labeling drawings—but rarely doing an experiment in the sense of really investigating a problem whose answer is unknown.

Today something more must be expected from school laboratory work. Active participation of the learner in some scientific investigation is needed if he is ever to glimpse the true nature and meaning of science, ever to appreciate the forces that motivate and activate the scientist (see Preface: For the Student). This *investigative* function of laboratory work requires a different approach and a revision of goals. It requires different and (often) more expensive kinds of materials and many more of them. It makes desirable more extensive laboratory facilities.

The investigative function of laboratory work does not displace the illustrative function; it complements it. For at least thirty years perspicacious biology teachers have striven to elevate this twentieth-century function to a place beside the honored nineteenth-century function. Both functions are represented in the investigations in the *Green Version* student's book.

The investigations are the heart of the course. At least 50 percent of the student's class time should be centered on them: planning, performing, observing, recording data, interpreting data, drawing conclusions, and relating the work to other sources of information.

Investigations have been placed within chapters at points where they fit the development of ideas. Sometimes they are initial; sometimes they are terminal; sometimes two or more succeed each other without intervening text. At times two or more investigations must be in progress simultaneously. And usually students should be discussing their reading of text material, reference assignments, and problems as work on the investigations proceeds. Nevertheless, to facilitate the management of such a complexity of activities in the classroom-laboratory and in the field, the authors have endeavored to place investigations in the student's book in such a manner that the textual material is not unduly fragmented.

Because of the importance of the investigations in the *Green Version* course, a special section is devoted to them (pages T15–T19).

**Summaries.** Each chapter ends with a summary (set on a longer type measure and bounded by horizontal lines). Summaries are not outlines, and the student will soon discover that they are no substitute for studying the chapters. However, summaries do bring together major ideas in their chapters, sometimes in new relationships with each other; they should prove useful to students as clinching devices and to teachers as bases for launching discussions.

**Guide questions.** These are based directly upon the chapter materials—both letterpress and illustrations. They require recall rather than reasoning, though there is some departure from this generalization in later chapters. They are placed all together at the end of a chapter, and the sequence is exactly that of the ideas in the chapter.

Thus, a teacher may break up a chapter for assignment in any way that he wishes, and the corresponding guide questions can readily be located.

It is intended that these questions be used by the student for his own guidance during his study. With some classes they may be used for checking student understanding of text materials. If confined to the guide questions, however, class discussion will proceed on a very low level and will result in the neglect of much material. Therefore, even with very slow classes the teacher needs to supplement the guide questions with some of his own, based on his understanding of the interests and attitudes of the students in each class. With average classes such supplemental questions should call for some reasoning. With above-average classes the guide questions should receive little attention in class discussion.

**Problems.** Unlike the guide questions, the problems require reasoning, computation, or research—sometimes all three. They are not intended as guides for the student while he studies the chapter, but as extensions beyond the chapter. Their sequence has no relationship to the sequence of ideas in the text. Although in some cases the problems may serve as material for class discussion, they should not be assigned *en masse*.

No attempt has been made to control either the vocabulary or the sentence structure of the problems. New terms are sometimes used without explanation. It is assumed that students who are sufficiently advanced to use the problems will also know how to use dictionaries and other references. It is not possible to rank the problems according to difficulty. Assignment should be made only after consideration of the interests as well as the abilities of individual students.

For the teacher, the principal value of the problems should be to provide suggestions for the invention of problems of his own. Problems with a local flavor or that bear upon biological topics currently receiving notice in news media are particularly valuable. Problems that lead the student into experimentation will, of course, be indistinguishable from the items entitled "For Further Investigation." Better students may be encouraged to develop their own problems.

**Suggested readings.** An effort has been made to limit the number of book titles. Some preference has been given to books available in paperback editions. The intention is to encourage the formation of *classroom* libraries where books may be constantly available to students, leaving the school library as a place for more extensive research. There many of the books listed in Part Two of this guide should be shelved. Since it is desirable to encourage further reading on the part of all students – not only those who read well – some easy references have been selected as well as some that will challenge the most advanced.

Periodical references have been confined to articles in *Scientific American, National Geographic*, and *Natural History*. This sparse selection from periodical literature does not imply that worthwhile material is lacking elsewhere. But librarians usually keep back files of these periodicals, while desired copies of many other periodicals are often hard to find. The *American Biology Teacher* regularly carries a column noting appropriate biological articles appearing in current issues of "popular" magazines. Many of the *Scientific American* articles are available in reprints.

**Appendix I.** This appendix contains general information needed for good laboratory procedure. It is needed before (or, at least, soon after) Investigation 1.1. But its inclusion with Chapter 1 seemed to the authors an impediment. Moreover, reference to it may be required at other times during the course. Hence its position as an appendix. But its existence should not be forgotten.

**Appendix II.** In this appendix the scheme of classification outlined in Section Two is presented in conspectus, enabling the student to see the levels of organization in close relationship to each other. The language has been kept as non-technical as possible, but not all terms are necessarily comprehensible at the time the student is studying Section Two. Illustrations are juxtaposed to their descriptions. This material is, of course, strictly for reference purposes. It would be desirable for the teacher to present an outline of one or two other schemes of classification for comparison with this.

**Index.** By now the reader of this guide must realize that the memorization of definitions plays a very minor role in *Green Version* biology. The discussion of word meanings in context, the usage of words – these *are* important matters. But they are not served by a list of pat definitions. Therefore, the student's book contains no glossary. However, the index of the textbook is quite comprehensive, so that the student has ready access to all the material in his book, including definitions in context whenever they occur (see, for example, "Amino acids," "Biosphere," and "Conifers").

## Investigations:
### Special Considerations

Good high school biology work has been accomplished in spacious and fully equipped laboratories; it has also been accomplished in small classrooms with primitive and improvised equipment. Obviously, in widely different physical environments procedures must also vary widely. Therefore, no prescriptions can be written for successful laboratory teaching. The following paragraphs are intended simply to alert the teacher to some sensitive areas of planning.

**Nature of the investigations.** The student's book contains 60 full-scale investigations and numerous suggestions "For Further Investigation." All of the 60 are an integral part of the course. They frequently present concepts or terms, an understanding of which is assumed in later development of ideas. None can be omitted without the same kind of checking and thoughtful balancing of time and objectives that should accompany the omission of any other materials in the student's book. In fact, keeping the fundamental aims of the course in mind, omission of investigations should perhaps involve more deliberation than omission of the textual materials.

A few investigations are recommended as demonstrations. For the most part these are ones in which the replication of the procedure by many students seems to serve no useful purpose or involves an inordinate amount of equipment. The number of demonstrated investigations ought to be kept to a minimum, even though many not recommended for demonstration *could* be presented in this manner. It might be argued that a demonstration would gain in effectiveness if the superior skill of the teacher is employed. But from a pedagogical viewpoint, demonstrations that are performed by special groups of students usually are superior to those done by the teacher.

⚓ **Organization of the investigations.** Because individual investigations contribute in different ways to the advancement of the student's biological knowledge and scientific understanding, no set pattern of internal organization is followed. In the high school laboratory there should be no straitjacket formulation of scientific investigation; there is none in the scientist's laboratory. However, every investigation has a general "Procedure."

But every effort must be made to create in each student an awareness of the purpose of his activity. He may see the purpose and still flounder about. But if he sees the purpose, he is the less likely to flounder and the more likely to grasp and carry out the procedure. In the first half of the year, the student is presented with a "Purpose" in each investigation. Later this practice is gradually dropped; the student is left on his own in this matter.

Almost every investigation has a "Materials and Equipment" list, which is mainly for the teacher and his laboratory aides. But such lists have also been found of value to

students in setting about their work, so they have been retained in the student's book.

Most investigations have some kind of follow-up to the procedure. This is often a section called "Studying the Data," in which directions are given for arranging data into tabular or graphic form and the meaning of data is elicited by suitable questions. It must be understood that the forms given in the student's book present only the scheme for recording data—size and amount of space required in his data book must be determined by the student.

Sometimes there is a "Summary." If an experimental situation justifies the use of the term, "Conclusions" are called for.

Sometimes investigations include "Background Information," material needed for understanding the procedure. Still other subheadings are used occasionally.

Suggestions "For Further Investigation" are plentiful. These are materials that can be explored by individual students who have more than average energy and drive—and, hopefully, above-average ability. Some call for fairly simple extensions of the procedures in the main investigation; some entail original thought and attention to design. In most cases, specific directions are lacking; the student must work out his own procedures. These materials are a step between investigations for classroom-laboratory use (necessarily structured to meet logistical considerations) and the open-ended experimental projects found in BSCS *Research Problems in Biology* (cited page T6).

Questions are inserted wherever they seem appropriate—even in an introduction. Most, of course, occur in sections such as "Studying the Data," "Discussion," or "Conclusions." In some investigations questions are woven into the procedure (Investigations 1.3 and 1.4, for example), and in others the whole procedure advances by means of questions (see Investigations 18.2 and 19.1). These methods make it desirable to place an identifying number (in parentheses) *after* a question rather than before it, so that the number does not separate the question from the foregoing statements that lead to the question. This placement of numbers has been used consistently throughout all the investigations. To facilitate the location of questions, which are often buried in paragraphs, a large dot (•) has been inserted at the point where a question begins.

**Data books.** Experience has shown that the most convenient way to handle the recording of data is by means of a bound (sewn) notebook. The use of such a *data book* is fully explained in Appendix I of the student's book.

Each student should be encouraged to regard his data book as a place of primary record. As such, it must meet the hazards of constant usage at the laboratory table and will receive records hurriedly made. Under such circumstances a data book is not likely to be a thing of beauty. Slovenly work cannot be tolerated in science; but many students, particularly the "better" ones, tend to equate slovenliness with mere lack of neatness. They must be taught to associate slovenliness with inaccuracy.

Although a data book is a personal record, not a report to the teacher, it should be checked occasionally to ensure that the student is using the most efficient methods of recording and organizing data. Checking should be accomplished on the spot, not by removing the book from the hands of the student, and should be disassociated from grading. Checking should be frequent at first, less so as the year progresses.

**Modifications.** In almost every investigation many variations are possible. Some of these are noted in Part Two of this guide. Others will be dictated by necessity. In the early part of the year, it is best to stick as closely to the printed form of the investigations as the local situation will permit. At this time connection between variations in procedure and variations in results must be established. It is therefore desirable to train the student to follow procedures carefully; and the fewer changes he has to cope with, the better. If many changes must be made, it would perhaps be best for the teacher to rewrite the investigation entirely.

Later, strict adherence to the printed procedures is not necessary—or even desirable. With more able classes, merely throwing out hints concerning possible changes may suffice to introduce valuable variations that may increase the teaching possibilities in the results. But beware of breaks in the reasoning process. Variations in procedure can degenerate into mere tinkering if links among procedure, data, and conclusions are not strongly forged.

Finally, the investigations in the student's book should in no way inhibit the teacher's efforts to devise new ones suited to his own facilities and situation. Rather, they should encourage him to do so.

**Looking ahead.** Careful planning is a hallmark of good teaching. It is especially important in science-teaching. In biological science it is crucial.

BSCS biology, with its emphasis upon experimental procedures involving living materials, calls for the utmost skill and ingenuity in planning. Simultaneously the teacher must often consider the disposal of materials from a completed investigation, the care of materials in one or more current investigations, the provision of materials for work to be accomplished in the next few days, and the procurement of materials for investigations that are two, four, six, or more weeks in the future.

Among the layers of planning responsibility, long-range foresight is the one most likely to be neglected. Yet it is essential. For example, in most parts of the country an investigation requiring young tomato plants is impossible to carry out in December unless the seeds have been planted in October. And the seeds may be difficult to obtain in October unless they have been bought in the spring or early summer.

**Initiating the work.** If the importance of laboratory work is to be established in the minds of students, there must be no delay in getting into it. Because very little procedure is involved, it is possible to set a class to work on Investigation 1.1 at its second meeting. But before Investigation 1.2 is attempted, some ground rules of laboratory work must be laid down. Among the matters to be considered are:

1. Need for thorough familiarity with the purpose (in the case of an experiment, the hypothesis) and the procedures to be followed.

2. Location of work stations and regulation of student mobility during laboratory work.

3. A scheme for distributing and collecting materials.

4. Principles of teamwork—leadership, acceptance of responsibility, and coordination of efforts.

5. Relationship between data book and the completed exercises.

6. Methods of evaluating student laboratory work.

Every student must assume responsibility for understanding the procedure of each investigation and, especially, his own part in it. The teacher has responsibility for relating the work to the accompanying textual materials and for adapting (when necessary) the procedure to his own classroom situation. The teacher is wholly responsible for the provision of the materials and equipment, though he may be able to delegate such responsibility to assistants—students or laboratory aides. All required materials and equipment must be on hand when work begins. Nothing is more detrimental to good classroom laboratory work than lack of an essential item at a critical moment.

**Finding time.** Having understood the basic importance of laboratory work and having leafed through the investigations in the student's book, the teacher immediately asks, "How can I find time to prepare all the material?"

No complete answer can be given to this question. Teachers *have* found the time—in one way or another. But every device suggested by teachers for providing more time seems merely to open up new opportunities for expanding laboratory activities. Thus teachers in the "best" situations are often as busy as those in the worst.

Where school systems have become convinced that extensive, truly investigative laboratory work is educationally important, various kinds of administrative action have been helpful. In some schools, science teachers are scheduled for one less class per day than are other teachers. The period freed from class instruction is available for preparation of laboratory and demonstration materials. In other schools, full-time laboratory assistants are employed. Still other schools provide part-time help by paying interested and qualified high school seniors to assist teachers in setting up laboratory and demonstration work for biology classes.

Even without overt administrative backing, the individual teacher can improve his ability to provide worthwhile laboratory work for his students. Something may be achieved by increased care in planning. In schools having more than one biology teacher, the sharing of preparatory tasks is time-saving and labor-saving—particularly when special skills are utilized. And much time can be saved by attention to organization of materials; a stock room or preparation room where all items have assigned places minimizes waste motion.

Most important, however, is the enlisting of voluntary aid from the students. In almost every class some students deem it a privilege and even an honor to be permitted to help in laboratory preparations. Not only do such students make a real contribution toward freeing the teacher from routine chores, but they also gain a realization that a certain amount of "dishwashing" is an essential part of laboratory work.

There is, of course, nothing new in this practice, but some suggestions may be useful. Students should be selected on an informal basis and never to the exclusion of others who may later become interested in helping. They should not be expected to correct papers, score tests, monitor classes, or perform other tasks that place them in positions of real or supposed advantage. Although their assistance may be greatest in routine work, they should be given instruction in some laboratory skills—partly in return for their aid and in encouragement of their continued effort, partly in hopes of discovering a few who may be especially deserving of guidance into careers in science or in laboratory technology.

Students who have already taken biology are often willing to become laboratory assistants during their free time. They can be assigned on a somewhat more formal basis than current students, since they are not members of the classes in which they assist. Among the criteria to be considered for the selection of such assistants might be (1) the students' interest in biology, (2) their scholarship in biology and related subjects, (3) their general scholarship, (4) their available free time, (5) their willingness to help other students, (6) their ability to get along with lowerclassmen, and (7) their general reliability and dependability. (Caution: No matter how much help he may have —paid or voluntary—the teacher retains sole responsibility for laboratory safety.)

**Checking the work.** It is possible for a student to become so preoccupied with preparations for future laboratory activity, so enmeshed in the mechanics of present laboratory activity, and so fatigued by the chores of cleaning up past laboratory activity that little time is left for the rounding out of his experience. Since there is little virtue in mere activity, this should never be allowed to happen. Every investigation should be followed by class discussion.

The kind of class discussion may vary with the kind of investigation. When an investigation is observational only, the teacher must be sure that students relate observations to the purpose of the investigation. When the investigation is experimental, the teacher must be sure that the course of the reasoning, from hypothesis through experimental design and data to conclusions, is understood. In any case, class discussion following laboratory work is the milieu in which an understanding of the true nature of science is best developed. No other means is as effective in placing before the student the rationale of science, the difficulties of research, the uncertainties of knowledge.

For many investigations a class discussion constitutes a satisfactory termination. Written reports for all investigations are neither necessary nor feasible. The teacher may easily be lured into a never-ending race with paper work. The results are a poor use of student time—in excessive writing—and a poor use of teacher time —in excessive reading. Which investigations to select for written report is a matter of personal choice. But it seems more reasonable to require such a report for an experimental investigation (such as 1.2) than for an observational one (such as 1.3).

A report that requires the student to copy lists of materials and long passages of procedure from his book is mere busywork and a sure way to undermine the purpose of the laboratory. In general, a written report might consist of (1) a title, (2) relevant data worked up from the data book, and (3) answers to the questions in the investigation. If complete statements are required in answering questions, grading is easier, and —more important—vague thinking is discouraged. At the beginning of the year's work, questions may be discussed in class before a written report is required. Later, when a pattern of acceptable response has been developed, this sequence may be reversed.

Written reports should be submitted as soon as possible after completion of an investigation. Prompt evaluation and return of the report to the student make a follow-up discussion possible.

## TESTS

No matter what the stated aims of a course may be, no matter how diligently the teacher may bend his efforts toward them, all is in vain unless the tests that are used to measure the student's progress reflect these aims. Whether much or little is made of marks in a school system, students remain realists; they will work toward tests. Therefore, it is of utmost importance that tests be firmly based on aims.

If student memorization of arbitrary, clear-cut definitions is the teacher's aim, then he should not be using the *Green Version*, which is certain to engender frustration in both himself and his students. But if this is *not* his aim, then he must be sure that his tests do not merely require rote memorization of terms. If the teacher really believes that laboratory work is as important as digestion of textbook information, then he must base his tests at least equally on laboratory work and textbook work.

All of this is probably self-evident. But granting the principle, the constructing of tests that reflect *Green Version* aims remains difficult. For some of the aims, no good group-testing procedures are yet known. And for all of the aims, good testing procedures involve the investment of much time and effort.

During the years in which BSCS materials were being tried out in classrooms, a committee of teachers, biologists, psychologists, and psychometricians worked to devise suitable tests to accompany the materials. The committee constructed, tested repeatedly with hundreds of classes, and normed quarterly tests for each of the three BSCS versions plus a comprehensive final test. These tests, revised for the 1968 editions, represent the best current efforts to measure BSCS aims in the conventional paper-and-pencil way. The set of tests designed for the *Green Version* can be obtained through the publisher, Rand McNally & Company, P. O. Box 7600, Chicago, Illinois, 60680.

Of course, quarterly tests fall far short of meeting the teacher's testing needs. Much more frequent tests are needed to allow the teacher to determine his successes and failures, and to indicate the areas in which intensified review is required. There is no substitute for teacher-made tests. With the crowded schedules already existing for science teachers and the increased time requirements of laboratory methods, it is to be expected that, in his construction of test items, the teacher will not always be able to match his performance to his ideals. But something more than a casual nod to such ideals will be necessary if the student is not to be demoralized by his first encounter with the quarterly tests. The teacher must have previously provided him with suitable test experience.

To assist the teacher in this task, the BSCS has provided two aids. In the *Biology Teacher's Handbook* (cited page T35), Chapter 16 is devoted to the construction of classroom tests. And in 1966 an experimental booklet of specimen test items, arranged by chapters, was published for each BSCS version. The test booklet for the *Green Version* is being revised at present, but, until the supply is exhausted, the 1966 edition can be obtained from Rand McNally (address above).

# SPECIFIC SUGGESTIONS
# FOR TEXT AND LABORATORY

# Section One  THE WORLD
OF LIFE:
THE BIOSPHERE

Whole living organisms are the center of attention throughout Section One. You should arrange to have the classroom plentifully supplied with them. Whether the room be large or small, whether provided with the latest biological equipment or not, it can be made a home for a variety of living things—ready, waiting, and conspicuous on the first day of school.

The "Preface: For the Student" may be read concurrently with the introduction to Section One. But resist the impulse to test the student's understanding; elaborate explanation at this stage can gain nothing, and it may destroy much. If, however, the reading level of the class is very low, you might read the student preface aloud to the students even before books are distributed.

In general, south of latitude 40°N., out-of-doors community studies are reasonably satisfactory until the end of October. If the school is in a region where inclement weather arrives earlier, Investigation 3.1 may be undertaken before the investigations that accompany Chapter 2 or even before those on the microscope (1.3, 1.4). Of course such order violates the logic of the individual-population-community sequence, but the violation is better than the omission of Investigation 3.1.

Throughout the section, you should try to keep constantly before the students the trio of ideas that underlie it: (1) individuals as biological units, (2) verifiable observations as the foundation of biological concepts, and (3) the flow of energy as the core of ecosystem function.

Section Illustration

Light filtering through leaves sets the tone for Section One and for the course as a whole—the biosphere is entirely a manifestation of solar energy.

CHAPTER

# 1

# The Web
# of Life

## MAJOR IDEAS

*The ideas presented here are not to be imposed on the student. Rather, they are intended to aid the teacher as he plans class discussions of the chapter. Therefore, they are stated in adult language.*

1. An understanding of the scientific enterprise—particularly of the processes of scientific work—is basic to any worthwhile study of science.

2. Organisms tend to maintain a steady state, both internally and externally, in the face of environmental change.

3. Energy flows from the sun through the living system back into the abiotic environment, from which it is irrecoverable.

4. Having been introduced into the living system in the form of light, energy is passed from organism to organism in chemical form.

5. The matter in living things is the same matter that is found in nonliving things.

6. In contrast to energy, matter moves cyclically between the living system and the nonliving world.

7. Earth's living system together with its supporting abiotic environment may be conveniently conceptualized as being the "biosphere."

8. Man—an integral part of the biosphere, yet possessed of extraordinary powers—is faced with enormous problems in maintaining a steady state in the biosphere. His own continued existence and that of all other living things will depend upon his biological understanding.

## PLANNING AHEAD

At the beginning of the school year the whole course lies ahead, but the requirements of the first week are the most pressing concern. Ideally, planning and ordering should have been done the year before and the materials for the first few investigations assembled or delivered a week or two before the arrival of students.

*If this has not been done, then—*

> First: procure and make labels for living organisms for Investigation 1.1. A photosynthetic flagellate is the most difficult to collect locally. Telephone a supplier for air-express shipment if necessary.
>
> Second: obtain seeds for Investigation 1.2.
>
> Third: prepare strips of small newspaper print and magazine photographs for Investigation 1.3.
>
> Fourth: order microorganisms for Investigation 1.4.
>
> Fifth: order snails and elodea for Investigation 1.5.

Now, with the most immediate needs attended to, check the lists of materials and equipment in Appendix B against the supplies in your school laboratory. Order what is lacking or begin to consider feasible substitutions.

Before work on Chapter 1 has proceeded very far, attend to the following needs for succeeding chapters:

1. Prepare a stencil to run off copies of five-cycle semi-log graph paper for Investigation 2.1. Printed paper is expensive.

2. Check the number of test tubes available for Investigation 2.2. The count will dictate the number of teams that can be accommodated. If you or your laboratory assistant have had little experience in preparing and sterilizing media, do these jobs well in advance to allow time for mistakes.

3. If the school is in a region where winter comes early, consider the possibility of doing Investigation 3.1 soon.

## GUIDELINES

Begin the year's work in the laboratory. If materials are at hand, Investigation 1.1 can be carried out as soon as routine organizational and administrative details have been disposed of. No previous reading assignment is necessary.

High school students seldom read prefaces, and high school teachers probably never assign the reading of prefaces. But in the *Green Version* the preface is essential matter. Its content is relevant to Investigation 1.1 and is a prelude to "The Scientist's Viewpoint" (pp. 5–7).

Investigations 1.1 to 1.4 are grouped together, but they need not all be carried out before proceeding with text materials. As work in the laboratory proceeds, study assignments can be interspersed: for example, pp. 2–7 (guide questions 1–5), 18–22 (guide questions 6–9), 22–26 (guide questions 10–14). Short study assignments are preferable while you learn the reading capabilities of your students.

It is recommended that Investigations 1.1–1.4 be done with as little modification as possible. This will lessen confusion, point up the importance of a careful reading of procedures, and build the student's confidence. Later, of course, you will often want to modify procedures to take advantage of special local circumstances.

Special attention must be given to proper use of the data book (student's book pp. 777–778 and guide p. T17).

In most modern school systems, students have gained quite enough physical and chemical knowledge in previous grades to provide a sufficient background for Chapter 1. In other systems a brief explanation of such basic terms as "element," "compound," "symbol," "formula," and "chemical change" is all that is needed.

The greatest danger the teacher faces in Chapter 1 is that of becoming enmeshed in the text. *Remember that this is an introductory chapter.* The dependence of producers on solar energy, the dependence of consumers on producers, the interdependence of the living system and the physical environment—throughout the course these things will always be in the background. Because they will be continually reappearing, the depth of understanding achieved at this point need not be great. Therefore, beware of bogging down in a morass of detail. Hit the laboratory hard, move through the text chapter quickly, and get on to Chapter 2 as soon as possible.

## TEACHING NOTES

### RABBITS AND RASPBERRIES
(pp. 2–5)

**p. 3, ¶ 4:** The terms "producer" and "consumer" are approximately equivalent to "autotroph" and "heterotroph." In some classes it may be desirable to use the latter pair, but the former have a firm place in ecological literature despite the distracting connotations that usually surround terms adopted from common language.

**p. 3, Fig. 1·2:** Energy passes from sunlight to producer (acacia) to first-order consumer (giraffe) to second-order consumer (lion). It is desirable to use a variety of organisms from a variety of places to illustrate food chains. Supplement the text and figure examples with examples in the students' own environment, as apple-man-mosquito, garbage-rat-cat-flea.

### THE SCIENTIST'S VIEWPOINT
(pp. 5–7)

**pp. 5–7:** This section does not lay down a "scientific method"; it merely describes the ways scientists work. Observation and verification are regarded as the fundamental processes without which there can be no science. The text material requires no discussion. The four investigations are the proper elaboration.

**p. 5, Fig. 1·3:** The biologist is Dr. Robert C. Stebbins of the University of California. He is shown at work on the pineal eyes of fence lizards. Some of his earlier work is the basis for Investigation 18.3. *Upper left,* field observation and recording of data; *upper right,* measurement; *lower left,* experimentation and use of instruments; *lower right,* assembling a report and graphing data.

## INVESTIGATION 1.1

### OBSERVING LIVING THINGS
(pp. 7–8)

The teaching objective of this investigation is the *process* of observation.

### Setting Up the Laboratory

In early fall a sufficient variety of *living* specimens is probably obtainable in any school situation. Though it is desirable that this investigation be started promptly, there are some advantages to enlisting the aid of pupils in gathering the materials. Pupil contributions, however, are likely to run to the more conspicuous animal forms; so the teacher will have to help. Aim for a balance among plants, animals, and protists.

The following are organisms that have been found useful in this exercise:

For observation under compound microscopes—*Euglena, Volvox, Spirogyra,* yeasts, rotifers, nematodes.

For observation under stereomicroscopes (or hand lenses)—*Rhizopus,* liverworts, mosses, lichens, *Planaria,* small annelids, small insects.

For observation by naked eye—kelps, mushrooms, ferns, *Lemna, Anacharis* (elodea), cacti, *Pelargonium* (flowering), *Begonia* (flowering), sensitive plants, sponges, earthworms, clams, snails, crayfish, centipedes, spiders, beetles, caterpillars, goldfish, frogs, toads, salamanders, snakes, lizards, canaries, rabbits, rats, hamsters.

*Euglena, Volvox,* or similar green, motile organisms are important for giving the student an opportunity to see the difficulty of grouping all organisms as either plants or animals.

Set up microscopes so that illumination and focus are optimal. Provide cultures rich enough so that no student manipulation of microscopes is needed. Of course, the microscopes will arouse much student interest;

but at this time the student should concentrate on what is to be observed; the means of observation will be considered later. Do not attempt too many things at once.

### Directing the Work

Observation time should be at least a minute and a half per specimen (for the first few specimens, somewhat longer). The number of specimens to be observed must be gauged by the time available in the period.

On the day before the observing, go over the directions with your students. The purpose must be made clear. Assign each student (or pair of students) the number of the specimen with which he will begin and announce the total number of specimens. Agree upon a signal for changing from one specimen to the next.

During the observation period the teacher merely gives the signals for change of station and makes sure that the operation proceeds smoothly. Students always feel quite insecure and try to ask innumerable questions about what to look for and how to record their observations. Answer no questions at this time, but encourage students to write in their data books any questions that arise while they are observing.

### Directing Discussion

By the day following observation, students should have worked up their data ("Studying the Data"). During class discussion your primary job is to stress *accuracy of observation*. For example, does a student report roots on a geranium plant because he *sees* roots – or because he thinks that a plant in soil must have roots? Here the distinction is between observation and inference. Secondly, you should try to arouse a *critical attitude* toward the points that students propose as characteristics of plants and animals, using the students' own knowledge of organisms to the greatest extent possible. Obviously no definite conclusion concerning the problem posed in the "Purpose" can be drawn from such limited data. This needs to be pointed out, and the students' natural uneasiness with the tentative and unresolved

must be quieted – perhaps after you conquer your own.

Remember: The *process* of observation rather than the *product* is the teaching objective of this investigation.

## INVESTIGATION 1.2

### THE GERMINATION OF SEEDS: AN EXPERIMENT (pp. 8–11)

This investigation is concerned primarily with the concepts encompassed by the terms "hypothesis," "variable," "control," "data," and "conclusions." The student should gain some insight into these concepts and should note the role of numbers and the use of graphic records in recording observations. He should also see the value of the team approach and the possibility of designing a procedure for simultaneously gathering data on two related hypotheses. The information concerning seed germination is incidental but not without value for chapters where the influence of environmental factors on populations is discussed.

### Materials

Garden seeds are generally available in stores only during the spring and early summer. They may be purchased in advance and stored in insect-proof containers in a cool, dry place. However, seeds used for pet food or for attracting wild birds may be purchased all year. The following are satisfactory: wheat, rye, corn, oats, barley, turnip, radish, vetch, bean (subject to mold, even when treated with fungicide), carrot, parsnip (slow), parsley (very slow), cucumber, squash, sunflower, marigold.

Many seed fungicides are sold commercially. They may be used according to the directions on the packages. However, several substances generally available in the high school laboratory are quite satisfactory: ethyl or isopropyl alcohol, 70% (soak seeds one minute); formaldehyde (dilute commercial formalin 1:500 and soak seeds twenty minutes); sodium hypochlorite (dilute commercial bleach 1:4 and soak seeds fifteen minutes).

Baby-food jars are quite satisfactory as containers for soaking seeds.

If there is a shortage of petri dishes, the soaked seeds can be planted in sand in half-pint milk cartons. Punch holes in the bottoms of the cartons for drainage.

The plastic bags are recommended because schoolrooms are usually rather dry and the dishes dry out quickly. If they are not available, add water as needed with a medicine dropper to avoid disturbing seeds.

## Procedure

Team sizes depend upon availability of materials; 4 or 5 students per team is good. To test the second hypothesis, each team should use a different kind of seed. Kinds that show a wide range of response should be selected. Radish represents one extreme; parsley, the other.

Treatment of seeds with fungicide reduces—but does not eliminate—loss of germination due to injury caused by fungi.

All seeds must be "planted" at the same time. Therefore, a schedule must be set up to insure that all groups of seeds are soaked the proper length of time. If necessary the soaking time for the last group of seeds may vary from two to four hours, depending upon the time at which the class meets on planting day. It is convenient to start the soaking schedule on a Friday and have some students take jars home, where soaking can begin on Saturday and Sunday. In this way a week of observation is available before another weekend occurs.

## Completing the Investigation

Though actual work occupies little time except on the first day and the planting day, the procedure for this exercise extends over many days. During this time it is easy to lose sight of the purpose. Particular attention must be placed on rounding out the experiment after the procedure is completed.

Many students require help in drawing bar graphs. Check the data forms to be sure that data are cumulated from day to day. Go over the sample bar graph (Fig. 1·5). Be sure a form for the recording of

data from different kinds of seeds is provided on the chalkboard. Check to see that teams record on this form only the results from seeds soaked 0 hours.

These are small matters, but attention to such details is especially needed at the outset; the reward for such attention will be clearer discussion at the end of this investigation and better work later.

### Notes on Student Responses

Class discussion of the numbered items in the "Discussion" and "Conclusions" is essential. Note that the questions are concerned entirely with experimental method, not with seed germination per se.

- (1): It may well happen that the difference in germination time for soaked *v.* non-soaked seeds is small. Raise the question of how *big* a difference is necessary before a Yes or No conclusion is valid. In better classes introduce the *idea* (but not the method) of statistical tests of differences.

- (7): The comparison of germination in different kinds of seeds involves a non-quantitative variable. Therefore, there can be no setup that serves as a control except on the purely arbitrary basis of picking one kind against which others are judged. A "control" in the technical sense is not a necessary part of an experiment; only some basis for comparison is needed.

## INVESTIGATION 1.3

### USE OF THE MICROSCOPE: INTRODUCTION (pp. 11–16)

Most students have a great interest in the microscope and the world it opens up for them. This motivation can be of value in introducing some basic ideas about the role of instrumentation in biology. Among these are the following:

1. The microscope is a tool that enables the biologist to extend the range

of his observations beyond that afforded by his unaided vision.

2. The way the tool is used determines the kind and amount of information that the scientist can obtain.

3. Information made available through instruments has given rise to problems that would never have been recognized if these tools had not existed. If the biologist had never been able to see *Euglena*, *Paramecium*, or bacteria, the problem of deciding which organisms are plants and which are animals would be far simpler than it is.

4. The development of science has been closely tied to the development and improvement of instruments that made available crucial information. The microscope is an excellent example of such an instrument.

## Materials

While not suitable for precise work at high magnification, No. 2 glass cover slips are entirely satisfactory for student use at both low and high power. They do not break as easily as the thinner No. 1 cover slips. Plastic cover slips soon become scratched and unusable; they may not represent any saving. It is better to use glass from the beginning and to stress proper handling.

Lens paper is usually supplied in booklets or large sheets. Store it in dustproof containers. Each piece of lens paper should be used only once, then discarded. Be sure students understand that lens paper is to be used for cleaning *lenses* only— *not* slides.

Slides may be cleaned with ordinary paper towels, but a softer grade of paper or cloth is preferable. Facial tissues such as Kleenex are satisfactory.

The print used for financial reports and sports statistics in newspapers is small enough to fit into the low-power field of view. Try to find pieces of newspaper with printing on one side only. The strips should be only about 1 cm long.

Almost any kind of water container can be used in place of finger bowls or beakers.

Ordinary transparent plastic rulers (bearing a metric scale on one margin) may be cut into several pieces with a saw. Short pieces are easy to handle on the stage of the microscope.

Seek out pieces of magazine photographs without printing on the back.

## Procedure

Description of the microscope is necessarily presented in general terms. Fig. 1·6 represents the type that was standard for most of the last half century and is still found in thousands of schools. But during the last decade radical changes have occurred in microscope design. The best course, then, is to exhibit an example of the type to be used by the students, pointing out on it the nomenclature of the parts.

The most elaborate microscope can be of only limited usefulness if illumination is poor. Often a dependable light of suitable color and intensity can be secured only by providing a lamp for each microscope.

Previous student experience, the amount and kind of equipment available, the level of student ability—these and many more factors determine the rate of progress of any particular class. However, most classes require part of a period for introduction of the microscope by the teacher and two full periods for student procedure. Undue haste at this time may result in faulty techniques and the development of poor attitudes toward careful laboratory work. Enough time must be provided so that the student *can* proceed carefully and *can* have an opportunity to do work of high quality.

The questions in the procedure concern observations or simple calculations from observations. Students should briefly note answers in their data books *at the time of observation*. There is no point in having these answers written out and handed in. Check notes informally as the students work.

The data-book notes should serve as a basis for a short class discussion at the completion of the observation periods. Since the notes are based on simple observation only, disagreements between students reflect differences in interpretation of instructions. Do not impose by fiat the "right" observation, but attempt to discover the source of difficulty and then establish consensus. Students have an inordinate yearning for recourse to higher authority; only by iron self-discipline will you be able to resist such flattery. But you *must*.

- (7): For most student microscopes: $10 \times 10 = 100$.
- (8): For most student microscopes: $10 \times 43 = 430$.
- (9): For most student microscopes: approximately 1.5 mm. Expect considerable variation in the estimation of the fraction. Point out that for future reference it is convenient to reach a class decision. But this is *not* a matter of, "He is right; you are wrong."
- (11): For most student microscopes (if $1500\mu$ is accepted as the diameter of the low power): $349\mu$.

Be sure that cleanup at the end of the laboratory period is quick and complete. If this is neglected now, bad laboratory habits will plague you for the rest of the year.

## INVESTIGATION 1.4

### USE OF THE MICROSCOPE: BIOLOGICAL MATERIAL
(pp. 16–18)

The student now uses his microscope to observe biological materials.

### Materials

To prepare iodine–potassium-iodide ($I_2KI$) solution, dissolve 15 g of KI in 1 liter of water. Dissolve about 3 g of iodine in this solution. Small bottles with dropper caps are useful for dispensing the stain.

White potatoes should be cut into 3-mm cubes (approximately). If placed in a little water in a dish, the pieces can be kept through several periods of the day.

To prepare a yeast culture, add approximately 1 g of dried yeast to about 5 ml of tap water and mix to form a thick paste. In a glass jar of approximately 400-ml capacity, place about 250 ml of molasses diluted to the color of strong tea. Pour the paste into the jar and stir to disperse the yeast. Place the uncovered jar in a warm, dark place. The culture should be set up several hours before use. Dispense in small beakers or in baby-food jars.

During September excellent cultures of mixed microorganisms can be dipped up from ponds. If opportunity to make natural collections is lacking, a laboratory culture of "mixed protozoa" may be purchased.

### Procedure

As in Investigation 1.3, students should jot down in their data books the answers — *in the laboratory and at the time of observation.*

A brief class discussion should follow the laboratory work, but there is no need to achieve consensus on all observations. Instead, emphasize the possible *reasons for differences* in observations.

- (2): Detection of the laminated structure of starch grains depends upon lighting. Many students will not see the structure. Does it exist, or are students who report it seeing something that isn't there? This is a good opportunity for a brief discussion of artifacts in microscopy.
- (4): Differences depend upon a gradient of stain concentration and may easily be missed as the stain spreads.
- (5): See • (2).
- (7): If potato starch grains turn up in the yeast preparations, students have not used sufficient care in cleaning slides.
- (8): Students may have difficulty recognizing that the presence of smaller organisms attached to larger ones indicates the occurrence of budding. An explanatory drawing may be needed. This may be recalled when the concept of an "individual" is discussed in Chapter 2.
- (11): It is unusual to see much structure in unstained yeasts. Nuclei might be seen in stained organisms.

• (13): This brings up depth of focus. A chalkboard sketch may help to clarify the idea.

• (14): In magnifying space, a microscope necessarily magnifies speed.

## THE FOUNDATIONS OF LIFE
(pp. 18–26)

**p. 19, ¶ 5:** The level of consumership is not an invariable property of each kind of organism but may change according to what is eaten. However, relatively few organisms are as omnivorous as man.

**p. 20, note 1:** This may lead to a discussion of the idea that *scientific* inquiry is limited to those questions for which verifiable data can be gathered from the natural world. There are questions of philosophy, aesthetics, and religion that are not within the realm of scientific inquiry. (A similar point is made by Problems 7 and 9.)

**p. 20, ¶ 4:** Elementary-school health courses seem to have been very effective in impressing the healthfulness of sunshine. Point out the animals that live in caves and in the deep sea totally without light. If time permits, vitamin-D synthesis may be mentioned. But insist that no way is known by which the energy absorbed while a human organism is lying on a beach can be transformed into the energy required for muscle contraction.

**p. 21, ¶ 2, lines 6–8:** The reference is to chemosynthetic bacteria.

**p. 21, ¶ 3:** This idea is developed further in Fig. 1 · 12.

**p. 21, ¶ 4:** The term "saprovore" is later used at times in the wider sense of anything that eats dead organic matter.

**p. 25, note 1:** Carping criticism is easy in biology. Even here we can bring up the matter of viruses, though it is doubtful that any student will do so. And, *if* viruses are alive, are they *organisms?*

**p. 25, ¶ 3:** Borrow a periodic chart from the chemistry teacher, but use it chiefly to show how few of the natural chemical elements are involved in the chemistry of organisms.

**p. 25, Fig. 1 · 15:** The absence of living things would have little effect upon the hydrologic cycle, but it would virtually eliminate the carbon cycle.

**p. 26, Fig. 1 · 16:** The biogeochemical cycles of all elements except hydrogen, oxygen, nitrogen, and carbon are similar to that of calcium.

## INVESTIGATION 1.5

### INTERRELATIONSHIPS OF PRODUCERS AND CONSUMERS
(pp. 26–28)

Unlike the other investigations in Chapter 1, this one is concerned primarily with the subject matter of the chapter rather than the methodology of science. It can easily be performed as a demonstration set up by a small team of students.

If the class has had little or no previous science, the teacher may demonstrate the properties of oxygen and of carbon dioxide. Directions for doing this can be obtained from any conventional manual for high school chemistry. But avoid becoming too deeply involved in the chemistry. If such demonstration seems unnecessary, a brief, silent demonstration of the effect of exhaled air on bromthymol blue is advantageous.

### Materials

If screw-cap culture tubes are not available, standard $20 \times 120$-mm test tubes, 4-oz prescription bottles, or 4-oz screw-cap specimen jars may be substituted. After the experimental materials are placed in them, containers should be tightly closed and sealed with paraffin.

Elodea and small snails are available wherever aquarium supplies are sold. You should culture them routinely.

Bromthymol blue is used because of its narrow pH range: pH 6.0 (yellow) to pH 7.6 (blue). An 0.1% stock solution may be prepared by dissolving 0.5 g of bromthymol-blue powder in 500 ml of distilled water. To the stock solution add, drop by drop, a very dilute solution of ammonium hydroxide until the solution turns blue. If the water in your community is alkaline, the addition of ammonium hydroxide may not be needed. (Note: Solutions of bromthymol blue purchased from supply houses are usually made up with alcohol; such solutions kill organisms.)

Use of fluorescent light will avoid excess heat.

## Discussion

In light a green plant *appears* to play a role in the exchange of $CO_2$ and $O_2$ opposite to that of animals:

$$\text{carbon dioxide + water} \underset{\text{respiration}}{\overset{\text{photosynthesis}}{\rightleftharpoons}} \text{food + oxygen}$$

But respiration, of course, goes on continuously in *both* green plants and animals. In light, green plants reuse almost immediately in photosynthesis the $CO_2$ released from respiration, so it does not accumulate in the environment. In darkness, however, photosynthesis does not occur; then the released carbon dioxide is not reused. Therefore, bromthymol blue in a culture tube containing elodea in darkness turns green, because carbon dioxide from respiration is accumulating in the water, acidifying it. When photosynthesis begins on exposure to light, carbon dioxide is used more rapidly than it is released. After a short time, the plant must begin to extract carbon dioxide from the water. As the amount of carbon dioxide in the water decreases, the bromthymol blue reverts to its blue color.

So much for the theory of the experiment. In actuality many strange things may happen, testing the ingenuity of teacher and students to explain. For example, Tube A2 may be green or yellow at the top and blue at the bottom. (In this case, it is usually found that the snail is at the top of the tube and the elodea at the bottom.)

- (1): In most cases the snail in Tube 1 dies first, but it may live longer than the snail in Tube 2 in the *dark*—since, in dark, both plant and animal are using $O_2$ from the water.
- (5): If many microorganisms are present in the pond water, their respiration

may produce sufficient $CO_2$ to cause a change in the indicator.

- (9): Use this opportunity to involve the class in making hypotheses. There are many that could be made, but focus attention on statements that *can be tested*. Examples: Both plants and animals give off $CO_2$ as a by-product of life activities. Light destroys $CO_2$ in the presence of plants.

---

## THE WEB OF LIFE (pp. 28–31)

**p. 28, note 2:** The best term for these "plant foods" (mostly inorganic and, in any case, not of bioenergetic importance) is "nutrient" (see p. 48).

**p. 28, ¶ 3:** Although frequently used in this sense, the term "food" is certainly not restricted by biologists. The reason for the arbitrary restriction is simplification. Attention is focused on energy flow and much ambiguity is avoided.

**p. 29, Fig. 1 · 18:** Note that individual arrows do not go to each kind of saprovore — but rather to all the first-order saprovores, all the second-order, etc., and that many arrows could run from the various saprovores to things that eat them. Organic objects (a dead leaf, for example) may be chewed by millepedes, ants, springtails, sow bugs, snails, mites, etc. This action helps to break down the leaf. The partially decomposed leaf, as well as the organic substances in the feces from these animals, makes a good substrate for growth of bacteria and fungi, which further reduce the substances. Finally the entire mess goes through the intestines of earthworms or roundworms. Whenever a saprovore is working on substances derived from plant material, it is a first-order consumer.

**p. 30, Fig. 1 · 19:** This diagram introduces an important concept—continuity of biological processes. Can both Figures 1 · 18 and 1 · 19 be read with equal confidence? Here is an opportunity to foster the habit of evaluating sources of data.

**p. 31, ¶ 3:** In our 1968 edition the most frequent current meaning of "biosphere" is used instead of the specialized meaning—the system of living things exclusive of their abiotic environment—used in the 1963 edition. In some respects this seems to be a regression in clarity, but the hoped-for increase in use of Lamont Cole's "ecosphere" (= "biosphere" in our present sense) has not occurred.

## MAN AND THE BIOSPHERE
(pp. 32–33)

From the viewpoint of the beliefs expressed in Part 1 (pp. T5–T7), this is the crucial and climactic section of Chapter 1. But excessive discussion at this time will not increase its effectiveness.

**p. 32, ¶ 1, line 5:** Note the "if." In their reaction to anti-evolutionists, biologists sometimes become overly dogmatic. We prefer to let the evidence speak for itself over the whole span of the book.

**p. 32, Fig. 1·21:** The questions, of course, are rhetorical.

**p. 33, ¶ 2:** The tardy and incidental acknowledgment of the meaning of "biology" is deliberate.

**p. 33, ¶ 3:** The questions are worded in such a way that they should be understandable—as *questions*—with only the background of Chapter 1. They should be much more meaningful at the end of the year's work in biology. All discussion of them should be postponed until that time.

## GUIDE QUESTIONS (p. 34)

**8.** Note that this question requires reading the caption to Fig. 1·12. This makes the point that most of the illustrations have content and must not be ignored.

## PROBLEMS (pp. 34–35)

**1.** Coal, oil, and gas are "fossil hydrocarbons"—remains of plants and animals that were only partially decomposed by saprovores before they were buried and that were later altered by heat and pressure within the earth.

**2.** The balance of nature would remain. But the point of equilibrium might be considerably shifted. Homeostatic adjustment of other populations would compensate for change in one population. How long is "permanent"? If an algal population is greatly increased, populations of consumers might increase. Effects of an increase in a fish population would depend primarily upon the consumer order of the fish.

**3.** If the earth is not itself considered to be derived from solar matter: volcanic and hot-spring energy, energy of radioactivity, nuclear energy, chemical energy in compounds formed by processes within the earth (but not chemical energy in substances—such as nitrogen compounds—formed by atmospheric processes).

**4.** It is virtually impossible to define life in a satisfactory way—and this is the point here. But if a student works at it, he can get some good *characteristics* of life.

**6.** A decrease in oxygen in the atmosphere and subsequent changes in the thermal climate resulting from changes in energy absorption and transmission in the atmosphere.

**8.** The main point here is to design a lowweight but highly efficient system that *recycles* materials. Consider starting with the widest *variety* of small producers and consumers, putting them in the kind of space environment they will be subjected to, and then letting the *system* select the proper group of organisms that will maintain a steady state.

**9.** This is another approach to the problem of limits to scientific inquiry. What kind of *data* can be collected to prove something is *absent*? This leads to a discussion of the nature of proof. There will be more on this later (p. 643).

**10.** Less than half a dozen years ago this might have been a difficult task. It is no longer.

## SUPPLEMENTARY MATERIALS

### Invitations to Enquiry

The "Invitations to Enquiry" in the *Biology Teacher's Handbook* (reference: page T35) are a valuable resource. In using them, the teacher must keep in mind both the subject-matter background of the students and their degree of sophistication in scientific methodology. For students of average ability and little background in biology, the following are recommended:

*Invitation 3* **(pp. 57–59 of the *Handbook*).** Both the subject (seed germination) and the topic (misinterpretation of data) are closely aligned with the work of Chapter 1. Because the written materials to be given the student are brief, this invitation lends itself to presentation by means of a series of transparencies on an overhead projector.

*Invitation 11* **(pp. 83–84 of the *Handbook*).** The subject matter requires no special knowledge on the part of the student. The topic (construction of hypotheses) provides greater depth for Investigations 1.2 and 1.5.

### Audiovisual Materials

In a broad sense, specimens and all the paraphernalia of the laboratory can be thought of as audiovisual materials. Here the term is used in a restricted sense. Primarily it means motion-picture films and filmstrips; occasionally it refers to phonograph records and a few miscellaneous items.

At the outset it is desirable to establish firmly the biologist's primary concern with living things and his need to work with them firsthand. Because such establishment requires a large amount of time in the laboratory, and because it is important to move rather quickly through Chapter 1, it is recommended that little time be devoted to audiovisual materials. But you may wish to use some of the following items:

**Filmstrip:** *Energy and Life* (Young America Films: "Principles of Biology," Part 1). Black & White. McGraw-Hill Book Co., Inc. An excellent summary of Chapter 1. But the somewhat juvenile character of the first few frames may make its use undesirable in classes sensitive to their senior-high status.

**Motion-picture film:** *The World of Life* (AIBS Secondary Film Series). 16 mm. Color. 20 min. McGraw-Hill Book Co., Inc. Dr. Bentley Glass discusses the nature of biological science. The film does not follow the content of Chapter 1, but it clearly develops the attitudes that are discussed in "Preface: For the Student" and "The Scientist's Viewpoint" (Chapter 1) and that are implicit in the laboratory investigations.

**Phonograph record:** *The Scientists Speak: Biology.* Harcourt Brace and Co., 1959. The first talk on this record (by Dr. George Gaylord Simpson) has the same purpose as the film *The World of Life*. It is, of course, less vivid, but it is shorter and has qualities that make it appeal to some students who are overwhelmed by the film. Moreover, it does not become involved in cellular and molecular biology.

### Teacher's References

The "Suggested Readings" in the student's book may be useful to teachers; conversely, some materials in the following list may be of value as assignments to certain students:

ABERCROMBIE, M., C. J. HICKMAN, and M. L. JOHNSON. *A Dictionary of Biology*. Baltimore: Penguin Books, 1961. (A good small dictionary that does more than list pat definitions.)

AMERICAN ASSOCIATION FOR THE ADVANCEMENT OF SCIENCE. *A Guide to Science Reading*. 2nd ed. New York: New American Library, 1966. (This paperback guide to paperback science books should be useful for advising interested students in their quest for printed resources.)

BATES, M. *The Nature of Natural History*. Rev. ed. New York: Charles Scribner's Sons, 1962. Chapter 18. (Provides good background on the nature of biological investigation.)

BIOLOGICAL SCIENCES CURRICULUM STUDY. *The Biology Teacher's Handbook.* New York: John Wiley and Sons, 1963. (Source for "Invitations to Enquiry." Contains useful discussions of classroom procedures and background in selected fields of science.)

CONANT, JAMES B. *Science and Common Sense.* New Haven, Conn.: Yale University Press, 1961. (A good brief background for some viewpoints implicit in Chapter 1.)

GATES, D. M. *Energy Exchange in the Biosphere.* New York: Harper and Row, 1962. (This goes far deeper than the understanding essential for teaching Chapter 1, but the teacher who reads it—even if he skips most of the mathematics—will gain an appreciation of a concept basic not only to the chapter but to the whole *Green Version.*)

GRAY, PETER. *The Dictionary of the Biological Sciences.* New York: Reinhold Publishing Corp., 1967. (A necessity in the school library; Abercrombie *et al.* suffices for the classroom.)

PHILLIPSON, J. *Ecological Energetics.* New York: St. Martin's Press, 1966. (Parallels Gates, but simpler.)

PYKE, M. *The Boundaries of Science.* Baltimore: Penguin Books, 1963. (A small book to supplement Conant.)

# 2

# Individuals
# and
# Populations

## MAJOR IDEAS

1. The individual organism—regardless of difficulties in definition—is a primary unit of biological study.

2. Individuals may be grouped in different ways. The indefinite
   but versatile term "population" is useful for such groupings.

3. Quantitative study of populations involves the idea of density—the number of individuals per unit of space.

4. Populations continually change in size. Such changes are
   determined by the interaction of four rates: natality, mortality,
   immigration, and emigration.

5. These rates are affected by biotic and abiotic environmental
   factors that are continually interacting.

6. Therefore, the study of natural populations is immensely complicated, and the application to natural populations of results
   from experimental populations is fraught with uncertainties.

7. In general, however, natural populations appear to be maintained in a steady state by the continuous operation of homeostatic mechanisms.

8. Mathematics is an essential tool in biology.

9. The species population is an entity of great practical and
   theoretical importance in biology.

## PLANNING AHEAD

If you have not already decided to move Investigation 3.1 forward, consider the season and the weather prospects in your locality. Perhaps this investigation had best be undertaken before the long Investigation 2.2 is started.

If Investigation 3.1 can be delayed, then preparations for Investigation 2.2 should be completed by the time that classwork on Chapter 2 is begun.

If Investigation 3.1 is to be done during classwork on Chapter 2, many decisions concerning procedure and equipment must be made at once.

Check the number of thermometers available for Investigation 3.2.

It is not too early to begin accumulating living animals for Chapter 4. Obtain as great a variety of individual animals as possible. Orders should be placed for the hydras, planarians, earthworms, crayfish, frogs, and brine shrimp or *Daphnia* required for Investigation 4.3.

## GUIDELINES

The light touch recommended for the teaching of Chapter 1 cannot be continued into Chapter 2. The concepts of "individual" and "population," first encountered here, form a foundation on which much of the remainder of the course rests. In Chapter 3 communities are regarded as interacting populations. In Section Two the species population is the unit of taxonomy. The "patterns" discussed in Section Three are composed of individuals grouped as species populations. Though these concepts sink into the background in the first part of Section Four, the individual emerges again as a unit of biological organization in Chapter 15. From then on, individuals and populations remain the focus of attention. So thorough study of Chapter 2 is essential.

Again in contrast to the recommendations for Chapter 1, work on this chapter should begin with the textbook. After a brief overview to enable students to discover its scheme of organization, Chapter 2 can best be assigned in three bites: pp. 36–43 (guide questions 1–6), 45–52 (guide questions 7–10), and 56–69 (guide questions 11–16). Soon after students have been exposed to the first of these assignments, attention may be shifted to Investigation 2.1. Later, after Investigation 2.2 has been started, the mathematical ideas in the first assignment can be more extensively developed. The second and third assignments may be taken up during the ten days required for growing the yeast populations of Investigation 2.2.

The student encounters many difficulties in this chapter, and the teacher must be prepared to assist him. The major difficulties are: abstract ideas; new vocabulary (sometimes disguised as familiar words); a long, difficult laboratory procedure in Investigation 2.2; and, worst of all (in the view of many students), mathematics.

For teachers and students who regard textbooks merely as fodder for memory work, the *Green Version* has proved to be disconcerting: it brings up issues and then fails to resolve them. On the other hand, teachers and students who use textbooks as a jumping-off point—a basis for discussion—welcome this characteristic. Such unresolved, open-ended exposition recurs throughout the book, but specific examples can be pointed out in Chapter 2: On page 37 (last paragraph), opportunity exists for pursuing the matter of definition in science. On page 38, the last paragraph raises a point that reappears as an important theme in Chapter 18. On page 59, paragraph 1, and on page 65, paragraph 4, other unresolved problems appear. The teacher who disregards such opportunities cannot begin to achieve BSCS objectives (pages T2–T3).

Study of population density and of the interaction of rates must be guided by the methods of the mathematics teacher; that is, examples must be worked through with the class, and then students must practice with numerous problems. Some practice can be obtained from Problem 1, page 70, and from the problems on pages T47–T49. But you will have to devise many problems of your own. Problems with a local flavor are, of course, best. Review of such problems should occur occasionally during the several months following "completion" of work on Chapter 2.

Both at the beginning and at the end of Chapter 2, the difficulty of definition is discussed – first in connection with individuals, finally with regard to species. From this the student might get the impression that slipshod language is characteristic of science. Fortunately the interposition of the concepts of density and rate, with their mathematical expression, helps to counteract such an impression.

## TEACHING NOTES

### INDIVIDUALS (pp. 36–38)

The term "individual" is appropriate. As a living unit of the biosphere, an individual can properly be said to be indivisible. Where divisibility exists, the result is new individuals. Portions of an individual can be maintained – as in tissue cultures – but this is obviously an artificiality.

**p. 37, Fig. 2 · 1:** The question in the caption is rhetorical.

**p. 37, ¶ 3:** The use of pseudo-precise language where ideas are imprecise involves just as much falsity as does the use of imprecise language for ideas that are precise.

### POPULATIONS (pp. 38–43)

**p. 40, Fig. 2 · 4:** The density is .0144 trees/m², or 144 trees/hectare.

**p. 40, Fig. 2 · 5:** The density of dusty clover is .0147 plants/m² in the field as a whole and .0424 plants/m² in the northwest quarter. Densities of blazing star and goldenrod can also be calculated and compared. This illustration is based upon studies of old-field succession in Michigan (S. A. Cain and F. C. Evans, *Contributions from the Laboratory of Vertebrate Biology*, **52:** 1–11, 1952 [University of Michigan]).

**pp. 40–41:** A rate of change in population size without consideration of the space factor can be calculated in the same way as a rate of change in density. For some students the size calculation may appear simpler; if so, the teacher may provide an example before considering the density case.

**p. 41, Fig. 2 · 6:** Relate the meaning of a change in slope to the interpretation of the line graph drawn in Investigation 2.1. The text example uses a decline because the investigation deals with an increase.

**p. 41, note 2:** A vertical line has a zero time component and therefore indicates infinity. A rate may approach but cannot actually reach it.

**p. 42:** Be sure that students actually consider each of the rhetorical questions.

**p. 42, note 5:** The density after three minutes would be 20.

### INVESTIGATION 2.1

### POPULATION GROWTH: A MODEL (pp. 43–45)

This investigation of a hypothetical population provides a basis for comparing the real populations encountered in Investigation 2.2 (a closed population with a fixed food supply and no provision for elimination of wastes) and Investigation 2.3 (an open, natural population). It also continues the task begun in Investigation 1.1 – to introduce the student to scientific methodology. Therefore attention must first be directed to pages 43–44, where the use of conceptual models and the role of assumptions are discussed.

### Materials

Semi-log graph paper may be obtained in 1, 2, 3, 4, 5, or more cycles. Such paper is logarithmic on one axis and is regularly spaced on the other. The 1971 population is 31,250 birds, and 5-cycle paper is sufficient for this. Paper satisfactory for this exercise can be produced on school duplicators from stencils prepared by the teacher. The finer subdivisions shown on commercial paper may be omitted.

### Procedure

The computations and the construction of the graph on the ordinary grid can be done at home. However, some previous groundwork must be laid in class. This should include at least some discussion of assumptions. In addition, many teachers find a review of line-graph construction advantageous. Often students attempt to solve the problem of choosing a suitable scale for the ordinary graph by arbitrarily changing the value of intervals on the vertical axis. Such students, of course, have no idea of the meaning of slope. Now, however, it is only necessary to point out that a scale must have some mathematical consistency.

To some students the semi-log grid appears as arbitrary as their own. But it is not necessary to become deeply involved in mathematics. Briefly develop the series $10^1$, $10^2$, $10^3$, $10^4$, etc.; note the correspondence of exponents to the number of zeros in the series 10, 100, 1000, 10,000, etc. Direct students to label the cycles on the semi-log graph paper *units, tens, hundreds,* etc. Point out that each succeeding cycle represents numbers ten times greater than those represented by the preceding cycle. Link this idea with the fact that within each cycle the system of second-order subdivisions separates spaces of decreasing width. Then illustrate the plotting of points, using numbers different from those used in the investigation.

The *model* is the whole construct. It involves a *hypothetical* population. This term is used because the population concerns an "If…, then…" situation.

### Discussion

- (1): The principal advantage of semi-log paper is that it permits the plotting of very large numbers in later generations while showing clearly the small increments in earlier generations. The straight line obtained on the semi-log paper indicates a con-

stantly accelerating growth rate. If it is known that a rate is of this kind, the plotting of only two points will establish the slope. Extrapolation is then easy. With most classes only the principal advantage need be stressed.

- (2) and • (3): Unfortunately, many students with competency in making graphs have little knowledge of how to interpret them. Therefore, considerable attention should be given to the concept of slope. The relation of slope to rate is basic in the interpretation of graphs. Here it is discussed simply, since all slopes in the graphs for this exercise are positive. But if there seems to be no danger of confusing the students, the significance of zero slopes and negative slopes can also be discussed, reducing the difficulties to be encountered in Investigation 2.2. The graphs in Chapter 2 should be helpful—especially Figure 2 · 6.

- (5): With a continuance of the assumptions, the line on the ordinary graph would approach the vertical.

- (6): On the semi-log graph the line would continue on the same slope.

- (7): The main point is the growth at an accelerating rate.

- (8): This should be left completely open to argument at this point. The idea of limiting factors and the impossibility of an infinitely large population will come later.

### Further Investigations

The last of these investigations invites the students to devise other problems. The usual difficulty here is vagueness in stating the assumptions.

---

### POPULATIONS AND ENVIRONMENT (pp. 45–52)

**p. 46, Fig. 2 · 8:** This is a retouched photograph of one of the pens used by Dr. Charles Southwick (now of Johns Hopkins) in the "crowding" experiment at the University of Wisconsin. The "English" experiments were conducted at Oxford by Drs. Peter Croweroft and F. P. Rowe. The original reports of these experiments appeared in *Ecology*, **36:** 212–225, 1955, and in the *Proceedings of the Zoological Society of London*, **199:** 359–370, 1937.

**p. 47, ¶ 4:** This points up the importance of careful description of methods in a published report of a scientific experiment. Without it no verification is possible.

**p. 48, ¶ 1:** Uncooked plant foods are, of course, frequently alive when eaten. Students are often surprised by this idea.

**p. 50, Fig. 2·11:** The upper photograph was taken in Arizona, the lower one in Idaho. The difference in density is at least in part a matter of difference in precipitation/evaporation ratio.

**p. 51, Fig. 2·12:** The south-facing slopes, because of their relationship to solar rays, receive more solar radiation per day and a greater total radiation per year than do the north-facing slopes. Therefore, the south-facing slopes are hotter and drier than the north-facing slopes. In a land where precipitation is barely enough for tree growth, these factors cause the striking difference between north and south slopes.

## INVESTIGATION 2.2

### STUDY OF A YEAST POPULATION
(pp. 53–56)

Students must obtain some firsthand experience with population dynamics. This investigation forms the hard core of such experience in the laboratory, and without it, Investigations 2.1 and 2.3 are meaningless. Investigation 2.2 builds upon the student's experience with experimental methods (Investigation 1.2) and applies his growing ability to use the microscope (Investigations 1.3 and 1.4). Furthermore, it greatly extends his conception of teamwork in science and his appreciation of the value of replication. The teacher *must* overcome any temptation to retreat before the manifold difficulties that are certainly present. Re-

member: this investigation *has been done* over and over again in a wide variety of classroom situations!

Considerations of time and space severely limit the choice of organisms. On both counts microscopic organisms are ruled out. Algae reproduce somewhat too slowly; bacteria are too small for the direct observation needed to provide a sense of reality. Common yeast seems to be the most suitable organism: it reproduces rapidly, its requirements are simple, it is easily visible with the "high dry" lens of the microscope, it responds readily to decrease in food concentration and increase in toxic substances, and it is an economically important organism already well known to students by name and appearance (Investigation 1.4).

Because of the time span it requires, this investigation should be set up early in the work on Chapter 2. Ideally, Investigation 2.1 should be completed before 2.2 is started, but this is not absolutely necessary; the purpose of Investigation 2.2 will be clear any time after 2.1 has begun.

From start to finish, this exercise requires two weeks, but much of the class time during this span is utilized in other work. Time needs can be broken down as follows:

1. Procedure A requires about two-thirds of a class period.

2. In each subsequent class period, inoculation requires not more than five minutes and involves only three students.

3. Procedure B requires two full class periods.

4. Discussion of the results, if it is properly done, will require at least one full period.

### Materials

The medium can be prepared by a group of students. For this job the following will be required:

2000-ml Erlenmeyer flask or Pyrex
    saucepan of similar capacity
Graduated cylinder
Large stirring rod or tablespoon
Source of heat

Test-tube basket

Autoclave or pressure cooker

Test tubes of about 20-ml capacity, 1 per student plus 1 per team of 10 students

Square of aluminum foil, large enough to form a cap over a test tube, 1 per student

Balance

Spatula

Clean, soft cloth

Yeast extract, 2.5 g

Monobasic potassium phosphate, 2.0 g

Glucose, 40.0 g

Peptone, 5.0 g

Distilled water, 1000 ml

You need 10 ml of medium for each student, plus 10 ml in addition for each team. (The quantities listed above will make a little more than 1000 ml of medium.) Compute the needed amount of each material. Weigh out the amounts of dry materials and add them to the required volume of water. Dissolve the materials by stirring continually over a low-heat source. When properly prepared, the medium is sparkling clear and slightly yellow in color.

Pour 10 ml of the medium into each tube (1 tube per student plus 1 tube per team). Shape a square of aluminum foil as a cap over the mouth of each test tube. With the caps fitted lightly over the tubes, sterilize at 15 lb pressure in an autoclave or pressure cooker for fifteen minutes. Tighten the foil caps and store the sterile, cooled test tubes in a refrigerator.

Few high schools have access to an autoclave. But a large pressure cooker of the kind used for home canning is an essential investment; later investigations, involving microorganisms, require it. For Investigation 2.2, however, it is *possible* to get along without a pressure cooker. With luck, a sufficient degree of sterilization may be obtained by boiling the medium and the tubes in water for ten minutes. If this is done, an uninoculated tube of medium should be boiled as a control.

Aluminum-foil caps are easy to make. Use a square of foil a little more than three times as wide as the test tube. Place the mouth of the test tube in the center of the square; fold the foil edges down by running the tube through a hole made by curving the forefinger around to the base of the thumb. Bacteriological cotton plugs *can* be used instead of foil, but making them requires an extra skill—and they are messy.

Brewer's yeast tablets, obtainable at any drugstore, may be substituted for yeast extract. Mix the tablets in about one-fifth the amount of water to be used in making medium sufficient for one class. Let stand overnight, decant, and then filter.

Sodium phosphate or dibasic potassium phosphate may be substituted for monobasic potassium phosphate.

Sucrose may be substituted for glucose, but this substitution is less desirable than those mentioned above.

Beef-bouillon cubes may be substituted for peptone. Two cubes are sufficient for 1000 ml of hot water. To remove the fat, cool the mixture somewhat and filter.

If the mineral content of the local water is low, tap water may be used in place of distilled water. Or the water may be treated with a demineralizer.

If any of the materials for preparation of medium and their substitutes are simply impossible to obtain, a water solution of molasses (about 10%) *not* containing sulfur dioxide may be used.

Though 10 ml is a convenient and efficient amount of medium per student, as little as 8 ml may be used—or as much as 15. But the amount in each test tube must be the same. If all the tubes have the same diameter, time can be saved in dispensing the medium by making a water "blank." Carefully measure out 10 ml of water and pour into the "blank" tube; then pour medium into each tube to the level of the water in the "blank."

When a pressure cooker is used, care must be taken to bring the contents back to room pressure slowly, to avoid having the caps blown off the tubes.

## Procedure A

The investigation is written with a class of 30 students in mind—three teams of 10. Each student is responsible for inoculating a tube. Students are numbered according to tube numbers; each tube number corresponds to the number of days the tube is to be incubated before counting day. On counting day students work in pairs—No. 1 with No. 2, No. 3 with No. 4, etc.

Of course, few classes consist of exactly 30 students. If there are fewer than 30, the number of incubation days can be reduced to 8 (requiring teams of 8 students), but then the chances of obtaining a clear decline in population are reduced. A better plan would be to have some students take responsibility for more than one tube. Such doubling up should be done with tubes having lower numbers, because they are less likely to require dilution on counting day.

For classes of more than 30 students, other kinds of adjustment are necessary. First, an additional student may be assigned to work with the tube inoculated on counting day, making the number of students on each team 11. Second, extra students may be assigned general duties connected with distribution of and accounting for materials—and they can also substitute for the inevitable absentees. Finally, a small separate team may be assigned the task of preparing the medium.

Each team should have a captain and a co-captain. They are responsible for seeing that the tubes are inoculated according to schedule by team members. Make a chart showing classes, teams, and tube numbers, with the name of the assigned student opposite each of the numbers. Placed on the bulletin board, such a chart helps remind students of their tube numbers and may be used to check daily inoculations.

For ease in handling the sets of tubes, it is advisable to designate each team with an individual letter that is not repeated in other classes: Teams A, B, and C might be in one class; Teams D, E, and F might be in another; and so on. With this system, containers holding each team's set of tubes can be distinctively labeled. The containers may be bacteriological culture baskets, or students may be asked to bring No. 3 cans from home.

Students may experience some difficulty using the glass-marking crayon on test tubes. Small pieces of masking tape or Labelon tape may be used instead. Both team letter and tube number may then be written with ordinary pencil. Test tubes with ground areas on which pencil may be used are also available. If desired, the eleventh tube may be placed with the team sets and marked O.

Experience has shown that fairly uniform initial populations can be obtained by the apparently haphazard method of inoculation. It *is* important to exercise some care in picking out grains that are as close to the same size as possible. It is not necessary that uniformity of grain size be obtained among teams—only within teams.

No matter which day of the week is chosen for beginning the inoculations, at least one weekend will be involved in the schedule. How can inoculations be made on weekends? One solution: the teacher may do the work himself. Another: students may inoculate the tubes at home.

The main objection to the latter solution is not so much the small error that is likely to result from the change in environmental conditions as it is the danger involved in students' carrying glassware —especially on a crowded school bus.

The cultures may be incubated at room temperature (normally considered to be 22°C). At this temperature the populations should be declining (the "death phase" of the growth curve) during the ninth and tenth days. It is important to keep the cultures from drafts and sudden changes in temperature. The cultures may be most conveniently kept in a cupboard against an inside wall of the building. The development of the population may be accelerated by increasing the temperature of incubation, or, conversely, it may be slowed down by lowering the temperature. If facilities for

| TEAM | DAYS | | | | | | | | | | |
|---|---|---|---|---|---|---|---|---|---|---|---|
| | 0 | 1 | 2 | 3 | 4 | 5 | 6 | 7 | 8 | 9 | 10 |
| A | 18 | 218 | 219 | 162 | 355 | 95 | 175 | 132 | 167 | 485 | 136 |
| B | 24 | 63 | 69 | 283 | 281 | 161 | 147 | 365 | 199 | 227 | 314 |
| C | 39 | 61 | 363 | 56 | 20 | 114 | 322 | 41 | 66 | 87 | 38 |
| D | 36 | 53 | 75 | 710 | 56 | 240 | 230 | 190 | 200 | 630 | 340 |
| E | | 30 | 210 | 45 | 59 | 46 | 82 | 453 | 93 | 60 | 88 |
| F | 47 | 71 | 73 | 170 | 20 | | 242 | 660 | 73 | 110 | 55 |
| G | 16 | 25 | 35 | 980 | 540 | 50 | 350 | 165 | 14 | 160 | 212 |
| H | 48 | 42 | 36 | 650 | 760 | 500 | 305 | 356 | 313 | 65 | 69 |
| K | 23 | 344 | 60 | 45 | 90 | 330 | 54 | 250 | 37 | 138 | 74 |
| Total | 251 | 907 | 1140 | 3101 | 2181 | 1536 | 1907 | 2612 | 1162 | 1962 | 1326 |
| Average | 31 | 101 | 127 | 345 | 242 | 192 | 212 | 290 | 129 | 218 | 147 |

Figure T–1

maintaining higher or lower temperatures are available, some classes might be assigned to incubate their cultures at such temperatures. On the whole, however, this is not recommended, and for two reasons: (1) it introduces a variable that, while interesting, is irrelevant to the purpose of the experiment; and (2) it reduces the number of replications available for "smoothing out" the population curve.

### Procedure B

In Investigation 1.4, students observed yeast organisms; but they have not attempted counts before, and they are still novices in manipulating the microscope.

A day or two before counting day, which is the day after Tube 1 has been inoculated, students may be given opportunity to practice the counting technique. First, ask for counts of the 20 individuals in Figure 2·14. Then provide a fairly dense culture of yeasts and have counts made under the microscope. Just as they will on counting day, have the students work in pairs, checking each other's counts. Have all students practice diluting, even though not all will need to do this on counting day. The medicine droppers should be calibrated for number of drops per milliliter; not all deliver 20 drops/ml.

If counting cannot be completed in one day, the cultures must be stored in a refrigerator, so that the population of the first day is maintained with as little change as possible. There is no need for sterile techniques on counting day, because the cultures will not be used again.

One of the most common sources of error in making cell counts is an uneven distribution of cells in the medium when the sample is removed. The student should shake the tube vigorously and then make a quick transfer to the slide. Since maintenance of sterile conditions is not essential, adequate shaking should be no problem. The dropper should be thoroughly rinsed after each sampling. Before counting is begun, the floating organisms should be allowed to come to rest.

Adequate instructions for making counts are included in the student's book. At this point the best advice for the teacher is to read instructions carefully and to anticipate (on the basis of his knowledge of students) as many difficulties as possible, taking steps to obviate them. And insist that students follow directions. Link this insistence not to obedience but to the scientific necessity for uniformity of procedure.

### Discussion

Check to see that all students have included the dilution factor ($\times 1$, if no dilution is made) in their calculations. The form shown in Figure T–1 is a convenient one for gathering data of all teams.

A wide range of numbers is likely to appear when counts of different teams are gathered together. Furthermore, fluctuations in the population—as measured by any one team—are likely to be so great that to detect any pattern of growth may be difficult. However, when the data from many teams are averaged, a fairly good growth curve usually results. Figure T–1 shows data obtained by three classes of somewhat less than average ability, and Figure T–2 is a graph based on the average of all nine teams.

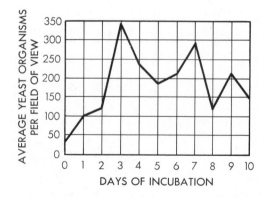

Figure T–2

To obtain a curve that is explicable in terms of population theory is, of course, desirable and very satisfying to students. But failure to obtain such a curve must not be interpreted as failure of the investigation. • (2) on page 56 is the pivot on which the investigation turns. No matter what the results, they will provide material for a fruitful discussion of sources of error in an experimental procedure and of the need for teamwork in some kinds of scientific work.

• (3)– • (5): Responses depend, of course, upon the nature of the graph obtained from experimental results. Comparison of Figure T–2 with the graph obtained in Investigation 2.1 shows that, initially, the growth rate of the yeast population accelerated somewhat as did the hypothetical sparrow population. But the yeast population soon reached a peak and began to fluctuate; moreover, superposed upon the fluctuations is a decline in the population. To explain the similarities and differences in simplest terms, you need only point out that both the sparrow and the yeast populations were initially small populations in a presumably favorable environment. However, assumptions in Investigation 2.1 made no allowances for the "facts of life" —the finite quantity of resources on the island. On the other hand, the yeasts exploited a constantly declining food supply and encountered an increasing accumulation of waste products in the environment. So environmental resistance operated only in the yeast experiment.

Regardless of the nature of the results, the hypothesis set up at the beginning of the investigation must be considered at its end.

## KINDS OF POPULATION CHANGES (pp. 56–61)

**p. 57, ¶ 2 and ¶ 4:** Note that this discussion depends for its meaning on the work done in Investigations 2.1 and 2.2. Dr. David Davis is now Chairman, Department of Zoology, North Carolina State University, Raleigh, N.C.

**p. 58, Fig. 2 · 18:** The investigators estimate that their counting methods involved about 10% error. Of course, rats may have immigrated from surrounding blocks, but Davis and his students found that rats seldom crossed streets unless the population was quite dense.

**p. 59, ¶ 1:** The word "cycle" should be given special attention because its sense here is different from its sense in Chapter 1 — particularly when Figures 1 · 14, 1 · 15, and 1 · 16 are compared with Figure 2 · 19.

**p. 60, Fig. 2 · 21:** The graph is based on studies by J. Davidson, *Transactions of the Royal Society of South Australia*, **62:** 342–346, 1938. Since sheep are entirely dependent upon man in Australia, changes in population reflect man's activities.

## INVESTIGATION 2.3

### POPULATION CHANGES IN OPEN SYSTEMS (pp. 62–64)

The graphs for the investigation can be prepared at home—and at any time after Investigation 2.1 has been completed. Consideration of the questions, however, should be delayed until Investigation 2.2 has been discussed. The conclusions to Investigation 2.3 constitute a summary of all three of the investigations.

The data on the Florida cotton mouse are from *Ecology,* **34:** 199–207, 1953; on the pheasants, from *The Murrelet,* **26:** 39–44, 1945; on the heath hen, from *Memoirs of the Boston Society of Natural History,* **6:** 491–588, 1928.

• (1)– • (8): The September-October portion of the curve resembles the growth of the hypothetical sparrow population, while the October-April portion resembles the declining phase that may have been obtained in your yeast population. The mouse

T 46

curve stabilized from April through August; this is a result of limiting factors, which were ignored in Investigation 2.1. There may be little apparent difference between the mouse and yeast curves. The mouse population is an example of an open population and, as such, illustrates seasonal increases and decreases around some steady-state level. Natality is highest in late summer and autumn. The effect of mortality is most apparent in late winter and early spring.

- (9)– • (11): The seasonal fluctuation of pheasants is due to the addition of young in late fall and early winter. This is a good example of a "new" population that has not yet reached the carrying capacity of the habitat. Counts at some time after 1942 would undoubtedly have shown a decrease in the rate of population growth – but it is not possible with these data to predict when this would have occurred.

• (12)– • (15): The increase of heath hens in 1915 is due to the preservation efforts, and the rise in numbers makes the curve similar to the pheasant curve. An excessive number of males not only reduces natality but also causes increased aggression. The population became extinct in 1932.

• (16)– • (19): The characteristic curve of "new" populations shows an exponential increase. The chief difference between the graph of the hypothetical population and those of the real populations is that it shows none of the variability inherent in real data. Also, given the assumptions, it can never show a decrease. The cotton-mouse curve best illustrates steady state; it shows annual fluctuations around a steady-state level.

SPECIES POPULATIONS (pp. 64–69)

**p. 68, Fig. 2·31:** Dimorphism related to sex and age is quite common in many or-

ganisms. Birds are used as examples because they are colorful and generally familiar. For other examples of dimorphism, see Figures 18·8, 18·9, and 18·17. Specimens of monarch and viceroy butterflies can be used to demonstrate similarity in two populations that are completely isolated reproductively. (In this case the species are even placed in separate subfamilies.)

PROBLEMS (pp. 70–71)

1. Simply add the rates of natality and immigration (43/year) and subtract the total of mortality and emigration (38/year). This means there was an addition of 5/year, owing mostly to surplus natality. In 10 years the box-turtle population would equal 65.

2. Ecologists are interested in *changes* in density; for this, estimates are quite useful if they are made by a consistent method and if the amplitude of population fluctuations is greater than the margin of error in the estimates.

3. The data can be obtained from several large almanacs. (*a*) The curve to date approximates that of the hypothetical population of Investigation 2.1. (*b*) The decline in rate of increase during the 1930's can be attributed to depression economics – a lower natality. (*c*) In the future the difference between immigration and emigration is likely to be negligible; the death rate will presumably continue its downward trend, and, though the birth rate may decline slightly, a continuing increase in population may be predicted. What you want, however, is not correspondence to this prognosis but any reasonable explanation. (*d*) To calculate densities, the area of the United States at the time of each census is required. (*e*) The plot of density parallels closely the total population curve.

4. The curve for your state may show accelerated growth (California, Florida, etc.) or a decline (Arkansas, Vermont). Or the density of your state may have

been stable for some years. When area is a constant, nothing is gained by figuring densities. Virginia is the only state that has changed in area, though some territories did before becoming states.

5. If A breeds with B, and B with C, then only one species is involved. If A became extinct, we would still have only one species. But with B gone we have two, since A and C don't interbreed.

6. The problem involves the time at which an individual becomes an effective part of the population. Is a seed a new individual at the time of zygote formation, at the time of dispersal, or not until germination? The same problem exists for animals, particularly egg-laying ones. For some purposes reproductive additions to a bird population may be counted from egg-laying, and for other purposes from hatching.

## SUPPLEMENTARY MATERIALS

### Additional Problems

As indicated previously, the ideas concerning population change must be developed chiefly through the consideration of problems. As much as possible, problems should be given local flavor. Those appearing below are far from adequate in number, but they may serve as a starting point.

1. What is the density of the student population in your English classroom compared with the density in your biology classroom?

2. On October 15, 1965, the beginning of the squirrel-hunting season for that year, biologists counted 75 gray squirrels in a 30-hectare woods. On December 15, 1965, 42 gray squirrels were counted in the same woods. What was the density of the squirrel population on October 15? On December 15? What determiners could have interacted to affect the density? What determiners must have predominated? [*2.5 squirrels per hectare on October 15; 1.4 squirrels per hectare on December 15. Some students are likely to know that the breeding season of gray squirrels*

*is virtually concluded by October 15 and that hunting mortality would probably be high.*]

3. In a certain city an eight-block area contained 1056 human beings and an estimated population of 1400 rats. Then an Urban Renewal Commission razed the wooden buildings in the area, and the area was occupied by 2480 human beings and an estimated population of 160 rats. Calculate the change in population density of both organisms. What determiners probably were predominant in effecting the changes in density? [*For human beings: + 178 persons/block; for rats: − 155 rats/block.*]

4. On a range of 450 hectares is a total of 1275 jackrabbits. Studies indicate the following rates for this population:

Mortality . . . . . . . . . . . 2225/year
Natality . . . . . . . . . . . . 3400/year
Emigration . . . . . . . . . . 775/year
Immigration . . . . . . . . 150/year

Is the population increasing? Decreasing? At what rate? Predict the population at the end of four years. What is likely to happen to the population of producers in this area during the four years? [*Increasing at a rate of 550 per year. Producers likely to be decreased.*]

5. In a cornfield the population of weeds (that is, all plants other than corn) is estimated at $35/m^2$. Half the field is treated with chemical A, half with chemical B. The density of living weeds in the A half:

end of first week . . . . $22/m^2$
end of second week . . $13/m^2$
end of third week . . . $8/m^2$
end of fourth week . . $6/m^2$
end of fifth week. . . . $7/m^2$

The density of living weeds in the B half:

end of first week . . . . $32/m^2$
end of second week . . $26/m^2$
end of third week . . . $18/m^2$
end of fourth week . . $7/m^2$
end of fifth week. . . . $5/m^2$

During the five weeks, what is the net rate of decline in the density of the weed population in each half of the field? Compare the rates of decline in the two halves during the first week after treatment. What population determiner is dominant in this situation? What population determiner is probably operating in the A half of the field between the fourth and fifth weeks? [*Decline in A: 5.6 weeds per week. In B: 6.0 weeds per week. Chemical A is initially more effective as a weed killer but does not act over as long a period as B. Natality surpassed mortality between the fourth and fifth weeks in the A half. Many more questions can be based on these data.*]

6. In a certain year observations were made of a mule-deer population on a 100-hectare island off the coast of British Columbia. Data:

Number of does, January 1 . . . . 90
Number of bucks, January 1 . . . 30
Births during year . . . . . . . . 75
Deaths during year . . . . . . . . 50
Number of deer, December 31 . . 155

What was the density of the population at the beginning of the year? At the end of the year? What were the effects of immigration and emigration on this population? [*Density January 1 = 1.2 animals/hectare; density December 1 = 1.55 animals/hectare. Immigration was 10 over emigration.*]

7. The number of meadow mice was recorded for a 14.2-hectare plot during a period of population "high" and its precipitous decline (O. P. Pearson, *Journal of Mammalogy*, **45**: 177–188, 1964). The number of meadow mice killed by carnivores was estimated by examination of bones in their fecal scats. These data have been approximated from Figure 2 of Pearson's article:

| Date | Number of Meadow Mice in 14.2 Hectares | Cumulative Number of Mice in Scats |
|---|---|---|
| June 15 | 2,800 | —— |
| July 1 | 4,300 | |
| Aug. 21 | 3,500 | 500 |
| Sept. 25 | 1,700 | 1,300 |
| Oct. 30 | 1,000 | 2,300 |
| Dec. 30 | 250 | 3,700 |
| Jan. 15 | 100 | 3,800 |
| Feb. 15 | 50 | 3,800 |
| March 15 | 0 | 3,800 |

What was the highest density of meadow mice? If you assume no natality, emigration, or immigration, how many meadow mice died between July 1 and

August 21? How many were found in fecal scats? What percentage of total potential deaths for that period were accounted for in fecal scats? Mortality rate should be calculated as deaths per unit time per 1000 mice present at the start of the period. For example, between October 30 and December 30 the death rate was 375/month/ 1000. What was the rate from September to October? [*About 302 mice/hectare on July 1. 800 mice died and remains of 500 were accounted for (62.5%). 700/1700 = 411/month/ 1000.*]

8. Estimates were made on the number of adult blackflies near Anchorage, Alaska, as follows: May 1 – 0; May 15 – 250; June 1 – 20,000; June 15, July 1, and July 15 – 20,000; August 1 – 5,000; August 15 – 400; September 1 and September 15 – 20; October 1 – 10; October 15 – 0. During which period is there the greatest rate of increase in adults? The greatest rate of decline? At which season does reproduction take place? If the population is in steady state, what is the *smallest* density of individuals that must be present in November? During which season is the mortality rate probably highest? [*May 15 to June 1 is period of greatest increase in adults. The greatest rate of decline is from October 1 to October 15 (death rate = 1000/month/ 1000). Reproduction takes place in the summer. The* smallest *number present in November is 20,000. The mortality rate is highest in late summer.*]

9. A study of cotton rats (*Ecological Monographs*, **34**:359–381) showed these estimates of cotton-rat density in Louisiana:

| Date | Rats Trapped/100 Traps |
|---|---|
| Nov. 1959 | 34.8 |
| Jan. 1960 | 35.0 |
| March 1960 | 0.0 |
| May 1960 | 0.0 |
| July 1960 | 0.1 |
| Sept. 1960 | 0.1 |
| Nov. 1960 | 0.6 |
| Jan. 1961 | 0.8 |
| March 1961 | 1.5 |
| May 1961 | 0.8 |
| July 1961 | 2.8 |
| Sept. 1961 | 6.9 |

What determiners of density were most significant in the early months of 1960? What environmental factors could stimulate these processes? If the density for May, 1960, is accurate, what could be responsible for the change by July? What is the most probable direction of population change after September, 1961? How would the rates of immigration and natality compare with the rates of emigration and mortality between July and September, 1961? [*Determiners most important were high mortality and emigration, and low natality and immigration. Severe winter cold. Initially immigration only, followed by immigration and natality. Continued increase in density into the fall. Immigration and natality are in excess of emigration and mortality.*]

### Audiovisual Materials

It is probable that more is to be gained by concentration on problems than by much use of time for films and filmstrips.

*Population Ecology.* 16 mm. Color. 21 min. Encyclopaedia Britannica Films. (Probably the best film available on the subject.)

*Grouse—A Species Problem,* BSCS Inquiry Film Loop. (Rand McNally #11-2976, 1968). Perhaps best used a few weeks after the species concept has been first encountered.

### Teacher's References

ANDREWARTHA, H. G., and L. C. BIRCH. *The Distribution and Abundance of Animals.* Chicago: University of Chicago Press, 1954. (A rather technical book that sets forth views still stimulating population research.)

BROWNING, T. O. *Animal Populations.* New York: Harper and Row, Publishers, Inc., 1963. ("For a quick elementary understanding. . . . Deals with experimentally tested concepts. . . . How environment influences populations and maintains the balance of nature." —AIBS *Journal.*)

HAZEN, W. E. *Readings in Population and Community Ecology.* Philadelphia: W. B. Saunders Co., 1964. (This collection of technical papers provides examples of some of the kinds of work being done by population ecologists.)

LACK, D. *Population Studies of Birds.* Oxford: Oxford University Press, 1966. (Birds probably provide the best existing data for studies of natural population dynamics. Reading this work should be balanced with reading studies of laboratory populations.)

MALTHUS, T., J. HUXLEY, and F. OSBORN. *On Population: Three Essays.* New York: New American Library of World Literature, Inc., 1960. (This paperback provides the most ready access to Malthus. Since human population is not stressed in Chapter 2 of the *Green Version*, the Huxley and Osborn essays may be postponed until study of Chapter 20.)

# 3

# Communities
# and
# Ecosystems

## MAJOR IDEAS

1. A biotic community consists of the sum of all interactions among the species populations at some particular time and place.

2. Various kinds of community interactions can be recognized; basically these relationships are concerned with the exchange of energy between species.

3. The significance of a community interaction is best determined by measuring its effect upon the population densities of the species involved.

4. The delimiting of communities is a subjective process; in nature there is always continuity in both space and time.

5. Every biotic community is part of an ecosystem, which is a complex of all biotic and abiotic interactions within a definable unit of space and time.

6. At any particular place a transition of ecosystems occurs through time. This is ecological succession.

## PLANNING AHEAD

The fieldwork of Investigation 3.1 may present opportunities to assemble specimens required for the investigations in Chapters 4 and 5. Many small invertebrates can easily be kept alive for several weeks. Likewise mosses, lichens, algae, and fungi for Investigation 5.2.

If leaves for Investigation 5.1 have not been collected, do not delay further, because it may soon be impossible.

Order cultures of *Serratia marcescens* and *Sarcina lutea* for Investigation 6.2 and a mixed culture of bacteria for use in Investigation 6.3.

If you have not already done so, become acquainted with the scheme of classification used in Appendix II of the student's book.

## GUIDELINES

The break between Chapters 2 and 3 is one of convenience. The sequence from individual to ecosystem overarches both chapters. The student should come to see this continuity clearly.

It is essential that the student gain direct experience with communities. Within the classroom walls simple laboratory communities can, of course, be maintained. Aquariums and terrariums are old standbys. In many schoolrooms students, their lunches, their viruses, houseflies, house mice (and, sometimes, crickets, dermestid beetles, and cockroaches) form a community that the alert teacher will use — especially in illustrating parasitism and commensalism. And work on Investigation 9.1 may be started at this time.

But in the view of the *Green Version* writers, all this is still inadequate. In city schools especially, it is important to get beyond the walls of the classroom, to show students that life is not entirely an *in vitro* phenomenon — that community interactions are not confined to glass test tubes, glass tanks, and glass buildings.

In addition to having firsthand experience with a local community, students should become acquainted with several other communities. Pages 73–76 are a step toward this. Pictures, especially motion pictures, can be helpful. In every case, attention should be directed toward the ecological relationships that bind the species in a community together; a mere enumeration of species does not depict a community.

The text of Chapter 3 fills only 29 pages. It does not lend itself well to short assignments. However, pages 72–76 should be read before the fieldwork for Investigation 3.1 is done; the rest, afterward.

With classes that can be trusted to glean for themselves the more obvious ideas from the textbook, the teacher can take time to stress some of the more abstract features of the chapter. First, the terminology of community relationships offers an opportunity to extend the discussion (begun in

Chapter 2) of definitions in science. Second, the paradox of change *v.* constancy — of steady state — is an idea that recurs frequently; it came early in Chapter 1 and again in Chapter 2. Third, the continuity of communities and ecosystems in time and space without real boundaries is merely a special example of the unity of biology.

Chapter 3 completes the series of ecological units begun in Chapter 2 and also marks the end of Section One. Therefore, it should be brought to a close with a careful review of the series: individual, population, species population, community, ecosystem. This may be the time for a test, but the student must understand that it is only an interim summary and ends nothing.

## TEACHING NOTES

### THE BIOTIC COMMUNITY
(pp. 72–76)

**p. 73:** Do not confuse a community with a society. In the usage adopted in this course, a community involves interspecific relationships; a society involves intraspecific relationships only. In a beehive there is a society, not a community (unless species in addition to the bees are also considered).

**pp. 73–76:** The description of the Florida river community is based on the work of Dr. John Crenshaw, now at the University of Rhode Island. Use this river community to stimulate discussion of similar communities in your neighborhood. Certainly you should not require the memorization of the specific animals and their relationships in the Florida community.

**p. 76, Fig. 3·4:** The question in the caption does not require at this point the use of the terminology developed later in the chapter, though you may want to come back to this illustration later.

### INVESTIGATION 3.1

### STUDY OF A BIOTIC COMMUNITY
(pp. 76–82)

Every investigation should be planned carefully, but one that takes students out of the school building demands doubled care. Unless both teacher and students know exactly what is to be done, this investigation can easily become a lark, without educational value. Given time and attention, however, it can be one of the most rewarding experiences of the year.

For reasons given on page 77, it is impossible to prescribe a single procedure for this investigation. Nevertheless, enough information has been given the student to enable him to take an active part in the planning. You, of course, should know considerably more about the methods of community study than is provided in the student's book. You will find *Ecology of Land Plants and Animals*, a BSCS laboratory block by E. A. Phillips (Boston: D. C. Heath & Co., 1963), valuable.

## General Procedure A

You, if not the students, should be thoroughly acquainted with the potentialities of your region. It is desirable that the area to be studied be as close to the school as possible so that repeated visits may be made. However, the desirability of repetitive visits may be outweighed by other considerations. If the resources in the immediate vicinity of the school are poor, and if administrative conditions permit, an excursion to a desirable site at a greater distance may be preferred.

*In no school is this investigation impossible.* Biotic communities exist even in the most urban situation. Look for vacant lots, the area around a billboard, even cracks in cement and asphalt—all these contain plants, insects, nematodes. Though the chief producers may be miles away, the city environment also contains larger organisms—mice, rats, cats, pigeons. Urban biology teachers should be acquainted with the following books:

BEEBE, W. *Unseen Life of New York as a Naturalist Sees It.* Boston: Little, Brown & Co., 1953.
FITTER, R. *London's Natural History.* London: William Collins Sons & Co., Ltd., 1945.

KIERAN, J. *Natural History of New York City.* Boston: Houghton Mifflin Co., 1959.
RUBLOWSKY, J. *Nature in the City.* New York: Basic Books, 1967.

Having chosen the area for study, visit it—together with a committee of students, if possible. With the area under observation, its possibilities can be sketched out.

## General Procedure B

Next, on the basis of the directly observed possibilities and the suggested procedures (pp. 78–82), the class can proceed to make detailed plans. The plans must be fitted to the personnel. Each student must have a definite place in the plans. He must have something to do, he must know what his responsibility is, and he must know how to carry it out. Each team leader must know the overall plan for his team. Figure T–3 is an example of a form (used in a woodland study) that provides the teacher and team leaders with a way of checking on individual responsibilities.

Written instructions are essential. Forms for recording data in the field may be devised; these, of course, must vary with the nature of the area to be explored. Some teachers have found it desirable to go through a "dry run" with their team leaders to check out directions and data forms.

If at all possible, Investigation 3.1 should be a *comparative* study. For example: the border of a woods may be compared with the interior; a grazed pasture may be compared with a mowed meadow; a well-trodden section of the school campus, with a less-disturbed section. Consider also the possibility of using studies by classes in successive years as bases for comparisons that can give firsthand meaning to the concept of ecological succession.

Population densities of several selected species may be obtained by counting individuals on measured quadrats. The mean densities in one habitat can then be compared with the mean densities in another. If a large number of quadrats are used, the difference between the means can be treated

## JOB SHEET

TEAM _____          TEAM LEADER _____

### PREPARATIONS

Staking out the area:          General description:

_____          _____          _____

_____          _____          _____

_____          _____          _____

_____          _____          _____

_____          _____          _____

### DATA COLLECTION

Trees:

_____          _____

Shrubs and saplings:

_____          _____

Herbs and seedlings:

_____          _____

Searching:

_____          _____

Litter and soil samples:

_____          _____

### TEAM EQUIPMENT

| | | |
|---|---|---|
| Stakes, 8 | Hammer, 1 | Rubber bands, 4 |
| String, 50 m | Old magazines, 6 | Plastic bags, 2 |
| Meter sticks, 2 | Collecting bottles, 4 | Wire circles, 2 |
| Rulers (metric), 4 | Forceps, 2 | Trowels, 2 |

Figure T–3

statistically against a null hypothesis; but at the level of sophistication appropriate for the tenth grade, it is probably sufficient in most classes to let the students decide subjectively whether or not the degree of numerical difference is "significant." Choice of species depends upon the habitats being compared. For instance, in comparing a much-trodden lawn with an out-of-the-way one, not grass but dandelions and plantains should be counted.

### General Procedure C

Get the fieldwork done while the weather permits. It is not necessary to process the data immediately; if a delay is necessary or seems desirable, take some 35-mm color photographs of the study area. These may be useful later, when the students' memories need refreshing.

Some teachers find it desirable to use organisms collected during the investigation as a basis for considering diversity among living things—a concept to be stressed in the next three chapters. Thus Investigation 3.1 can serve as a connecting link between Sections One and Two. But collecting is not an aim of Investigation 3.1, and care must be taken that the enthusiasm students often display for collecting does not interfere with the community study.

### Specific Procedure B

The dimensions to separate trees from saplings are arbitrary and can be varied.

### Specific Procedure C

Small specimens can best be collected in jars containing dilute formalin (1 part of commercial formaldehyde solution to 7 parts of water) or 70% alcohol (isopropyl is satisfactory).

### Specific Procedure D

When collecting nematodes from the soil, remember that the populations vary greatly, depending upon whether the sample is from a rich organic soil, from an area poisoned with insecticide, etc. The Berlese funnel works best if there is a considerable

temperature gradient in the soil—thus the bottom of the soil should be cool and the top warmed by the light. Anything that weakens the gradient lowers the efficiency of the apparatus.

### Studying the Data

If at all possible, assemble a labeled collection of the species most likely to be encountered. This may be difficult when you do the investigation for the first time, but the collection can be increasingly comprehensive in later years. Use this collection as a basis for students to identify their organisms. Although specific identification is not necessary to obtain acquaintance with a community, students love to have names for things, and this increases their sense of accomplishment. But do not let identification become the goal of the work.

Discussion of the questions is more effective if delayed until the section on "Community Structure" has been studied.

Either before or after the class discussion of the questions, each student should write his own report on the work as a whole. It should include the purpose of his investigation, a brief account of the methods used, a summarization of the data, and (most important of all) his own detailed interpretation of those data in the form of a description of the community structure and relationships.

Throughout the work on Sections Two and Three, reference should be made whenever possible to the results obtained from this fieldwork.

---

### COMMUNITY STRUCTURE
(pp. 83–94)

**p. 83, Fig. 3 · 9:** The lion is a predator, the giraffe prey, the vultures commensals. Compare with Figure 1 · 2.

**p. 84, Fig. 3 · 10:** The corn is a host, the smut a parasite.

**p. 86, Fig. 3 · 11:** Fleas of mice are not likely to parasitize a hawk (parasites are usually rather host-specific); but if they weaken a mouse, they could make predation by the hawk easier. Or if they carried infectious organisms that killed off enough mice, they could reduce the number of mice available to the hawk.

**p. 88, Fig. 3 · 14:** The hydra obtains food produced by the algae; and the algae obtain a habitat, protection, and presumably some raw materials. Thus the relationship can be called mutualism.

**p. 89, note 1:** Numerical data are the most readily verifiable data. But note that even with numerical data a subjective judgment still must be made as to whether the harm or benefit is enough to warrant the term called for in the classification. Hence, we still have not avoided a decision that someday, with addition of more information, might be changed.

**p. 89, Fig. 3 · 16:** The graph is based on work of D. A. MacLulick, *University of Toronto Studies* **43:** 1–136, 1937.

**p. 90, ¶ 1:** You may want to point out —if some student does not do it—that throughout this chapter microorganisms have been neglected.

**p. 91, ¶ 3:** The relationship between high species diversity and high stability has been observed often enough to establish it as a fact. What is not certain is whether high species diversity *causes* the stability, or the reverse (great environmental stability *causes* high species diversity). In other words, while the correlation is observed, the cause and effect relationships are not well known.

**p. 93, ¶ 4:** A climax community is often referred to as a "stable" community. But stability is a relative matter: a lichen community may persist for a very long time and, as the next paragraph indicates, climax communities are mutable.

## ECOSYSTEMS (pp. 94–97)

**p. 94, note 1:** Lichens and mosses do not usually gain footholds on sandbars: the first plants are usually willows, grasses, or sedges, whose long root systems bind the sand.

**p. 95, Fig. 3 · 18:** The succession shown here is in the Colorado Rockies.

**p. 97, ¶'s 2 and 3:** Use Figure 1 · 19. The ideas expressed here constitute a deliberate repetition of ideas from pp. 30–31. Do any of your students recognize this? Those who do are really studying biology; those who do not are perhaps merely reading pages in a book.

**p. 97, Fig. 3 · 20:** All the energy in the food eventually becomes heat energy. But before that happens it appears, for example, as muscle movement and electrical forces in human bodies. And some of it passes through the human body still in chemical (food) form and enters the life processes of saprovores in sewage disposal systems.

## INVESTIGATION 3.2
### ABIOTIC ENVIRONMENT: A COMPARATIVE STUDY (pp. 98–99)

### Procedure

This investigation not only concerns the ecosystem concept but is related to matters of tolerance and ecological distribution that arise in Chapter 8. One team per class may be delegated to do the fieldwork.

Differences in temperature among the three habitats are more pronounced early in the autumn than later. For best results vegetation should not yet have become dormant, and the sun should be fairly high in the sky. Of course the work should be done on a sunny day. The three habitats should be as near to each other as possible, so that topographic differences are minimal.

For meeting student questions concerning relative humidity, refer to H. J. Oosting, *The Study of Plant Communities* (complete reference, p. T60).

In this investigation, sling psychrometers are difficult to use—and at the 0-cm height, impossible. But if available, they hold the two thermometers conveniently. If the bulb sleeves are used repeatedly, distilled water should be used to soak them.

### Studying the Data

If you have several teams, gather data into a form drawn on the chalkboard.

- (1) – • (10): These depend upon the results obtained in the investigation. On a sunny day, bare ground is usually the warmest and driest habitat at all levels; vegetative habitats are cooler and moister below the top of the vegetation than above it. In general these measurements illustrate the modifying effect of vegetation, the conversion of radiant energy of sunlight to heat on contact with the earth, and, finally, the idea of microclimatic variations.

- (11) and • (12): Microclimates are generally of importance to an organism whose size does not transcend the extent of one distinguishable microclimate (beetle and gnat) but of little importance to an organism whose size encompasses the whole range of microclimatic variation (cow).

- (13): Shade is a microhabitat factor important to producers. Air currents, related (along with relative humidity) to the evaporation rate, may also be important.

## Figure T–4

RELATIVE HUMIDITY (percentage)

Dry-bulb temperature (degrees C)

| Difference between dry-bulb and wet-bulb readings | 10 | 11 | 12 | 13 | 14 | 15 | 16 | 17 | 18 | 19 | 20 | 21 | 22 | 23 | 24 | 25 | 26 | 27 | 28 | 29 | 30 |
|---|---|---|---|---|---|---|---|---|---|---|---|---|---|---|---|---|---|---|---|---|---|
| 0.5 | 94 | 94 | 94 | 95 | 95 | 95 | 95 | 95 | 95 | 95 | 96 | 96 | 96 | 96 | 96 | 96 | 96 | 96 | 96 | 96 | 96 |
| 1.0 | 88 | 89 | 89 | 89 | 90 | 90 | 90 | 90 | 91 | 91 | 91 | 91 | 92 | 92 | 92 | 92 | 92 | 92 | 93 | 93 | 93 |
| 1.5 | 82 | 83 | 83 | 84 | 85 | 85 | 85 | 86 | 86 | 87 | 87 | 87 | 87 | 88 | 88 | 88 | 88 | 89 | 89 | 89 | 89 |
| 2.0 | 77 | 78 | 78 | 79 | 79 | 80 | 81 | 81 | 82 | 82 | 83 | 83 | 83 | 84 | 84 | 84 | 85 | 85 | 85 | 86 | 86 |
| 2.5 | 71 | 72 | 73 | 74 | 75 | 75 | 76 | 76 | 77 | 78 | 78 | 79 | 80 | 80 | 80 | 81 | 81 | 82 | 82 | 82 | 83 |
| 3.0 | 66 | 67 | 68 | 69 | 70 | 71 | 71 | 72 | 73 | 74 | 74 | 75 | 76 | 76 | 77 | 77 | 78 | 78 | 78 | 79 | 79 |
| 3.5 | 60 | 61 | 63 | 64 | 65 | 66 | 67 | 68 | 69 | 70 | 70 | 71 | 72 | 72 | 73 | 74 | 74 | 75 | 75 | 76 | 76 |
| 4.0 | 55 | 56 | 58 | 59 | 60 | 61 | 63 | 64 | 65 | 65 | 66 | 67 | 68 | 69 | 69 | 70 | 71 | 71 | 72 | 72 | 73 |
| 4.5 | 50 | 51 | 53 | 54 | 56 | 57 | 58 | 60 | 61 | 62 | 63 | 64 | 64 | 65 | 66 | 67 | 67 | 68 | 69 | 69 | 70 |
| 5.0 | 44 | 46 | 48 | 50 | 51 | 53 | 54 | 55 | 57 | 58 | 59 | 60 | 61 | 62 | 62 | 63 | 64 | 65 | 65 | 66 | 67 |
| 5.5 | 39 | 41 | 43 | 45 | 47 | 48 | 50 | 51 | 53 | 54 | 55 | 56 | 57 | 58 | 59 | 60 | 61 | 62 | 62 | 63 | 64 |
| 6.0 | 34 | 36 | 39 | 41 | 42 | 44 | 46 | 47 | 49 | 50 | 51 | 53 | 54 | 55 | 56 | 57 | 58 | 58 | 59 | 60 | 61 |
| 6.5 | 29 | 32 | 34 | 36 | 38 | 40 | 42 | 43 | 45 | 46 | 48 | 49 | 50 | 52 | 53 | 54 | 54 | 56 | 56 | 57 | 58 |
| 7.0 | 24 | 27 | 29 | 32 | 34 | 36 | 38 | 40 | 41 | 43 | 44 | 46 | 47 | 48 | 49 | 50 | 51 | 52 | 53 | 54 | 55 |
| 7.5 | 20 | 22 | 25 | 28 | 30 | 32 | 34 | 36 | 38 | 39 | 41 | 42 | 44 | 45 | 46 | 47 | 49 | 50 | 51 | 52 | 52 |
| 8.0 | 15 | 18 | 21 | 23 | 26 | 27 | 30 | 32 | 34 | 36 | 37 | 39 | 40 | 42 | 43 | 44 | 46 | 47 | 48 | 49 | 50 |
| 8.5 | 10 | 13 | 16 | 19 | 22 | 24 | 26 | 28 | 30 | 32 | 34 | 36 | 37 | 39 | 40 | 41 | 43 | 44 | 45 | 46 | 47 |
| 9.0 | 6 | 9 | 12 | 15 | 18 | 20 | 23 | 25 | 27 | 29 | 31 | 32 | 34 | 36 | 37 | 39 | 40 | 41 | 42 | 43 | 44 |
| 9.5 | | 5 | 8 | 11 | 14 | 16 | 19 | 21 | 23 | 26 | 28 | 29 | 31 | 33 | 34 | 36 | 37 | 38 | 40 | 41 | 42 |
| 10.0 | | | | 7 | 10 | 13 | 15 | 18 | 20 | 22 | 24 | 26 | 28 | 30 | 31 | 33 | 34 | 36 | 37 | 38 | 39 |
| 10.5 | | | | | 6 | 9 | 12 | 14 | 17 | 19 | 21 | 23 | 25 | 27 | 29 | 30 | 32 | 33 | 34 | 36 | 37 |
| 11.0 | | | | | | 6 | 8 | 11 | 14 | 16 | 18 | 20 | 22 | 24 | 26 | 28 | 29 | 31 | 32 | 33 | 35 |
| 11.5 | | | | | | | 5 | 8 | 10 | 13 | 15 | 17 | 19 | 21 | 23 | 25 | 26 | 28 | 29 | 31 | 32 |
| 12.0 | | | | | | | | | 7 | 10 | 12 | 14 | 17 | 19 | 20 | 22 | 24 | 26 | 27 | 28 | 30 |
| 12.5 | | | | | | | | | | 7 | 9 | 12 | 14 | 16 | 18 | 20 | 21 | 23 | 25 | 26 | 28 |
| 13.0 | | | | | | | | | | | 6 | 9 | 11 | 13 | 15 | 17 | 19 | 21 | 22 | 24 | 25 |
| 13.5 | | | | | | | | | | | | 6 | 8 | 11 | 13 | 15 | 17 | 18 | 20 | 22 | 23 |
| 14.0 | | | | | | | | | | | | | 6 | 8 | 10 | 12 | 14 | 16 | 18 | 19 | 21 |
| 14.5 | | | | | | | | | | | | | | 6 | 8 | 10 | 12 | 14 | 16 | 17 | 19 |
| 15.0 | | | | | | | | | | | | | | | 5 | 8 | 10 | 12 | 13 | 15 | 17 |
| 16.0 | | | | | | | | | | | | | | | | | 5 | 7 | 9 | 11 | 13 |
| 17.0 | | | | | | | | | | | | | | | | | | | 5 | 7 | 9 |
| 18.0 | | | | | | | | | | | | | | | | | | | | | 5 |
| 19.0 | | | | | | | | | | | | | | | | | | | | | |
| 20.0 | | | | | | | | | | | | | | | | | | | | | |

## PROBLEMS (pp. 100–101)

1. In lightless caves, producers cannot live; but organic substances enter the caves, mainly with flowing waters, and serve as food for the saprovores that are at the base of cave food webs.

2. The essence of this problem is that a predator-prey action is harmful (negative) to the individual being killed but may have a long-run positive effect on the prey *population*. The Kaibab deer story is also given in Odum, *Fundamentals of Ecology*, pp. 239–240.

3. The point of the contrast between aquatic and terrestrial Antarctic communities is a comparison of abiotic conditions. The terrestrial habitat is so extreme that few species can survive — yet in the water, where the violent fluctuations in atmospheric conditions are modified, a greater number of species can find niches.

4. All three of these communities are similar in that they depend upon a continual input of foods.

5. This problem can lead the student in many directions. It is a good preliminary to the concepts of infectious diseases developed later (Chapter 7). Chestnut blight is an example of a host-parasite relation that has not evolved into a steady state. Immunity has not developed, and the parasite has decimated the population of the host organism. On the other hand, in whooping cough host immunity has developed — hence there is low fatality to the host. Also, artificial immunization of the host can be used so that the disease is no longer a population hazard.

6. No single answer can be given to these questions. The important thing is for students to realize how much energy is imported to the city and how much the biotic community is dependent upon man. Be sure the commensals of man — such as house mice, Norway rats, and cockroaches — are not forgotten.

## SUPPLEMENTARY MATERIALS

### Additional Problems

1. The frontier farm is often said to have been self-sufficient. What does this mean in terms of biotic communities? [*Most of the biotic energy was captured and expended locally; food was raised and consumed on the farm.*]

2. Why may it be reasonable to include the wheat fields of Kansas, the cotton fields of Texas, and the fishing banks of Newfoundland in the biotic community of New York City? [*A modern city may be thought of as a biotic community, but its energy system cannot be understood unless study is extended far beyond the city limits.*]

3. In Figure 2·21 the smoothing of a graph line between plotted points is shown. To explain this further, the teacher may present other examples of population data plotted on a grid and have the class draw smoothed curves for each set of data. (See W. C. Allee *et al., Principles of Animal Ecology*, Philadelphia: W. B. Saunders Co., 1949, pp. 309, 329, 385, and E. P. Odum, *Fundamentals of Ecology*, pp. 199, 232.)

4. "Pheasants eat several kinds of fleshy fruits. The seeds of these fruits pass through the digestive tract and are distributed throughout the countryside, and surprisingly, are better able to germinate than seeds that have not been eaten by pheasants." Discuss the interrelationships illustrated by this quotation and formulate an experiment that might help to classify the type of interspecies relationship. [*The plant species gain in two ways from this mutualistic relationship. The germination rate of the seeds is increased by the action of the pheasant's gizzard, which abrades the tough seed coats. And the distribution of the seeds is increased by the wandering of the pheasants. The pheasants gain nutrients from the fruits and from some of the seeds.*]

5. Cattle stomachs contain enormous numbers of microorganisms, some of which digest the cellulose which is abundant in the plants eaten by cattle, and in so doing produce substances that are useful nutrients for the cattle. Evaluate the relationship between cattle and these microorganisms. [*The microorganisms get a place to live and easily digested chunks of food; the cattle benefit by having cellulose digested into substances they can use.*]

## Additional Investigation
## COMPETITION BETWEEN TWO SPECIES OF PLANTS

### Introduction

Many problems of human ecology involve such artificial biotic communities as gardens and cultivated fields. In this investigation intraspecific competition between species of garden plants that do not naturally occur together is the basis of an experiment. Students should set up a hypothesis that seems reasonable for the suggested procedure.

### Materials (for each team)

Soil (a good loam), enough to fill three flats
Trowel
Wood block
Wooden flats (boxes), approximately
    55 × 35 × 10 cm, 3
Sharp pencil
Tomato seeds, about 450
Radish seeds, about 450
Sheet glass, enough to cover 3 flats
Scissors
Paper toweling
Triple-beam balance, sensitivity to 0.1 g

### Procedure

Prepare the soil by removing stones and breaking all lumps. Place in flats and smooth out to a level surface. Use a block of wood to press the soil down firmly, but do not pack it tight. Use enough soil to make a firmed layer at least 7 cm deep. Water and allow to stand twenty-four hours.

With a sharp stick or pencil, draw furrows on the surface of the soil, parallel to the long sides of the flat, about 2 mm deep and 5 cm apart. In one flat, place tomato seeds about 1 cm apart along each row. In a second flat, place radish seeds about 1 cm apart along each row. These flats are "pure cultures." In the third flat, place tomato and radish seeds alternately 1 cm apart along each row. This is a "mixed culture." Use the wooden block to firm the soil again along the lines of planting. This will barely cover the seeds with soil.

To reduce evaporation from the soil until after the seeds germinate, cover the flats with sheets of glass and place in a warm, shaded place. When germination begins, flats should be moved into the light. Later the glass should be removed. By this time the plants will be large enough to be sprinkled gently without being disturbed. Keep all flats equally moist. If the flats are kept on the classroom windowsill, turn them daily so that the plants on all sides of the flats receive about the same amount of light over a period of days.

The experiment may be brought to a conclusion in 35 to 50 days—when the plants are fairly large but before they begin to topple over. At that time all the tomato plants in the mixed culture need to be clipped (with scissors) close to the soil and weighed together. Then clip off and weigh all the tomato plants in the pure culture. Pull up all the radishes in the mixed culture, carefully wash the soil from the fleshy roots, blot dry on paper toweling, and weigh together. Follow the same procedure with the radishes in the pure culture. Since there were only half as many radish seeds and tomato seeds in the mixed culture as there were in the pure cultures, it is necessary to divide the weights of the plants from the pure cultures by 2.

### Studying the Data

Represent the data in the form of a bar graph, with *weight* on the vertical axis and *type of culture* on the horizontal axis. Arrange the bars along the horizontal axis, from left to right, in the order in which the cultures are weighed.

• Is there a difference between the total weight of the tomato plants grown in pure culture and those grown in mixed culture? If so, how do you account for the difference? (1) • Is there any difference between the weight of the radish crop grown in pure culture and that grown in mixed culture? If so, how do you account for the difference? (2) • Does the growing of tomatoes and radishes together have more effect on the tomatoes or on the radishes? Or is the effect equal? Or is there no effect? (3) • Attempt to explain how the effects you noted may have occurred. (4)

The effects of competition are being judged by the weight of the "crops" developed—a quite reasonable method from the viewpoint of an agriculturist. On pp. 88–89 the basis on which ecologists prefer to judge the effects of community relationships is discussed. • Explain why the weights of the crops may be considered *indirect* evidence of competition. (5)

### For Further Investigation

Carry out the same experiment, using other kinds of plants. Spacing between plants and the depth of planting may have to be varied to suit the kinds of plants used.

### For the Teacher

This is a simple experiment that can easily be turned over to a small team. The work can be done at home if sufficient window space is available. However, growth of the plants in the laboratory arouses interest and discussion that should make the team's report of the results more meaningful to the class.

The seeds may be treated with fungicide, as described in Investigation 1.2.

The procedure assumes that the roots of the tomato plants represent a negligible weight factor. If students object to this assumption, it is possible to harvest the whole plants by gently washing the soil away from the root systems.

• (1) – • (3): These questions follow directly from whatever data are obtained.

• (4): If differences are found between the pure cultures and the mixed cultures for either species, they can perhaps most readily be explained on the basis of more effective absorption of water or nutrients by one species in the presence of the other. At later stages, however, one species may overtop the other and thus reduce its supply of radiant energy.

• (5): The definitive judgment of competition must rest on its effect on the populations of the two species. Since these species do not reproduce vegetatively, the effect depends upon the quantity and viability of the seed produced. Any conclusions based on the results of this experiment depend upon the assumption that the size of a plant, as indicated by weight, is related to its ability to produce viable seed.

Some students may want to investigate *intra*specific competition, though it is more closely related to the idea of crowding (discussed in Chapter 2) than to community study. Such an investigation could parallel 3.2. One kind of seeds should be used, but they should be planted in several flats. The intervals between seeds should be different in each flat. The effects of spacing can be measured by weight. If peas, which are self-pollinating, are used, the effects of spacing can be correlated with the quantity of seeds produced. There is value in allowing students to see that pertinent data may be obtained from an experiment in a variety of ways.

### Audiovisual Materials

The concepts introduced in Chapter 3 lend themselves rather well to visual instruction. Many relevant filmstrips and motion pictures are available, but most are pitched on a level that should be too superficial for tenth graders.

**Filmstrips:** *Symbiosis—Strange Partners in Nature* ("Darwin's World of Nature,"

Part 8). Color. New York: LIFE Filmstrips. The pictures are good, but the captions are full of teleology and anthropomorphism. The term "symbiosis" is used in the restricted sense—i.e., equivalent to "mutualism."

*The Ecological Succession.* McGraw-Hill Book Co., Inc., 1960. Contains accurate terminology, though rather more than necessary. The picturing of bare-rock succession parallels our description.

*The City as a Community.* McGraw-Hill Filmstrips. Useful to give city students some ideas for conducting a community study.

*Life in a Fallen-Log Microcommunity.* Society for Visual Education, Inc. Fits well with the idea of microhabitats emerging from Investigation 3.2 and with the idea of indefinite community boundaries.

**Motion-picture films:** *Life in a Woodlot.* National Film Board of Canada. 16 mm. Color. 17 min. Shows the factors that affect the dynamic balance of populations in a woodlot community through the cycle of the seasons.

*The Cave Community.* Encyclopaedia Britannica Films. 16 mm. Color. 11 min. A good example of the flow of energy through a community.

*The Community.* Encyclopaedia Britannica Films. 16 mm. Color. 11 min. Depicts the interrelationships that comprise a biotic community. Food webs of several communities are illustrated.

*Succession—From Sand Dune to Forest.* Encyclopaedia Britannica Films. 16 mm. Color. 16 min. In depicting succession on the southeast shore of Lake Michigan, this film shows many good examples of community relationships. An alert teacher can exploit these more effectively than the narrator does.

*Plant-Animal Communities: Physical Environment.* Coronet Films. 16 mm. Color. 11 min. The slant of this film leads to the subject matter of Chapter 8. It could be used to pick up the thread of ecological thought in beginning that chapter.

## Teacher's References

References for Chapter 3 overlap those for Chapter 2 because the division between these two chapters is rather arbitrary. Of the "Suggested Readings" listed in the textbook, the book by Odum is of particular importance to the teacher. See references to Chapters 4 and 5 in the student's book for help in identifying organisms encountered during Investigation 3.1.

DICE, L. R. *Natural Communities.* Ann Arbor: University of Michigan Press, 1952. (Dice attempts to interweave materials for both plant and animal ecology.)

HANSON, H. C., and E. D. CHURCHILL. *The Plant Community.* New York: Reinhold Publishing Corp., 1961. (A more recent book than Oosting's. Contains a considerable amount of material on the methodology of community analysis.)

OOSTING, H. J. *The Study of Plant Communities.* 2nd ed. San Francisco: W. H. Freeman & Co., 1956.

PIMENTEL, R. A. *Invertebrate Identification Manual.* New York: Reinhold Publishing Corp., 1967.

RUTTNER, F. *Fundamentals of Limnology.* 3rd ed. Toronto: University of Toronto Press, 1963. (This book is a good place to begin an acquaintance with the limnologist's view of communities.)

# Section Two  DIVERSITY AMONG LIVING THINGS

During the twentieth century all the major developments in biology have tended to strengthen the concept of a fundamental unity in life processes. But the diversity of organisms remains an obvious and inescapable fact. Biologists—at least *some* biologists—must deal with it. And any biology course having primarily cultural aims ought to deal with it. This diversity should be considered early in the course, because students need a mental map on which to arrange the numerous organisms that must be used to illustrate the workings of biological principles and processes.

The chief intellectual burden of Section Two is *not* the characteristics of the numerous groupings into which taxonomists have sorted organisms. All such groupings involve a large element of subjectivity; they are mutable, if not ephemeral. Much depends upon still-accumulating paleontological evidence, and much depends upon the way in which the groups are defined. "The alligator belongs to the class Reptilia" is a kind of statement frequently heard —as if the class Reptilia were an *a priori* entity to which alligators must conform. Today such a statement is merely a matter of convenience; to the modern biologist it does not have Aristotelian implications. But it certainly will have such implications for students unless they are cautioned to interpret the statement thus: "Alligators have characteristics that allow us most conveniently to place them in the Reptilia—as that class is defined by most zoologists." With such an interpretation, drill on the proper disposition of organisms into one of the many possible schemes of classification becomes absurd.

What, then, is the chief burden of the section? It lies in three abstract ideas: first, the purposes and the nature of biological classification (Chapter 4); second, the scheme of biological nomenclature (Chapter 5); third, the difficulties inherent in attempts to fit the facts of nature into a conceptual mold (Chapter 6). Whatever time you allow for class discussion should be devoted primarily to these three ideas. Because the number of major ideas in Section Two is fewer than the number of pages might indicate, a schedule should be adopted that is in proportion to the density of ideas rather than to the number of pages.

**Section Illustration**

Animal, plant, and protist (the last in the decaying wood) are represented in this scene from a woodland ecosystem. The animal is a chipmunk.

# 4

# Animals

## MAJOR IDEAS

1. Despite the bewildering diversity of animal forms, some major patterns of structural characteristics can be discerned in the animal kingdom. These patterns form the basis for the hierarchical ordering of taxonomic groups.

2. Because the taxonomist often finds it convenient to work with dead specimens—and, in the case of extinct species, must do so—the structural characteristics of organisms have been most frequently used in classification. But other kinds of characteristics are increasingly employed by modern taxonomists.

3. In different species, structures having obviously similar basic components vary in detail; these variations appear to fit any given species for efficient functioning in a particular environment. This is the concept of structural adaptation—an important element in all evolutionary theories, but equally applicable to a theory of special creation.

4. Since the time of Darwin, the similarities among organisms have been ascribed to common evolutionary development. By means of levels of classification, the modern taxonomist seeks to express the varying degrees of evolutionary divergence; but simultaneously he seeks to provide biologists with convenient means of grouping organisms.

## PLANNING AHEAD

Considerable time may be needed to mount the leaves to be used in Investigation 5.1. Once done, however, most of the mounts should last for several years. Save some dried leaves for use in Investigation 7.4. And be sure you have a few twigs and dried insects for the same investigation.

Try to accumulate as many kinds of living plants as possible for display in your laboratory during work on Chapter 5. In gathering these, keep in mind the assortment of kinds desirable for Investigation 5.2; employ living specimens so far as practicable.

If you have not ordered the cultures of bacteria needed for Investigation 6.2, do not delay any longer. While you are doing so, you should also consider acquiring a culture of *Agrobacterium tumefaciens* for Investigation 7.2. Because this organism is a plant pathogen of considerable importance, many states have regulations concerning its shipment, and it may be necessary to obtain a permit from appropriate authorities (see p. T104). This may take some time, so steps in this direction should be taken immediately.

You will also require potted bean, tomato, or sunflower plants for Investigation 7.2. Because this is an off-season for plants, you will probably have to grow them yourself. Start now.

## GUIDELINES

Diversity of form among animals is the pervading idea in this chapter. To the greatest degree possible, students should have opportunity to see this diversity in living animals. Investigations 4.2 and 4.3 serve to some extent. Visits to a zoo or an aquarium help. Even so, pictorial means must be used to give students a still broader view of the diversity of animal forms. The pictures in the student's book should be fully exploited. In addition, bulletin boards, filmstrips, and slides should be employed. For bulletin-board materials *National Geographic Magazine*, *Natural History*, and *Life* magazine are particularly good sources. Students vary greatly in their acquaintance with animals; you must gauge the experiential background of your classes and then select materials accordingly.

The chapter begins (pp. 104–108) with the abstract concept of classification. There follows a long part (pp. 113–138) concerned with descriptions of major animal phyla strung together on the theme of structural adaptation—a theme important later, especially in Chapters 10 and 18. The concluding part (pp. 142–146) returns to abstraction with an exploration of the meaning of biological classification.

The most logical first assignment is pp. 104–108 (guide questions 1–3), during which Investigation 4.1 can be carried out as a homework assignment and then discussed in class. However, if reading difficulties are anticipated, this investigation might better be carried out in class with immediate teacher direction after the study of pp. 104–108 has been completed. If the basic concept of a hierarchical classification is difficult for students, you may find it helpful to have students first discuss a classification for a group of not unduly diverse manipulatable objects—an assortment of bolts, screws, and nails of various sizes and types, for example.

The next block of text can be conveniently divided into two reading assignments: the first, pp. 113–124 (guide question 5), about chordates; and the second, pp. 124–138 (guide questions 6–13), beginning with the arthropods and continuing through the rest of the animal phyla that have been chosen for discussion. This is not material for exhaustive study; the facts are plentiful but are not intended to be committed to memory. Spice this highly with as much illustrative material as possible. Investigation 4.2 then serves as a summary of some ideas concerning animal organization while it also introduces the idea of taxonomic keys. The remainder of the chapter can then be covered in one reading assignment, pp. 142–146 (guide question 15), to be immediately followed by Investigation 4.3, which brings the student back from abstraction to the concreteness of living animals.

Finally, you should make frequent reference to Appendix II, "A Catalogue of Living Things," though several such references occur in the student's book. Call attention to the introductory paragraphs on p. 782 and point out the reversal of sequence.

DIVERSITY AMONG LIVING THINGS

## TEACHING NOTES

### THE PRINCIPLES OF CLASSIFICATION (pp. 104–108)

**p. 104, ¶ 2:** Many so-called primitive peoples of the present day have large nomenclatures for the organisms surrounding them, and these are by no means restricted to organisms that are immediately harmful or beneficial.

**p. 106, Fig. 4 · 1:** The technical form of each group name has been used in the chart, but in class discussions you are urged to employ the English forms whenever possible. Thus, say "chordates," "arthropods," "mammals," even "canids"; leave "Chordata," "Arthropoda," and "Mammalia" for formal use. Students should know technical forms exist, but they do not need to burden themselves with exotic spelling and pronunciation (unless they individually wish to do so).

**p. 107, Fig. 4 · 2:** To most students, wolf and coyote look most alike. If some students think that either resembles the fox more closely than the other does, call attention to the fact that the forelimbs of the fox are more lightly constructed and the whole animal is relatively smaller. Most of the structural differences between *Canis* and *Vulpes* that are important to taxonomists are not visible in the drawings.

### INVESTIGATION 4.1

### THE LEVELS OF CLASSIFICATION (pp. 108–113)

For students who have attained a ninth-grade reading level, this investigation is quite feasible — with a few hints from you — as an independent home assignment. However, for some classes various degrees of assistance must be given — to the extreme of working out the entire investigation in class with your direct guidance.

#### Procedure

In some cases *explicit* information concerning the group in which a specific animal is classified is not in Appendix II. This will no doubt lead to some degree of healthy frustration on the part of the student and also to a more careful and searching scrutiny of this appendix — resulting in a better understanding of the dimensions of animal diversity.

Specific difficulties that may arise are:

p. 109, Fig. 4 · 3: *(e)* If the past four items have led students to expect chimpanzee and gorilla to be differentiated from man on all counts, this item may be puzzling. The number of incisors is the same for all three species. Although both chimpanzee and gorilla are illustrated in Appendix II, they are not explicitly identified as apes.

p. 110, Fig. 4 · 4: *(a)* No picture is required for this. *(c)* Some inference is required here, because in the figure the clavicle is only indicated in black, not named. *(d)*, *(e)* Identity of canines and incisors should be carried over by the student from Figure 4 · 3. Although no dog (order Carnivora) is shown in Appendix II, the necessary information is included in Figure 4 · 1. Neither is a cat (genus *Felis*) shown, but the cheetah is sufficiently catlike that most students will, by inference, locate the order of the cat.

p. 111, Fig, 4 · 5: *(a)* Your laboratory should contain a specimen of a frog for students to examine. *(b)* See note on Figure 4 · 4, *(a)*. *(c)* You may want to briefly explain the difference between "warm-bloodedness" and "cold-bloodedness" or to refer to p. 117, ¶ 2, and p. 119, ¶ 2. The necessary information on dogs is available in Figure 4 · 1. An illustration of a tree frog (A · 159) is in Appendix II.

p. 111, Fig. 4 · 6: *(c)* Some students may call the brain of a bird small, but point out that the job here is to make comparisons and that compared with the brain of the crayfish, the bird brain is large, even considering relative body size. *(d)* This is another case where attention is called to a point that does not distinguish; all have paired appendages, though some students may call attention to a difference in numbers. *(e)* All students recognize the embryonic similarity between man and bird. Some may, nevertheless, complain that they cannot definitely answer the question with respect to the crayfish. They are right, of course.

Some difficulty in establishing the phylum to which the crayfish belongs may be experienced, because only blue crabs and water fleas represent the Arthropoda in Appendix II. If no student does so, call attention to the close similarity between a lobster and a crayfish. Then Figure 4·1 resolves the difficulty.

## Discussion

- • (1)– • (5): Students sometimes try to make these questions more complicated than they are, attempting to give reasons for the classification by repeating the structural features noted in the charts instead of merely citing the classification levels. This results from misreading: the question is not concerned with the evidence itself but the way the evidence is expressed in the hierarchy of classificatory levels.
- • (6): Species C and D are more closely similar than species A and B. On the basis of the evidence given, it is impossible to make any other general statement.

Be sure during discussion that details do not obscure the basic point of the investigation: that the hierarchy of classificatory levels is an expression of degrees of likeness — the greater the likeness between two organisms, the lower the level at which they are grouped together. At the species level, organisms to be grouped together must be so very much alike that they are capable of interbreeding.

## THE ANIMAL KINGDOM
(pp. 113–138)

This discussion is confined to animals living today and excludes (as does Appendix II) animals known only from fossils. This simplifies (and, of course, somewhat distorts) the picture of animal diversity.

**p. 113, Fig. 4 · 7:** The caption question is rhetorical but some students may very well come up with some ideas such as "two eyes," "mouth," or even the more penetrating (and ultimately the more important) "backbone." Probably very few will think of "bilateral symmetry" unless they have read ahead. A short discussion on the figure—without teacher comment—is a good motivational device at the time the reading assignment is given.

**p. 114, Fig. 4 · 8:** This is a photograph of a cleared specimen.

**p. 115, ¶ 2, line 3:** Note the wording "are placed." No organism "belongs" in a taxonomic group except on the basis of some set of characteristics specified by someone making a classification. This is a basic point in all of Section Two, and it needs constant emphasis by the teacher. We regret that we have not ourselves always been able to avoid the misleading "belongs" terminology.

**p. 115, Fig. 4 · 10:** Sand shark: 5 pairs of pharyngeal openings (gill slits or clefts) are present.

**p. 117, ¶ 2:** Many of the characteristics used by vertebrate taxonomists are in the skeleton. The importance of this becomes evident in Chapter 10. You might want to mention a few such mammalian characteristics: (1) the much smaller number of skull bones as compared with reptiles, (2) the formation of the auditory arch by three bones instead of one, as in reptiles, and (3) the clear differentiation of tooth types (with a few exceptions).

**p. 117, ¶ 4:** Most students should be able to mention many structural adaptations in mammals—beginning with themselves. Also refer to Figure 4 · 11.

**p. 117, Fig. 4 · 12:** Spoonbills sweep their distinctively shaped beaks back and forth through the water to separate out small marine organisms that form their principal food. The peculiar beaks of crossbills enable them to pry out the seeds from pine and spruce cones very efficiently; many other birds must expend a great deal of effort or wait until the cones have opened before their food supply is available to them. The strong, hooked beaks of eagles are well adapted for tearing the flesh of the relatively large animals that they use for food. The relatively narrow and sharp beaks of robins permit them to grab and hold earthworms pulled from burrows and to capture soft insect larvae. The pouchlike beaks of pelicans enable them to collect and manipulate small fish, eliminating excess water from the catch, and also enable them to temporarily store the fish before swallowing them or feeding them to young.

**p. 117, ¶ 5:** What is a feather? This is a good reference question for an interested student. Interest in birds is often high, and there are many other questions that might be pursued. Among the multitude of bird books, two that can be recommended are: J. C. Welty, *The Life of Birds* (New York: Alfred Knopf, 1963) and J. Van Tyne and A. J. Berger, *Fundamentals of Ornithology* (New York: John Wiley & Sons, 1959). The latter is the more technical.

**p. 118, Fig. 4 · 13:** Except for fishes, probably no group of vertebrates shows as much color diversity as birds. Yet blue pigments do not occur in birds, and green is rare, not occurring in quetzals. Some student might like to study "structural color."

**p. 120, note 6:** Movement through a narrow burrow, not much wider than the animal living in it, would be impeded by appendages extending out from the animal's body. Friction between the body surface and the burrow walls, plus the squirming motions characteristic of many burrowing animals, makes possible efficient locomotion in a very confining space.

**p. 123, note 1:** In general, fast-swimming fish have a slender, tapered, streamlined body form. In slower-swimming species the body is usually much less elongated, and movement of pectoral and pelvic fins is of greater importance in propelling the fish through the water. In some fish, trunkfish for example, the body is quite rigid and fins play the major role in locomotion. Locomotion of fish is actually quite a complex matter. Three references that may be of help to students interested in this problem are: F. D. Ommanney and the Editors of LIFE, *The Fishes* (reference: p. T73); N. J. Berrill, *Biology in Action* (New York: Dodd, Mead & Co., 1966), pp. 474–478; and U. Lanham, *The Fishes* (New York: Columbia University Press, 1962), pp. 39–51.

Structural adaptations of bottom-living fish may include flattened body, shift in position of eyes, alteration of fundamental patterns of body symmetry, modification in shape, and position of fins.

**p. 124, Figs. 4 · 19 and 4 · 20:** For background information consult N. J. Berrill, *The Origin of Vertebrates* (New York: Oxford University Press, 1955).

**p. 127, note 5:** The complete reference is F. Lutz, *A Lot of Insects* (New York: G. P. Putnam's Sons, 1941).

**p. 128, Fig. 4 · 25:** In flies, the posterior wings are represented only by balancing organs (halteres). The relatively small but powerful anterior wings are well adapted for hovering and for rapid flights of short duration. Normal cruising speed in still air is approximately 8 km/hr. The large wings of the type of butterfly shown in the illustration (a swallowtail) are well adapted for short periods of relatively active flight, alternating with periods of gliding on favorable air currents. Speed of flight is approximately 20 km/hr. The long, slender wings of dragonflies, unlike those of butterflies, beat independently, the forward ones rising as the rear ones fall. This permits not only rapid forward flight but also well-coordinated hovering maneuvers. Speed of flight is approximately 40 km/hr. In beetles the anterior pair of wings form thick, hard structures that cover and protect the membranous posterior wings. In many cases, these anterior structures reduce the effectiveness of the posterior pair of wings, the only ones used in flight. Many beetles fly for only short periods of time. The proximal halves of the anterior wings of stinkbugs are thickened — somewhat as are those of beetles, but not as much so. They probably supply some motive power, but the posterior, wholly membranous wings are probably more effective. The delicate, ornate wings of lace bugs are relatively poor flight organs.

**p. 129, Fig. 4 · 26:** Mosquito: Mouth parts form a piercing organ with a groove through which saliva (containing an anti-clotting substance) is injected and the blood of the victim is lapped.

Honeybee: Paired mandibles are used for shaping and crushing wax used in comb building. A long, tubelike proboscis is employed in sucking nectar from flowers.

Grasshopper: The strong, hard, paired mouth parts are used for biting and chewing vegetation.

Butterfly: The long, coiled proboscis is used for sucking nectar from flowers. It can reach deeper into tubular flowers than can the proboscis of a honeybee.

Ant: Paired mouth parts are used for seizing, biting, and chewing a wide variety of food, depending upon the species.

**p. 130, note 1:** Millepedes and centipedes have many structural features in common. The basic body plan includes a head and an elongated trunk, made up of many similar leg-bearing segments. Both groups have a single pair of antennae, and the mouth parts show basic similarities. Both groups are often included in a single class, the Myriopoda. Yet many taxonomists — including the ones responsible for our Appendix II — are more impressed by the differences.

**p. 130, note 2:** Terrestrial crabs are commonly nocturnal and live in burrows; both of these habits reduce exposure to dry air. In coconut crabs (*Birgus*), the gills are reduced; most respiratory exchange takes place through the surfaces of highly vascular folds of epithelial tissue, which hang from the top of enclosing branchial chambers. All these adaptations reduce rate of water loss to the point where the animal can absorb sufficient oxygen without becoming excessively dehydrated.

**p. 136, ¶ 2:** Do not lose any opportunity to point out that taxonomists can usually agree on the facts of animal characteristics, but they often disagree about the importance of those characteristics or about their meaning for classification.

## INVESTIGATION 4.2

## STRUCTURAL CHARACTERISTICS IN THE IDENTIFICATION OF ANIMALS (pp. 139–142)

Much of the advice given for Investigation 1.1 applies equally well to this investigation.

### Materials

Since the keys in the second part of the investigation are very simple, they do not take into consideration exceptional representatives of the groups. Therefore, in choosing specimens, take care to select those that will "key out." Suggestions:

For Chart 1: rat or mouse, dogfish, frog or salamander, bat, canary or parrakeet, snake, turtle, goldfish, lizard, lamprey.
For Chart 2: earthworm, crayfish, jellyfish, hydra, butterfly or moth, starfish, clam or oyster, beetle, spider, grasshopper, planarian, snail (but avoid slugs), clam worm, millepede, centipede, tick.

Living animals should of course be used as much as possible.

The charts are rather cumbersome to draw. Some teachers find it convenient to duplicate the charts and have students paste the copies in their data books. The number of columns in the charts depends upon the number of animals to be observed.

### Procedure

At the beginning of observation, two minutes should be allowed at each station.

This time can be reduced as students become familiar with the charts, but it is unlikely that more than twenty specimens can be examined in a single period. If diversity is to be evident despite this limitation, a judicious choice of specimens is important.

Although most of the terminology in the charts has been encountered by the student during his study of previous pages, some explicit definitions may have to be developed as students work out this investigation. Those most likely to cause difficulty are, for convenience, noted below.

*Chart 1*. Bony skeleton: a skeleton in which most of the parts are hard and relatively rigid, because of the hard mineral matter they contain.

Cartilaginous skeleton: a skeleton in which all the parts are tough but flexible, because they are composed of cartilage—a substance that does not contain hard minerals.

*Chart 2*. Exoskeleton: a skeleton on the outer surface of an animal, enclosing the animal.

Radial symmetry: a plan in which the parts are arranged in a circular manner around a central point or region—as in a bicycle wheel.

Bilateral symmetry: a plan in which the parts occur in pairs along the right and left sides of a line running from one end of the object to the other—as in the body of a bus.

Body segmentation: a structural pattern in which the body is divided into a series of more or less similar sections, the boundaries of which are usually indicated by grooves encircling the body.

Tentacles: slender, very flexible structures usually capable of being lengthened or shortened and usually attached near the mouth.

Antennae: slender structures that can be waved about but cannot be changed in length, usually attached to the head.

Procedure B can be assigned as homework. However, in classes where many students have reading difficulties, you should assist in working several examples through the keys before leaving students to independent work. It is important to call special attention to the cautions in the last two paragraphs of Procedure B.

For further experience with taxonomic keys, see Investigation 5.1 and teacher's guide material for Investigation 15.2.

### For Further Investigation

Any vertebrate with feathers can immediately be placed in the class Aves. Any invertebrate which has jointed appendages can immediately be placed in the phylum Arthropoda. Any arthropod without antennae can be placed in the class Arachnida. Any adult arthropod with 3 pairs of legs on the thorax can be placed in the class Insecta.

---

## THE MEANING OF BIOLOGICAL CLASSIFICATION (pp. 142–146)

Chapter 18 is entitled "Evolution," but the writers of the *Green Version* regard the theory of evolution (considered distinct from the theory of natural selection) no less fundamental to the science of biology than the molecular theory is to the physical sciences. The idea that organisms change through time has been implicit from the beginning. It is still implicit in this section of Chapter 4—the word "evolution" does not occur here—but a few questions lead to that idea as a simple way to account for a vast wealth of facts. Without that idea one is left in chaos; there is no scientific meaning to the facts.

**p. 143, note 1:** A trick of sophists is to substitute analogy for demonstration or evidence. Teachers are prone to this fallacy. Help your students to catch you up.

**p. 144, Fig. 4·41:** Do not overlook the caption of this figure. All the organisms shown can be readily found in Appendix II (either by direct comparison with a figure there or by reference back to this figure) except the Portuguese man-of-war, a colonial hydrozoan (Coelenterata).

**p. 146, ¶ 2:** Another analogy!

## INVESTIGATION 4.3

### DIVERSITY IN THE ANIMAL KINGDOM: A COMPARATIVE STUDY (pp. 147–149)

This investigation is not intended to be an abbreviated "type study" of animal phyla. Its primary purpose is to sharpen the student's observation of living animals. Second, through it the student becomes acquainted with five major patterns of animal structure; these are organisms that are good examples for many purposes and are used frequently, especially in Chapter 14. And third, it provides firsthand evidence for the important theme of structure-function relationship (see p. T3).

### Materials

The principal teaching problem is one of logistics. It is sometimes difficult to assemble all the animals—in a healthy, active condition—simultaneously. All the species are worth maintaining as permanent denizens of the laboratory. Therefore, some attention to culturing these animals on a permanent basis is justified. If cultures are routinely maintained (see Needham, reference: p. T73), the problem of timing orders from suppliers is eliminated. You may wish to add or substitute other animals. Suggestions: *Daphnia, Tubifex*, crickets, grasshoppers. Of course, if substitutions are made, you must revise the specific directions.

### Procedure

Note that reference to the student's data book is dropped here and in most subsequent investigations. It is assumed that the use of the data book for all laboratory records is now an established habit.

The five stations should be as far from each other as the plan of the laboratory permits. Movable tables and peripheral facilities allow the best arrangement, but adaptations can be made in other situations. Six students per station is perhaps ideal, but eight can be accommodated. Each group should be permitted about ten minutes at each station. Therefore the observation time

occupies all of an ordinary class period. Consequently, directions for observation must be thoroughly studied before the laboratory period; and everything must be in readiness at all stations when the class arrives.

It is unlikely that the procedure can be followed exactly as written. You may direct students to omit some of the general questions or to add others. (But be sure that any added questions can be answered *from the material available;* this is not the time to send students scurrying to an encyclopedia.) Some of the directions for specific animals may have to be bypassed—feeding the frog probably causes the most difficulty.

### Discussion

Concentrate first on the structure-function idea in the "Summary." Then return to specific observations if time allows.

---

### GUIDE QUESTIONS (p. 150)

**2.** The second part of this question can be answered in part on the basis of material in the first reading assignment (pp. 104–108). But it becomes more understandable at the end of the chapter (p. 145, ¶ 3). Return to it when you reach that point.

### PROBLEMS (p. 151)

**2.** This problem incidentally illustrates the principle of adaptive convergence discussed on pp. 369–370. (*a*) Lampreys lack jaws and bony skeletons. (*b*) Snakes have three-chambered hearts and amniote eggs. (*c*) Salamanders lack scales, claws, and amniote eggs. (*d*) Armadillos have mammary glands and sparse hair. (*e*) Bats have hair and mammary glands and lack feathers.

**4.** Taxonomy will continue to develop because: (*a*) additional fossil forms will continue to be discovered; (*b*) new kinds of evidence indicating different relationships will undoubtedly be discovered; (*c*) new species of organisms will continue to appear as a result of evolution.

5. See Simpson and Beck (reference: p. 151) for a discussion of patterns of symmetry in relation to motility in animals.

6. Moment (reference: p. 574) has a short discussion of this problem. However, the student should also consult other college zoology textbooks that have a phylogenetic approach, e.g., Buchsbaum, and Storer and Usinger (references: p. 151).

7. This one should be easy, but it also gives a hint of an approach to Problem 2.

8. The class Monoplacophora (p. 794) had already been established, but it was known only from fossils. Moment briefly tells the story. Another example of the same kind of event was the discovery of *Latimeria* in 1938. But probably most major changes in classification during the past century have resulted from the discovery of fossils rather than of living organisms. If the problem is allowed to include such discoveries, it is a very wide one. Just one example: the discovery of the toothed birds in 1872.

## SUPPLEMENTARY MATERIALS

### Audiovisual Materials

**Slides:** Of materials for projection, the best for this chapter are $2 \times 2$ slides. Large stocks of such slides, offering illustrations of almost all animal phyla, are available from the principal biological suppliers: CCM: General Biological, Inc., 8200 S. Hoyne Ave., Chicago, Ill. 60620; Carolina Biological Supply Co., Burlington, N.C. 27216 (or Powell Laboratories, Gladstone, Ore. 97027); Ward's Natural Science Establishment, P. O. Box 1712, Rochester 3, N.Y. (Ward's of California, P. O. Box 1749, Monterey, Calif.). From these stocks the teacher can select slides showing animals that are unavailable as living specimens.

**Filmstrips:** Except for human physiology, no topic in biology has been more abundantly treated in filmstrips than has classification. For the most part, however, filmstrips that the *Green Version* writers have seen are unsuitable for our purposes, either being too greatly involved with anatomy and cellular detail or approaching classification from an authoritarian viewpoint. As indicated above, the teaching of animal diversity is better accomplished with slides; you are then free to discuss alternative systems of classification.

**Motion-picture films:** The comments on filmstrips apply in some degree to motion-picture films. The following are relatively free of the disadvantages mentioned above.

*Introducing Insects.* National Film Board of Canada. 16 mm. Color. 17 min. Illustrates well the diversity among insects and discusses classification. Includes some good slow-motion and time-lapse sequences.

*Echinoderms.* Oxford Biological Films, distributed by Ealing. Super-8 film loop. 4 min. The dimension of motion is especially desirable in presenting this phylum, with which most students can have little firsthand acquaintance.

*What Is a Fish?, What Is an Amphibian?, What Is a Reptile?, What Is a Bird?, What Is a Mammal?* Encyclopaedia Britannica Films. 16 mm. Color. Various lengths. A good series if your laboratory is deficient in living specimens and if opportunities for your students to visit aquariums and zoos are few.

*Life in the Ocean.* Film Associates of California. 16 mm. Color. 13 min. This film is not particularly concerned with classification, but it has beautiful photography of sea animals that most students are not likely to see otherwise.

### Teacher's References

BORRADAILE, L. A., and F. A. POTTS. *The Invertebrata.* 4th ed. New York: Cambridge University Press, 1961. (An excellent systematic reference on the invertebrates. Contains numerous line drawings.)

CARR, A., and the Editors of LIFE. *The Reptiles.* New York: Time, Inc., Book Division, 1963. (Excellent pictures. The authoritative text goes rather far beyond the scope of our Chapter 4, but it includes much on adaptations.)

CARRINGTON, R., and the Editors of LIFE. *The Mammals.* New York: Time, Inc., Book Division, 1963. (Contains excellent illustrations.)

FARB, P., and the Editors of LIFE. *The Insects.* New York: Time, Inc., Book Division, 1962. (Contains excellent illustrations.)

NEEDHAM, J. G. *Culture Methods for Invertebrate Animals.* New York: Dover Publications, Inc., 1937. (An old standby for information on culturing laboratory invertebrates.)

OMMANNEY, F. D., and the Editors of LIFE. *The Fishes.* New York: Time, Inc., Book Division, 1963. (See remarks under Carr above.)

PETERSON, R. T., and the Editors of LIFE. *The Birds.* New York: Time, Inc., Book Division, 1963. (See remarks under Carr above.)

ROTHSCHILD, N. M. V. *A Classification of Living Animals.* New York: John Wiley & Sons, Inc., 1961. (Perhaps the best recent systematic overview of the animal kingdom.)

SIMPSON, G. G. *Principles of Animal Taxonomy.* New York: Columbia University Press, 1961. (An important summarization by a paleontologist who has devoted many years of careful thought to the philosophy and practice of taxonomy.

YOUNG, J. Z. *The Life of Vertebrates.* 2nd ed. New York: Oxford University Press, 1962. (Good background for teacher rather than student.)

# 5

# Plants

## MAJOR IDEAS

Classification and structural adaptation continue to receive emphasis in Chapter 5. Additional major ideas are:

1. Binomial nomenclature developed during the age of world exploration, when the need arose for an orderly system that would provide distinctive names for each of the multitude of newly discovered organisms.

2. Through the application of a few simple rules, the binomial system has resulted in relative stability and clarity in biological nomenclature for nearly two hundred years.

3. The great majority of familiar land plants can be grouped together in one phylum. This phylum, the Tracheophyta, is characterized by a vascular system, through which liquids are conveyed.

4. Plants of other phyla either are aquatic or grow best in rather moist habitats.

## PLANNING AHEAD

You may want to set up Investigation 6.1 before you complete Chapter 5 (see note to p. 173, ¶1 – p. T79).

If you are unfamiliar with techniques for handling microbes, you should try out those required in Investigations 6.2 and 6.3 before attempting to guide students. You may find the following film loops helpful: *Bacteriological Techniques I*, Super-8, Color, 4 min., 30 sec.; and *Bacteriological Techniques II*, Super-8, Color, 3 min., 15 sec. (BSCS Techniques Series, Thorne Films, Boulder, Colorado). If you have not ordered cultures of *Serratia marcescens* and *Sarcina lutea* for Investigation 6.2, do so immediately. Check the quantities of glassware available for Investigation 6.2; the result will determine the size of your teams. Also, prepare the glass tubes needed to set up Investigation 6.4.

Some form of incubator will be useful for Investigation 7.1. Check p. T91 and consider the possibilities for your own laboratory. Securing *Agrobacterium tumefaciens* sometimes involves some letter writing. Consult p. T104 and take whatever steps may be necessary in your state.

Seeds for Investigation 8.1 are difficult to obtain locally in the autumn. If you do not have seeds on hand, order some from a biological supply house.

## GUIDELINES

It has been customary to wrap the whole of taxonomy in a neat package of abstractions that are quickly and superficially covered, quickly and completely forgotten. The authors believe that taxonomy both explicitly and implicitly permeates all areas of biology. Moreover, they believe it to be an intellectual achievement, an important facet of human cultural development, and, therefore, a matter of importance in a humanistically oriented high school biology course (p. T6). The result of these beliefs is an attempt to avoid locking taxonomy into a compartment by itself. Experience indicates that taxonomy is more clearly understood—and (we think) better appreciated as an intellectual achievement—when it is divided into parts and taught at several appropriate points than is the case when it is presented in one massive lump. So the species concept came first (Chapter 2); classification followed (Chapter 4); now comes nomenclature.

For assignment the obvious divisions of the textbook chapter are pp. 153–157 (guide questions 1–4), 157–171 (guide questions 5–11), and 171–184 (guide questions 12–16). The first of these is rather short, but, as has been mentioned previously, number of pages is not necessarily a good guide to number of ideas. In this chapter nomenclature requires a major share of discussion time.

Investigation 5.1 can be introduced immediately following completion of the first study assignment. Students have already become familiar with dichotomous keys through their work in Chapter 4. They should, therefore, have little real difficulty in working out this investigation, which does not really depend—except for its title—on any study of pp. 157–164. However, it is best to defer Investigation 5.2 until the study assignments have all been completed. It provides a good means of reviewing many of the ideas and much of the information presented in the chapter.

Refer to the "Guidelines" of Chapter 4 for suggestions concerning the treatment of the diversity concept. If you follow the student's book, you will avoid becoming entangled in alternation of generations—traditionally a "Slough of Despond" during any pilgrimage through the plant kingdom. What Marston Bates calls "the botanist's obsession with sex" should not be allowed to deter the student from gaining a panoramic view of plant diversity. In due time reproductive cycles will be dealt with—in Chapter 16.

## TEACHING NOTES

### PLANT CLASSIFICATION
(pp. 153–154)

**p. 154, ¶ 3:** A student report on the life of Linnaeus might be useful. Encyclopedia accounts are dull—and Linnaeus himself certainly was not. But even an average tenth grader ought to be able to contrive an interesting report from *Green Laurels*, by D. C. Peattie, Chapters 4, 5, and 6 (New York: Simon & Schuster, Inc., 1936).

### A PROBLEM: NOMENCLATURE
(pp. 154–157)

**p. 155, Fig. 5 · 2:** The Latin name is translated: "simple wild pink, sweetly blushing." Note that the term "caryophyllus" was used for pinks in addition to the term "dianthus"; Linnaeus combined the two in designating the carnation binomially (p. 156, ¶ 1).

**p. 156, ¶ 2:** Students may ask, "What prevents duplication of names?" Basically the answer to this is the rule of priority. The first person to publish a name establishes that name as valid. An example is Linnaeus' name for the carnation. If someone now published another name for it, that name would become a synonym. This has happened quite frequently because it is difficult to know about all publications of names. For vascular plants alone it has been estimated that there are 3 times as many names as species. The system *is* simple, as the text says, but regulating it is complex; this is the business of several international organizations of taxonomists, who do not always agree but have a better record, on the whole, than international political organizations.

**p. 156, Fig. 5 · 3:** For some groups of organisms that were poorly known in Linnaeus' day, other beginning points for the rule of priority have been agreed upon. For example, most nomenclature of fungi dates from Fries's *Systema Mycologicum*, 1821.

**p. 157, ¶'s 1–3:** Some expansion of the discussion may be interesting to students. Further examples of short generic epithets are *Pica* (magpies), *Sus* (pigs), *Acer* (maples), *Bos* (cattle), *Rhus* (sumacs), *Erica* (heaths), *Ficus* (figs), *Ilex* (hollies), *Chen* (snow geese), *Anas* ("puddle" ducks), *Iva* (marsh elders), *Aix* (wood ducks). On the other hand, the layman's view has some justification; consider *Strongylocentrotus* (sea urchins) and *Dolichocephalocyrtus* (beetles).

Some further examples of generic epithets far from classical Latin and Greek are *Fothergilla, Forsythia, Cunninghamia, Koelreuteria, Torreya, Kickxia, Muhlenbergia,* and, of course, *Welwitschia* (Figure 5 · 13) —all these are plants named for botanists; *Lama, Nasua,* and *Fayra*—mammals with names derived from American Indian languages; *Peggichisme*—it looks Greek, but try pronouncing it; *Arizona, Sonora*—snakes with names derived from geographical terms of American Indian origin; *Ginkgo* —a gymnosperm tree with a Chinese name.

## TRACHEOPHYTES (in part)
(pp. 157–164)

**p. 157, notes 2 and 3:** Establish the habit of using anglicized forms of names: "tracheophytes" rather than "Tracheophyta." Where completely English words are available, use them: "liverworts" rather than either "Hepaticae" or "hepatics."

**p. 159, ¶ 4:** "Why are stamens and pistils believed to be modified leaves?" a student who has begun to acquire the spirit of this course may well ask. A full answer, involving paleontological evidence, is difficult to give at this point, but you can show that stamens often grade into petals in "double" cultivated flowers such as many roses and begonias.

**p. 160, ¶ 3:** In addition to the illustrations in Figure 5 · 4, you should try to have on hand an assortment of flowers for students to examine for firsthand appreciation of diversity. At the season in which this chapter is likely to be studied, wild flowers are not available in the northern states and are likely to be mostly composites southward. Visit a florist and ask for sprays of flowers that have deteriorated too much to be salable.

### p. 161, Fig. 5 · 8

*Poppy:* The mature fruit or capsule has a ring of openings, or pores, at its top and is developed at the tip of a long stalk. When the capsules are shaken by the wind, the tiny seeds sift out through the pores, a few at a time, and are carried away.

*Maple:* The paired, winged fruits (samaras) are well adapted to be carried away from the parent plant by the wind.

*Touch-me-not:* In this species the mature fruit is a fleshy capsule. If a fruit is pinched, or even touched when ripe, the capsule wall suddenly splits into a number of segments that roll up with considerable force, thereby scattering the seeds.

*Cocklebur:* The paired pistillate flowers are enclosed in a protective coat composed of hooked, spinelike, involucral bracts. When the fruit is mature, this outer covering serves to attach the fruits to the fur of mammals that brush up against the plant. If the animal later dislodges the fruit, a very efficient adaptation for seed dispersal has operated to transfer the seeds of the parent plant to a new location, often at a considerable distance from it.

*Dandelion:* Each single-seeded fruit is equipped with a "parachute" (pappus), actually made up of delicate filaments derived from the calyx of the flower. When the fruit is mature, winds or air currents detach the fruits from the disc of the inflorescence and carry them away from the parent plant.

**p. 162, Fig. 5 · 9:** Much of the monocot seed shown here is endosperm, but this part is not labeled because presence or absence of endosperm is not a feature that distinguishes between monocots and dicots.

**p. 163, Fig. 5 · 10**

*Sweet pea:* The leaflets of the compound leaves of this legume are developed as tendrils that curl around any available supporting structures and enable the shoots of the plant to maintain its position in space. Most of the photosynthetic activity is carried on by the large, paired stipules attached at the base of the leaf.

*Pitcher plant:* The cuplike, highly modified leaves become partially filled with rainwater. The waxy, inner surface of a cup is provided with hairs, all pointing toward the base. Insects that fall into the cups find it difficult or impossible to climb out. They eventually drown and are digested by the bacteria and enzymes in the water in the cup. The outer surfaces of the leaf carry on normal photosynthesis.

*Venus's-flytrap:* The terminal part of each leaf in this plant consists of two toothed halves that are attached to one another by a median hinge. Three sensitive hairs (invisible in this picture) project from the inner surface of each leaf half. If an insect touches any two of these hairs in succession or a single hair twice, the two halves quickly snap shut and the insect is imprisoned between them. Glands then secrete enzymes

which bring about the digestion of the prey. Eventually the two halves separate, and the leaf is ready to capture its next victim.

Both the pitcher plant and the Venus's-flytrap are species that are adapted to live in soils deficient in soluble nitrogen-bearing nutrients. By digesting and absorbing nitrogenous compounds in captured insects, the species are presumably better able to survive in such soils than are other species lacking such insect-capturing structures.

*Victoria regia:* The floating leaves of this plant may exceed 2 m in diameter. The petioles extend upward from a tuberous rhizome embedded in the mud a meter or more below the surface of the water. Stomates located only on the upper surface of the leaf blade, airspaces in the leaf mesophyll, and numerous perforations (stomatodes) are all adaptations permitting the photosynthetic leaves of this water plant to function as effective organs at the surface of the water. For an interesting account of the two existing species of *Victoria*, see L. H. Bailey, *The Standard Encyclopedia of Horticulture*, Vol. III, pp. 3466–3469 (New York: The Macmillan Co., 1930–17th Printing, 1958).

*Cactus:* In the species shown, an *Opuntia*, or prickly-pear cactus, the green photosynthetic tissue of the shoot is located near the surface of the flattened but thick stems. Although very small leaflike structures are present on young stems, these do not persist. On older stems the spines, which discourage herbivores from eating the succulent photosynthetic tissues, are believed by many botanists to be highly modified leaves.

## INVESTIGATION 5.1

### DIVERSITY IN ANGIOSPERM LEAVES (pp. 164–165)

As the most abundant and conspicuous groups of plants known to students, angiosperms deserve special attention. Emphasis on diversity of leaf structure can be justified because materials for study can be so readily obtained and preserved.

Attention to this diversity through work on key construction is desirable because it continues emphasis on the mechanisms of classification and because it produces further student facility with keys. As mentioned earlier, learning to use a key is a truly educational objective because it tends to free a student from dependence upon others for the identification of organisms.

## Materials

Each student should individually work out a dichotomous key for the ten leaves in a set. Thus each class of 30 students requires 30 sets of named leaves (Set A) and also 30 sets of leaves without names (Set B) to use in checking the keys. Each set includes 10 different leaves. $30 + 30 = 60$; $60 \times 10 = 600$ leaves. That is a lot of leaves, particularly if they must be obtained at a time when many species, at least in the northern parts of the country, are not in leaf.

Obviously you can reduce the supply problem by collecting, pressing, and mounting sets of leaves prior to the time they are needed for this investigation. Collecting leaves of 10 different species presents no problem in spring, summer, or early fall.

Pressing, if a standard press is not available, can be quite satisfactorily accomplished by interleaving specimens in old telephone directories. Every day or every other day, depending upon the thickness of the specimens and the relative humidity, move the leaves to dry pages in the books. Completely dried specimens can then be mounted on herbarium sheets and labeled.

You can do an even better job of mounting by making use of clear transparent vinyl or acetate film, which can be obtained precoated with adhesive. Such materials can usually be obtained in paint or hardware stores. Somewhat more expensive materials are available from biological supply houses. Three methods of mounting have been used satisfactorily: (1) The leaf is placed between two sheets of adhesive vinyl plastic, adhesive surface against adhesive surface.

(2) The leaf is placed on a sheet of acetate and then covered with a sheet of adhesive vinyl that bonds to the acetate. (3) The leaf is placed on a sheet of thin cardboard and then covered with a sheet of adhesive vinyl that bonds to the cardboard. In each of the first two methods, a slip of paper bearing a number and name (for Set A) or a number only (for Set B) is mounted with the leaf. In the third method the label can be written directly on the cardboard before the adhesive vinyl is applied. Methods 1 and 2 have the advantage that with them the patterns of venation can easily be seen if the mount is held up to the light. But in terms of expense and time, Method 3 is preferred. If a hole is punched in the upper left-hand corner of each mount, sets can be assembled and then kept together by means of looseleaf mounting rings. Such sets of leaves, when used with reasonable care, are quite durable and should remain in good condition for a number of years.

The particular species included in each set of leaves is of course not crucial, but a fairly wide range of diversity is desirable. Black locust, ginkgo, hickory, sycamore, maple, sweet gum, horse chestnut, sassafras, tulip tree, red and white oak, linden, cottonwood, willow, privet, cherry, and beech are all usually rather easily obtained. Leaves do not necessarily have to be obtained from woody plants, but such leaves are usually firmer than those from herbaceous plants and more easily dried without wrinkling. Some attention should also be given to leaf size, since it is desirable that the mounts be of about the same size. A selection of 10 different species from a group such as the one mentioned above will provide plenty of evidence of diversity.

## Procedure

The sample key presented on p. 164 employs the same principle as that used in the keys of Chapter 4; only the format is new. But the format is so obvious that most students require little or no help.

You should be especially concerned with establishing a learning pattern so that students achieve a clear understanding of the dimensions of diversity in terms of differences between specimen and specimen and between species and species. Comparison of keys prepared by students in a given class almost always shows no two keys alike. Even the criteria used for constructing the keys (really the criteria used for classifying) usually differ from student to student. Finally, the need for careful observation and description is clearly demonstrated when two students attempt to use and then evaluate each other's keys. Thus, because the points are made in the doing, a minimum of discussion is required at the conclusion of the work.

The project suggested "For Further Investigation" is an excellent assignment for homework immediately following completion of this investigation.

## TRACHEOPHYTES (cont.)
(pp. 166–171)

**p. 166, ¶ 1:** The distinction between gymnosperms and angiosperms is a rather more technical matter than this paragraph allows. This is of no great importance for the purposes of this chapter, but really inquisitive students may present you with two somewhat embarrassing specimens: the "fruits" of yew and of ginkgo, both of which may occur in the autumn around many schools. A little examination shows that the yew seed is rather well buried in the pulp but is not completely surrounded by it, as is the seed of a peach. The ginkgo seed seems to be completely encased in pulp; however, the pulp is a part of the seed itself, not a structure developed from an ovary, as are the pulp and stone around a peach seed. Therefore, ginkgoes simply bear single, naked seeds, not fruits.

**p. 168, note 5:** The age of a tree, particularly one living in middle and high latitudes, can be determined accurately if the annual rings, shown in a cross section of the trunk (or in a core that has been taken by boring into the center of the trunk),

are counted. The level at which either cross section or core is obtained should be as close to the ground as is feasible. See Figures 13·15 and 13·24.

**p. 170, Fig. 5·17:** Do your students recognize the typographical distinction between the names and understand the reason for it? *Ophioglossum* and *Marsilea* are technical generic epithets and are therefore capitalized and italicized.

**p. 170, ¶ 1:** Students who want to prepare a herbarium will find that ferns are good plants for them to start with. Ferns are easily collected; most can be pressed without difficulty; they present a good appearance without causing the disappointment involved in the loss of color from flowering plants; and most are not in any critical danger of extinction.

## NONVASCULAR PLANTS
(pp. 171–179)

**p. 171, ¶ 3:** Because nonvascular plants are even less familiar to students than are tracheophytes, it is especially important to have as many specimens, preferably living, as it is possible for you to gather together.

**p. 173, ¶ 1:** It is not inappropriate to set up Investigation 6.1 at this time. Some of the "microorganisms" that result from it are fungi.

**p. 173, ¶ 2:** The term "mycelium" for the mass of hyphae has been eliminated from the 1968 edition because the authors could find no real need for it. You may wish to reintroduce it, but before you do so ask yourself the question: "Are my students going to use 'mycelium' so often that it will have distinct advantage over the more cumbersome 'mass of hyphae'?"

**p. 173, ¶ 3:** None of the common terms applied to fungi—mold, mildew, mushroom, etc.—has any taxonomic significance. Plants bearing these names are scattered among the fungal classes.

**p. 174, Fig. 5·26:** Spores of a field mushroom are located at the tips of specialized hyphae, the basidia. These project from the surface of the gills (plates) that radiate from the center of the cap.

**p. 175, Fig. 5·27:** Spores of an ascomycete, such as the cup fungus shown, are formed in elongated sacs (asci) that, together with sterile, non–spore-bearing hyphae, are located in a layer on the inner surface.

**p. 175, ¶ 1:** The classification of species of *Penicillium* as members of the ascomycetes is not approved by some mycologists. Since no perfect forms are known for a majority of the species included in the form genus *Penicillium*, a case could be made for relegating them to the Fungi Imperfecti (p. 177). However, their inclusion in Ascomycetes seems justified by (1) the close similarity between the asexual (conidial) stages of many *Penicillium* species and ascomycete genera having identifiable sexual stages, and (2) the fact that most Fungi Imperfecti, upon the discovery of their sexual stages, turn out to be ascomycetes. None of this need be brought to the attention of most students; but for some, this can be used as an excellent illustration of the difficulties in taxonomy.

**p. 175, Fig. 5·29:** The story of penicillin has been told so often that most tenth-grade students probably know something of it. However, a good student report on Fleming's discovery can do three things at this time: (1) relieve steady attention to taxonomy, (2) remind students of the role of serendipity in scientific research—with due attention to the principle that chance favors the prepared mind, and (3) remind students of the complexities of ecological relationships.

**p. 176, Fig. 5·30:** The phyla of each of the genera illustrated are as follows: *Enteromorpha* and *Ulva*—phylum Chlorophyta; *Laminaria, Fucus,* and *Ascophyllum*—phylum Phaeophyta; *Chondrus* and *Polysiphonia*—phylum Rhodophyta; and *Oscillatoria*—phylum Cyanophyta. This can be deduced from color alone because none of the algae illustrated in this figure represent

any of the numerous color exceptions, but all are also listed under their phylum names in Appendix II. *Oscillatoria* may cause some difficulty, as the Cyanophyta have now been placed in the kingdom Protista. This transfer of kingdom does not, however, alter the fact that they can be referred to as "algae," a term that is essentially a common name without taxonomic significance. Note also that in this figure identification is by generic epithet only; each of the genera contains a number of species, but the species depicted has not been designated.

**p. 177, ¶ 3:** A good variety of freshwater algae can be maintained in your classroom aquariums. You should have some examples of marine algae mounted on herbarium sheets. (Mounted algae are obtainable from biological supply houses.) Students should also be allowed to scrape the sides of an aquarium to collect and examine microscopically the diatoms usually found there. Some microscope time might also be devoted to prepared slides of diatoms and desmids, which are fascinating in their diversity.

**p. 179, ¶ 2:** Here is another place where your students are not told what to think. How are they bearing up under this treatment? How are *you* handling matters of this sort when you construct a quiz?

## INVESTIGATION 5.2

### THE CONCEPT OF "PRIMITIVE CHARACTERISTICS"
(pp. 179–183)

Students generally have far less acquaintance with plants than with animals; therefore, more effort is required to broaden the concept "plant." Such is the primary purpose of this investigation. The secondary purpose derives from the last portion of Chapter 4 (pp. 142–146). From the idea that classification reflects kinship (genetic) relationships, it logically follows that characteristics of organisms have diverged through successive generations in the past. That some present-day organisms may have retained more, and others fewer, of their ancestors' characteristics is but a corollary of this proposition.

## Materials

The student is being asked to observe. Inference should be kept at a minimum. Therefore the plant materials should show as many as possible of the characteristics needed for correct scoring. For example, gymnosperm specimens should include seeds; angiosperm specimens should have fruits or flowers; mosses, ferns, and lycopods should bear spore cases. Some distinctions—as between shrub and tree—are difficult to exhibit in specimens small enough for the laboratory.

The easiest plants to obtain, of course, are just those that tend to confirm the popular stereotype. Considerable effort (and, if necessary, money) should be expended to provide a true diversity of plants; perhaps not more than 3 of the 10 specimens should be angiosperms, and not more than 1 of these should be herbaceous.

Suggestions for plant materials follow: For microscope—green algae (*Spirogyra, Oedogonium, Ulothrix*); yeasts. For hand lens or stereomicroscope—molds (*Rhizopus, Aspergillus*); liverworts (*Marchantia, Conocephalum*); mosses (*Polytrichum, Mnium, Pogonatum, Dicranum*); lichens. For naked eye—*Lycopodium;* ferns (*Polystichum, Polypodium*); pine; spruce; begonia; *Zebrina;* household geranium; fire thorn (*Pyracantha*). If you wish to consider blue-green algae as plants, the chart allows you to do so.

As always, fresh material is preferable to that which is preserved. Most of the plants listed above are fairly easy to obtain in the autumn. To obtain bread molds, start about ten days before the work is scheduled. If possible, use home-baked bread or rolls, since commercial bread usually contains mold inhibitors. Break the bread into 10 pieces to avoid later handling. Spores of the mold are usually abundant in the air; after the bread has been exposed to air in the laboratory for a day, sprinkle it with water, cover, and keep in a warm, dark place.

## Procedure

The chart on pp. 180–181 bears a superficial resemblance to a dichotomous key. The resemblance enables the student, who has had experience with keys in Investigations 4.2 and 5.1, to grasp the plan of work quickly. But of course the chart is not a key, because it does not lead to identification.

Begin the work by dividing the class into groups of 2 to 4 students and assigning each group to a station. Each station should be supplied with a specimen of each kind of plant. If sufficient specimens of each kind of plant are not available, some plan of rotation among stations is required. By this time students should be able to move from station to station readily. Work is expedited if you run through the scoring of a specimen (one not included in the investigation) before setting students to work.

## Discussion

The numbers in the chart have been worked out so that, when summed along possible courses through the chart, they will provide low scores for plants generally considered primitive by botanists and high scores for plants generally considered advanced. For the purposes of this investigation, "primitive" and "advanced" are adequately explained in the "Background Information" on p. 182. You must bear in mind and communicate to the students the controversial nature of the scores. For example, it is probable that many mycologists would justifiably object to the rather low score that is assigned to fungi.

- (1): If species were formerly fewer and simpler, then the more numerous and more highly developed species of later times would logically be more diverse—that is, there would be more kinds.

- (2)–• (4): The greater the difference in score between characteristics at any one dichotomy, the more important the difference was considered to be by the maker of the chart.

• (5) and • (6): This entails listing characteristics common to plants that scored low and high respectively.
• (7): It is dichotomously branching on the basis of contrasting characteristics.
• (8): It does not lead to an identification.

## PROBLEMS (p. 184)

1. The dark spots, usually arranged in a definite pattern, are groups of sporangia called sori, which in some species of ferns are partially covered with a protective structure, the indusium. Typically, sori are more conspicuous on the older leaves of a fern, but they can be seen in various stages of development as progressively younger leaves are examined. The presence of sori—and sporangia—is of course entirely normal in a healthy fern plant.

2. Compounds containing elements in which the soil is deficient can be obtained by insectivorous plants through absorption of digested material derived from captured insects. See comments on pitcher plant and Venus's-flytrap in Figure 5 · 10 (p. T77).

3. In helping students work out answers to these questions, you can avoid some confusion if you contrast a plant such as a species of *Penicillium,* which produces only asexual spores, with a seed-bearing species such as a bean. "Advantage" and "disadvantage" should be interpreted in terms of reproductive effectiveness. Since both spore bearers and seed bearers are abundant today and both have been abundant for long geological ages, it follows that "advantages" and "disadvantages" have balanced in the long run. With the above as the ground rules, some pertinent characteristics are:

*Advantages* (seed-bearing plant): (*a*) Embryos in seeds are provided with a "built-in" food supply. (*b*) Adaptations

of fruit or of seed coats may provide protection and a variety of mechanisms for dispersal. (*c*) Great variety of offspring is possible because seeds are sexually produced (not a likely idea from students at this point).

*Advantages* (spores): (*a*) Because they are small in size, spores can be produced in tremendous numbers. (*b*) They have a low density and high surface-to-volume ratio, which are good characteristics for dispersal by winds and air currents. (*c*) Because they are asexually produced, new plants developed from them have characteristics of the parent; if the parent is well adapted, so also will be the offspring.

*Disadvantages* (seed-bearing plant): (*a*) Since seeds contain foods, they may be used by many animals as a source of nutrients; unless protected by resistant coats, the seeds are destroyed. (*b*) In many cases seeds are produced in relatively small numbers.

*Disadvantages* (spores): (*a*) The food stored in the spore is necessarily very limited. (*b*) Since all the offspring resemble the parent closely, if they are distributed to environments quite different from that of the parent plant, the probability of any of them being able to survive is low.

In discussing this problem with students, keep in mind that in due course you will be discussing the microspores and megaspores produced by seed-producing tracheophytes and also that many spores are produced as the direct result of sexual reproduction. Thus the discussion, if not held within the bounds of the "ground rules" noted above', may lead more to confusion than to enlightenment.

4. The parts of plants that we use as concentrated sources of foods are precisely those in which the plant has stored foods for its own use or for its offspring's. Food storage in seeds represents an adaptive characteristic increasing reproductive effectiveness per dissemi-

nule. Storage of foods in underground parts of herbaceous plants serves to protect the plants' food supply from animal depredation and, in certain climates, from damage by extremes of environmental temperatures or by desiccation. This protection is obviously of survival value to the species concerned.

5. All producers do not appear green, although all contain at least one of the several kinds of chlorophyll that may be involved in photosynthesis, but accessory pigments may mask the green color of the chlorophylls. Common terrestrial examples: red maples, red cabbage, *Coleus* species, copper beeches, etc. And students should remember the variously colored algae.

## SUPPLEMENTARY MATERIALS

### Audiovisual Materials

The remarks concerning audiovisual materials for Chapter 4 apply equally well to Chapter 5.

**Filmstrips:** *Classification of Plants.* United World Films, Inc. Color. Although this filmstrip uses the ancient cryptogamphanerogam classification, it is clearly organized in a way that can easily be related to more modern classification. The drawings are excellent. Only a few of the names in this British film are likely to be unfamiliar. One error: roots of the sporophytes of ferns and horsetails are called rhizoids.

*What Makes Up a Flower Family?* Society for Visual Education. Color. Uses the Liliaceae as an example. Describes how a plant is named scientifically.

*Great Names in Biology: Carolus Linnaeus.* Encyclopaedia Britannica Films. Color. Good for biographical background.

**Motion-picture films.** *Fungi.* Encyclopaedia Britannica Films. 16 mm. Color.

*Simple Plants: The Algae.* Encyclopaedia Britannica Films. 16 mm. Color.

*Gymnosperms.* Encyclopaedia Britannica Films. 16 mm. Color.

These three films are part of a series covering the plant kingdom. As a whole, the series places too much emphasis on phylogeny for our purposes in Section Two of the *Green Version* course; but taken individually, the films may be useful for emphasizing plant diversity with students who have poor experiential backgrounds.

*Carnivorous Plants.* Super-8. Color. Film loop. 2 min. Ealing. Good, if your students do not have an opportunity to become directly acquainted with this example of plant diversity.

### Teacher's References

ALEXOPOULOS, C. J., and H. C. BOLD. *Algae and Fungi.* New York: The Macmillan Co., 1967. (A concise account, including basic information on morphology, physiology, and biochemistry.)

BENSON, L. *Plant Classification.* Boston: D. C. Heath & Co., 1957. (A general text on plant taxonomy, but it emphasizes vascular plants.)

BOLD, H. C. *The Plant Kingdom.* 2nd ed. Englewood Cliffs, N.J.: Prentice-Hall, Inc., 1964. (A brief but well-organized summary of the plant kingdom. Of particular interest is a table showing several different systems of plant classification.)

HILL, J. B., L. O. OVERHOLTS (deceased), H. W. POPP, and A. R. GROVE, JR. *Botany: A Textbook for Colleges.* 3rd ed. New York: McGraw-Hill Book Co., Inc., 1960. (Uses a good up-to-date classification.)

JENSEN, W. A., and L. G. KAVALJIAN (eds.). *Plant Biology Today.* 2nd ed. Belmont, Calif.: Wadsworth Publishing Co., Inc., 1966. (A collection of papers on a variety of topics. The sections on biochemical methods in systematics and on lichen symbiosis are of particular interest.)

PORTER, C. L. *Taxonomy of Flowering Plants.* 2nd ed. San Francisco: W. H. Freeman and Co., Publishers, 1967. (A basic reference including information on most aspects of the taxonomy of angiosperms.)

SAVORY, T. *Naming the Living World.* New York: John Wiley & Sons, Inc., 1963.

(An excellent introduction to the principles of biological nomenclature.)

SCAGEL, R. F., G. E. ROUSE, J. R. STEIN, R. J. BANDONI, W. B. SCHOFIELD, and T. M. C. TAYLOR. *An Evolutionary Survey of the Plant Kingdom.* Belmont, Calif: Wadsworth Publishing Co., Inc., 1965. (Definitely not for the student, but you may find it good background if your training included little of this or was obtained long ago.)

SOKAL, R. R., and P. H. A. SNEATH. *Principles of Numerical Taxonomy.* San Francisco: W. H. Freeman and Co., Publishers, 1963. (The Linnaean system of binominal nomenclature is not likely to disappear overnight, but the teacher ought to be aware of new developments in the field of biological nomenclature.)

The series of identification manuals cited at the end of Chapter 4 includes several that deal with plant groups.

# 6

# Protists

## MAJOR IDEAS

Structural adaptations, classification, and nomenclature should continue to receive emphasis during work on Chapter 6. Additional ideas to emphasize are:

1. All that we know of microorganisms has come to light within the era of modern science. This knowledge—representing a whole new dimension in biology—has been integrated into the older biological knowledge slowly, with difficulty, and (still) incompletely.

2. Science is an international enterprise, sustained by the efforts of many men in many countries. (This, of course, is an idea that should carry through the entire year, but it is especially appropriate for emphasis in Chapter 6.)

3. The more man learns about nature, the less easy he finds it to fit his knowledge into compartments. The boundaries between taxonomic groups seem sharp when a scheme of classification is studied in a book but indistinct when organisms themselves are observed.

## PLANNING AHEAD

With everything in readiness for the laboratory work of Chapter 6, you also have much of your preparation for Chapter 7 completed, because both chapters are concerned primarily with microbiology. However, check specifically: facilities for incubating cultures (Investigation 7.1); clearance of your *Agrobacterium tumefaciens* order (Investigation 7.2); availability of plants of sufficient number and size for inoculation (Investigation 7.2). It may also be advisable to collect soil samples for Investigation 7.3 if it seems likely that the weather might make that difficult later. And make sure that you have the materials for Investigation 7.4, particularly dead insects, dead leaves, and twigs.

It is not too early to survey your pictorial and projection materials for Chapter 8. That chapter requires student experience with various biomes, and—except for the biome in which you live—that experience can be gained only vicariously through still and motion pictures and audio recordings.

## GUIDELINES

Animals are very familiar to students, plants (except in a general way) less familiar, and protists quite unfamiliar. Consequently, though shorter than Chapters 4 and 5, Chapter 6 presents more difficulties. Providing firsthand experience with protists is a task incommensurate with the size of the organisms. Yet, if protists are not to be mythical beasts, you must show them to students. Therefore the core of this chapter, even more than others, is the laboratory work.

A good beginning is made with Investigation 6.1. It has previously been suggested (p. T74) that this may be set up well before the end of Chapter 5. Many of the organisms that appear in the cultures fall in our plant kingdom and others in our protist kingdom—and microbiologists have never been very careful about distinctions between kingdoms. Thus Investigation 6.1 not only forms a good bridge between Chapters 5 and 6; it also again stresses the artificiality of classificatory schemes.

If you have not begun Investigation 6.1 previously, start it as soon as possible. While the cultures are developing, have students read pp. 186–189, the first of several illuminating excursions into the history of biology. (Others: pp. 339–340, 378–381, 426–433, 466–469, 641–647, 673–682, and 725–729.) Stressing the international nature of the scientific enterprise, which is a necessary corollary to a history of science, is an important aspect of teaching science humanistically. Whatever other time may be available for discussion is best devoted to the problems involved in human attempts to impose order upon the facts of nature—as illustrated by difficulties of classification at the kingdom level, for example, or by doubts concerning the status of viruses. From the first chapter students have been exposed to the idea that learning science is not the memorizing of a prescribed system, into which facts are to be fitted with Procrustean determination, but rather a seeking after new and better ways to order an ever-widening array of facts. Said the Abbé Galiani, "La science est plutôt destiné à étudier qu'à connaître, à chercher qu'à trouver la vérité." ("Science is destined rather to study than to know, rather to seek truth than to find it.") Chapter 6 offers a fine opportunity to bring this attitude to the forefront.

If students have studied cells in a previous course, the question of the cellularity of protists may be raised. Are ciliates, for example, single cells, or are they organisms that have lost cellularity—or did they ever have cells? How do we interpret cellularity in slime molds?

## TEACHING NOTES

### THE DISCOVERY OF MICROORGANISMS
(pp. 186–189)

**p. 187, ¶ 2:** The first scientific society was probably the Accademmia dei Lincei, of Florence. It exists today, but it has not been continuously active, as has the Royal Society.

**p. 188, note 3:** As indicated under "Guidelines" above, this is primarily a chapter of laboratory investigations. You can start Investigation 6.4 at any convenient time. It lasts for six weeks and so does not reach a conclusion until long after you have left the rest of Chapter 6 behind.

**p. 188, ¶ 4:** Much of the technology that students employ in Investigations 6.2 and 6.3 came from Koch's laboratory. Petri dishes were invented by one of his students. The use of agar-agar was suggested by the wife of one of his students.

## INVESTIGATION 6.1

### A GARDEN OF MICROORGANISMS
(pp. 189–191)

Investigation 6.1 allows the biology teacher to lay claim (temporarily) to some of the olfactory ill fame usually monopolized by the chemistry department. This is not necessarily bad public relations; in some schools it has called attention to the fact that there is life in the biology laboratory!

The terminological distinctions made in "Background Information" are important. The chapter is titled "Protists" and begins with a discussion of microorganisms; the student can therefore easily fall into the delusion that protists are microorganisms and vice versa. However, the terms "microbes" and "microorganisms" *are* synonymous, though there is a slight differentiation in usage, the latter being a little more dignified and formal, perhaps.

### Materials

If finger bowls are in short supply, any glass or plastic container more than 10 cm in diameter and having more or less vertical sides at least 4 cm high may be substituted. Small plastic refrigerator dishes are good; but they cannot be stacked, so they require more space after being filled. It is desirable that all the containers used in any one class be alike.

The recommended media have been chosen with an eye to culturing a wide variety of microorganisms; there are, of course, many other possible choices. If necessary the number per team may be reduced, but the media recommended for Bowls 1, 3, 4, 5, and 8 should be retained. Peppercorns (Bowl 10) are recommended because of their historical association with Leeuwenhoek's work. The kind of fruit for Bowl 1 can be varied from team to team; so can the kind of water for Bowl 3. Students can supply most of these materials.

Hand lenses may be used in place of stereomicroscopes, but they are not really an adequate substitute in this investigation.

Tap water may be used in setting up the cultures (except for Bowl 3); but if the water contains much chlorine, it should be allowed to stand twenty-four to forty-eight hours in a shallow container. Chlorine can diffuse from the large, exposed surface of the water.

### Procedure

It is convenient to set up three teams of 10 students each. Each student is responsible for 1 of his team's 10 bowls. (Few classes have exactly 30 students; see p. T42 for suggested alternatives.)

It is important to note that all bowls must be clean at the outset (and of course should be cleaned thoroughly afterward). Here "clean" means not sterile, but chemically clean—that is, free of all soap or detergent. After washing the bowls, rinse them thoroughly at least four times.

If the bowls are set up on Friday, they may be observed macroscopically (and olfactorily) during the following week. Each day at the beginning of the class period, the bowls should be placed in an accessible place so that each student can observe all bowls —at least in a cursory way. But it is too time-consuming to have all students make detailed notes on all bowls; each should concentrate on the bowl he set up.

One week after they have been set up, the materials in the bowls should be ripe for microscopic observation. Students having like bowl numbers should work together as a group. Provide each of these (ten) groups with whatever optical equipment it seems to require. For example, a team observing organisms in Bowl 3 requires monocular microscopes, but it has little use for hand lenses or stereomicroscopes.

In a classroom situation it is not feasible to attempt identification of microbes all the way to the genus and species levels; in most instances one must be content with identification at the phylum level. Some students may, however, wish to pursue the matter further with the aid of the following:

FROBISHER, M. *Fundamentals of Microbiology.* 8th ed. Philadelphia: W. B. Saunders Co., 1968.

T 88

HENRICI, A. T. *Molds, Yeasts, and Actinomycetes.* 2nd ed. New York: John Wiley and Sons, Inc., 1947.

JAHN, T. L., and F. F. Jahn. *How to Know the Protozoa* (reference: p. 213).

PRESCOTT, G. W. *How to Know the Freshwater Algae.* Dubuque, Iowa: W. C. Brown Co., 1964.

## Discussion

The first step is to have the reports of observations exchanged among the students either orally or by means of duplicated sheets.

- (2): Usually molds are found in the largest number of dishes. Partly this is because bacteria, which are probably actually more widespread, are difficult to find without special techniques (Investigation 6.3), while molds are readily visible. And partly it is because molds grow better at the temperatures prevailing in most laboratories. If cultures were incubated at 35°–40°C, more bacterial colonies might be observed.

- (3): This depends upon how long observations are continued. For example, sometimes "rotting" begins (probably mostly from bacteria), and later the material becomes covered with visible mold. A succession of "protozoa" might be observed in Bowl 3, but this kind of succession is more likely to be detected in Investigation 9.1 (pp. 312–314). In Chapters 4 and 5 ecological relationships were allowed to sink into the background. In Chapter 6 ideas and terms from Chapters 2 and 3 are being picked up again. You should be aware of this swing back toward ecology; actively exploit it, because it prepares the way for a full-fledged return to ecological concepts in Section Three.

- (4): A definite diminution of material should be noticeable, in Bowls 1, 6, and 8 especially. To some extent this may be attributed to desiccation, but for the most part the food is being consumed by the organisms.

These questions present opportunities for discussion to proceed in many directions. It is particularly desirable to stress the fact that in this "garden," *foods*—not merely inorganic nutrients—are provided for the microorganisms, since the great majority are consumers. As most of the organisms occur in situations where decomposition is proceeding, it is obvious that most are saprovores, though there is no clear-cut way to distinguish them from other consumers. Also, the possible presence of predators and parasites cannot be excluded.

At this point the discussion might be turned to such questions as: Why the odors, and why different kinds? Where did the microorganisms come from? (This is a good prelude to Investigation 6.4.) How can you account for the changes in a given bowl over a period of time?

## THE PHYLA OF PROTISTS (in part) (pp. 191–194)

**p. 191, ¶ 5:** This is the point at which to consider the questions, What is an animal? What is a plant? These questions were deliberately bypassed in Chapters 4 and 5, but they were raised in Investigation 1.1. Have students refer to their data-book records of that investigation when you consider these questions.

**p. 191, ¶ 7:** As a grouping of convenience, the protist kingdom is somewhat like the Lichenes, which some botanists use as a group in the plant kingdom, or like the Deuteromycetes. No one claims that all the phyla in the protist kingdom are related to each other—not even as distantly as the phyla grouped in the plant kingdom or in the animal kingdom. We may regard the protist phyla as representing different ways in which organisms have carried along a varying set of characteristics from very ancient times. The animal and plant kingdoms, then, represent two other ways in which organisms have developed from ancient ancestors. Every taxonomist knows that we will develop *better* classifications as we learn more about living things. However, the taxonomic problem is not unique in science. The door is never finally closed on any major scientific problem. At any time, a new discovery may reopen any question.

**p. 192, ¶ 3:** Perhaps the most obvious way in which bacterial photosynthesis differs from that of other photosynthetic organisms is its lack of oxygen production.

**p. 192, Fig. 6·5:** Having discussed nomenclature in Chapter 5, you should take every opportunity to use biological names —but without ostentation. The names of microorganisms are suitable for this purpose, because most lack "common" names. Be sure students note the great disparity in magnifications.

## INVESTIGATION 6.2

### MICROBIAL TECHNIQUES: POPULATIONS (pp. 194–198)

This is a complex investigation, but it is worth the effort involved. It pays dividends more in appreciation than in specific knowledge. Moreover it provides a good test of the extent to which students have learned to understand and follow directions, to work together in teams, and to relate procedures to outcomes. It is also a good test of the extent to which you have mastered laboratory logistics.

Before any other action is taken, a careful check of materials must be made. Keeping in mind the quantities of glassware available, decide upon team sizes. Teams of 2 require, for example, 375 test tubes and 375 petri dishes, if you have five classes of 30 students each. Such quantities may be entirely impracticable. Using teams of 3 or 4

cuts them and still provides opportunity for each student to participate actively. By staggering the scheduling of the investigation for different classes, you can cut down the quantities still further.

### Materials

Standard nutrient agar can be purchased, but the preparation of the medium is a good project for a special team. To prepare 60 culture tubes, the team requires:

Pipette, 10-ml
Test tubes, 18 mm × 150 mm, 75
Glass-marking crayons
Heat source
Distilled water, 1000 ml
Graduated cylinder, 500-ml
Beaker, 1000-ml
Balance
Agar, granulated, 15 g
Peptone, 5 g
Beef extract, 3 g
Stirring rod
Funnel, 4- or 5-inch
Ring stand and ring
Rubber tubing, to fit funnel tube
Pinch clamp or spring-compressor clamp
Nonabsorbent cotton
Wire test-tube basket or other suitable container
Autoclave or pressure cooker

Using the pipette (or a small graduated cylinder), place 15 ml of water in a test tube and mark the water level with a glass-marking crayon. Pour out the water. Using this tube as a ruler, mark the 15-ml level on enough tubes to provide 5 for each team.

Heat the water to just below boiling. (If the tap water bears no unusual amounts of dissolved minerals, it may be used in place of distilled water.) Dissolve the agar first; then add peptone and beef extract. Heat until the mixture comes to a boil, stirring continuously. For dispensing the prepared medium into tubes, attach a short piece of rubber tubing to the stem of a large funnel and place a pinchcock on the tubing. Support the funnel on a ring stand at a convenient height. While the liquid is still warm (above 55°C), pour it (a portion at a time) into the funnel. A little practice in using the pinch clamp facilitates filling the marked tubes. Plug the tubes with cotton.

Place all the tubes in wire baskets, and sterilize in an autoclave at 15 lb pressure for fifteen minutes.

With a little trial and error you can make inoculating loops that hold close to 5 mm³ (1/200 ml).

*Serratia marcescens* is a bacterium having a red pigmentation; *Sarcina lutea* is yellow. These organisms are relatively harmless. They are safe for use by high school students and are large enough to be easily studied. Cultures can be obtained from most biological supply houses.

Grids on sheets of plastic are useful, though not essential, in counting colonies; they, too, are available from supply houses.

Figure T–5

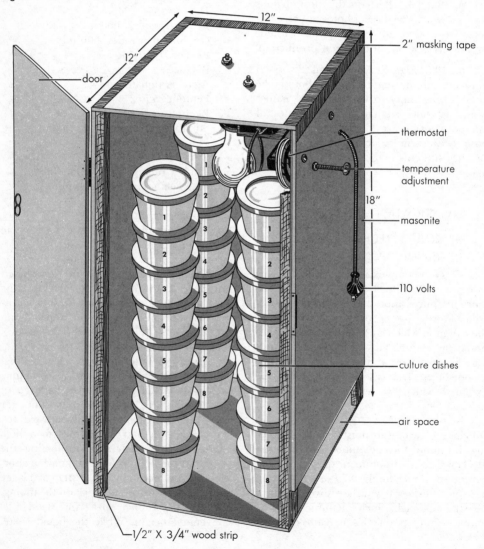

## Procedure

If you have little bacteriological background, make use of the BSCS film *Bacteriological Techniques* (reference: p. T96). In addition consult the BSCS Laboratory Block by Sussman (reference: p. T97). The BSCS technique film may be shown to classes. Since it is quite short, the showing can be repeated a number of times. But even with its use, demonstrate all steps in the procedure.

It is desirable that the cultures be incubated at an even temperature. Generally room temperature is sufficient, but if you desire to maintain a higher and more even temperature and lack a bacteriological incubator, you may use a Temperature Gradient Box (Fig. T–5). This is one of the pieces of apparatus developed by the BSCS Laboratory Block Committee. For details see R. E. Barthelemy, J. R. Dawson, Jr., and A. E. Lee, *Innovations in Equipment and Techniques for the Biology Teaching Laboratory* (Boston: D. C. Heath & Co., 1964). You may adapt the box as an incubator by taping cardboard over the spaces at the bottom and setting it up in a draft-free location.

Although the bacteria being cultured are ordinarily harmless, sterile procedure should be observed throughout the work, not only because the demonstration of safe handling of microorganisms is one of the purposes of the investigation but also because it is possible for pathogenic organisms accidentally to get into the medium and multiply. Therefore, at the end of the work *all tubes and petri dishes must be sterilized* in an autoclave or pressure cooker before the medium is cleaned out of the glassware.

## Discussion

- (1): 1,800,000,000. The populations can also be explained by calculating in reverse order, from 1,800,000,000 live bacteria per cm³ in the original mixed culture: Into Tube 1 we transfer 1 loopful ( = 5 mm³ = $\frac{1}{200}$ cm³) of this suspension. In this volume there will be $\frac{1,800,000,000}{200}$ = 9,000,000 or-

ganisms. If each of these organisms develops into a visible colony, there should be approximately 9,000,000 colonies present in the pour plate prepared from this tube. Thus every colony on this plate represents 200 organisms per cm³ present in the original culture. If we now take a loopful of agar from Tube 1, included in that loopful there should be 3000 bacteria. (We introduced 9,000,000 organisms into 15 cm³ of agar medium: each cm³ will as a result include $\frac{9,000,000}{15}$ = 600,000 bacteria per cm³. A loopful will therefore include $\frac{600,000}{200}$ = 3000 organisms.) This loopful is now introduced into Tube 2. In the pour plate prepared from this tube there should develop approximately 3000 colonies. Thus each colony represents 600,000 organisms present in the original mixed culture. In a loopful of the agar present in Tube 2 there will be $\frac{1}{200} \times \frac{1}{15}$, or $\frac{1}{3000}$, of the organisms present in Tube 2. $\frac{1}{3000}$ of 3000 = 1. Therefore we would expect only 1 organism to be introduced into Tube 3, and only 1 colony would develop in the pour plate prepared from it. Therefore each colony in this plate represents 1,800,000,000 organisms present in the original mixed culture.

In these dilution procedures there are, of course, a number of sources of error which may be identified by alert students and will serve as good starting points for discussion. One source, of minor import, is the fact that the organisms removed from Tubes 1 and 2 by means of the loop are not present in the pour plates prepared from them. Another, of far greater significance, is the fact that organisms may not survive the rigors of the handling and dilution procedures and will therefore not give rise to visible colonies. Also, incomplete mixing of organisms introduced into the tubes leads to large sampling errors. Finally, variations in the dimensions of the loops used by different teams can result in differences in data.

- (4): The assumption involved is that all plates are contaminated equally.
- (6): *If* you lift only from a single colony, then all organisms on the loop should be of a single kind, since all in the colony descended from a single individual.
- (7): This would be a pure culture.
- (9): This is the same as the number of kinds of colonies—assuming that all kinds produce colonies distinctively different in appearance. The assumption is probably warranted in this case of a deliberately constructed "mixed culture." But generally speaking, "kinds" cannot be equated with "species" because in many bacterial species various kinds of colonies may be produced depending upon environmental circumstances and "strains" within species.
- (11): See last paragraph of notes on "Procedure" (above).
- (13) and • (14): In general, Procedures A and C are concerned with the determination of population density, and Procedure B with obtaining a pure culture.

Evaluation of procedures should be a habit by this time. Have the class consider the following: (*a*) What are some possible sources of error in estimating the number of bacteria in a culture by the methods used in this investigation? (*b*) How might the kind of medium and the temperature of incubation influence the number of colonies? (*c*) How could you use the pour-plate method to compare rates of growth for two different kinds of bacteria in a mixed culture?

## INVESTIGATION 6.3

### MICROBIAL TECHNIQUES: MICROSCOPIC STUDY OF BACTERIA (pp. 198–200)

#### Materials

If your biology laboratory is not equipped with sufficient gas outlets and if alcohol burners are unavailable, you may be able to arrange an exchange of laboratories with the chemistry teacher for one period. The actual laboratory time for this investigation need not exceed thirty minutes, exclusive of time for studying directions and for cleaning up.

The peppercorn infusion from Investigation 6.1 should contain a good variety of bacteria. This may be mixed with materials obtained from the cultures of Investigation 6.2.

To prepare crystal-violet stain, dissolve 2 g of crystal violet (gentian violet) in 20 ml of ethyl alcohol (95%) and add 180 ml of distilled water. Filter just before using.

#### Procedure

Though sterile technique is not critical in this investigation, flaming the loop before and after use should be practiced for the sake of bacteriological principle.

Mounting the stained film by adding a few drops of glycerin and a cover slip makes the color of the stain appear more brilliant and permits the "high dry" objective to be used at maximum resolution—an important factor in the study of such small organisms.

Some teachers provide blank slide labels. The student may mark such a label with the name of the organism, the date, and his initials, affix the label, and keep the finished slide as a souvenir. (If glycerin has been used, it should be rinsed off in several changes of water.) Because students are often proud of these tokens of their achievement, knowledge of the activities of the biology classes may be disseminated through the school. You can make a permanent mount by placing a few drops of Canada balsam or of Permount on the dry film and adding a cover slip.

The oil-immersion lens is not essential; after all, Leeuwenhoek observed bacteria in a peppercorn infusion with a lens magnifying 270X. But an oil-immersion microscope always adds some interest to the observation of stained bacteria. To point up the extent of magnification possible with the oil-immersion microscope, a simple comparison can be made: To the center of the chalkboard fasten a 1-mm square of white paper; around this mark off a 1-m square. The bacteria, when viewed under the oil-immersion microscope, are magnified to a similar degree. From this the students can get an indication of the minute size of bacteria.

\* \* \*

Completion of Investigations 6.2 and 6.3 provides students with rudiments of technique that can be further developed on an individual basis. Possibilities of further investigation are endless; the two ideas at the end of Investigation 6.2 are samples. The Laboratory Block by Sussman (reference: p. T97) should be put in the hands of any students who show interest.

## THE PHYLA OF PROTISTS (cont.)
(pp. 200–209)

**p. 200, ¶ 2:** Unlike the photosynthetic bacteria, the blue-green algae do give off oxygen. But the blue-green algae resemble bacteria in their reproduction by simple fission and in their lack of a distinct, organized nucleus. If you have copies of the 1963 edition of the *Green Version*, you can emphasize the mutability of classification by showing the shift of Cyanophyta in successive editions of a book. However, the shift was not made simply to illustrate this point!

**p. 200, Fig. 6·14:** Again (previously in connection with Figure 5·30) remind students that the use of generic epithets only does not violate the binomial system of nomenclature. It is legitimate identification

at a level less precise than that of species in cases where such a level of identification is considered unnecessary (as here) or where it is not possible on the basis of available information.

**p. 202, ¶ 3:** Another reminder that Section One, with its attention to ecological relationships, is not a closed matter. Often students' past experience has been such that they find it difficult to believe that they are expected to carry over any understanding from one "unit" to another. This can only be overcome by constant attempts to tie past experience to the present.

**p. 204, note 1:** The diameter of the field of a monocular microscope using a 10X (16 mm) objective and a 10X Huygenian (not wide-field) ocular is approximately 1.4 mm. There are 3600 seconds in an hour. $3600 \times 1.4 = 5040$ mm $= 5.040$ m. The rate of movement is therefore approximately 5 m per hour—perhaps a little better than a "snail's pace."

**p. 205, ¶ 1:** If students consulted Appendix II to check on sporozoans, they found there a malarial parasite named *Plasmodium vivax*. Now, in this paragraph, they find the word "plasmodium" unitalicized, uncapitalized, and referring in a very general way (not taxonomically) to slime molds. This is sure to be confusing. Help them.

**p. 206, ¶ 2:** If you wish to demonstrate slime-mold growth, see pp. T165–T166.

**p. 206, note 3:** Figure 6·22E shows a mosaic disease of squash. The *symptom* is similar in tobacco mosaic, but the *pathogen* is different; these two terms are soon to be encountered in Chapter 7.

**p. 207, Fig. 6·21:** If these photographs are to mean much, the magnification must be noted. And they should be compared with those in other figures, especially Figure 6·5.

**p. 209, ¶ 2:** See comments concerning p. 179, ¶ 2 (p. T80).

## INVESTIGATION 6.4

### EXPERIMENTS ON SPONTANEOUS GENERATION (pp. 209–211)

There is no need for more than one setup per class; the thinking is much more important than the manipulations. But if you have more than one class, replication by classes may reveal that there can be some variation in the results.

### Materials

Filtering can be avoided if peptone is available; use about 8 g of peptone in place of the bouillon cube.

If flasks do not have a ground-glass area that can be written on with lead pencil, label them before sterilizing by using cardboard tags tied on with string. Do *not* use a glass-marking pencil on flasks that are to be heated or autoclaved.

### Procedure

A few students working outside of class time may prepare the materials. Those who prepared the medium for Investigation 2.2 can prepare the medium with a minimum of teacher supervision. The work with glass tubing is new, however, and should be closely supervised. Be particularly careful in inserting the glass tubing through the rubber stoppers; cork borers may be used to make this operation safer. Choose a cork borer with an inside diameter just large enough so that the tubing fits into it. First insert the cork borer through the hole in the stopper. Then slide the tubing through the borer to the desired distance. Finally, holding the tubing in place, withdraw the borer from the stopper.

Pre-class preparations can include mixing the medium, bending the tubing, constructing the stopper combinations, and autoclaving Flasks 4, 5, 6, and 7. (Stoppers should be loose in necks of the flasks during autoclaving.) Then the preparation team can conclude the work in front of the class by boiling Flasks 2 and 3 and sealing the tops with paraffin. (Be sure the stopper of Flask 3 is tilted in the mouth of the flask during the boiling.) If flasks have been labeled with tags during the preparations, they can now be relabeled with glass-marking crayon.

During the weeks while observations are being made, flasks may be picked up for examination; but they should not be violently shaken.

If all goes well, put aside Flask 7 at the conclusion of the investigation and save it for use at the beginning of Chapter 16.

### Discussion

Typical results are as follows:

Flask 1 becomes turbid within a day or two. In this and the other flasks that become turbid, patches of mold often develop on the surface of the medium.

Flask 2 usually becomes turbid a day or two later than Flask 1. Before the conclusion of the experiment its contents have usually evaporated.

Flask 3 may take a very long time to become turbid; indeed, it may never become turbid. Nevertheless, though many microbes are killed by boiling, the resistant spores of some bacteria may survive and eventually produce turbidity.

Flask 4 usually becomes turbid at about the same time as Flask 2. Its contents usually disappear by evaporation.

Flask 5, with its small opening, may not become turbid for many days or (if there are few air currents) even weeks. But if it is kept long enough, turbidity will appear.

Flask 6 often remains clear long after the experiment has been concluded.

Flask 7 should remain perfectly clear for as long as it is undisturbed. Some flasks of this kind have been dated and kept for years as exhibits. The design of the S-shaped tube is comparable to that of Pasteur's "swan-neck" flask.

Students may doubt that the turbidity of the broth is caused by bacteria. (If the course is doing what it should, they will demand evidence.) Make a check on Flasks 2 and 4, using the methods of Investigation 6.3. Usually some good slides of bacilli and cocci will be obtained, and these can be compared with prepared slides of known bacteria.

- (1) and • (2): If Flask 3 becomes cloudy, it usually does so much later than Flask 2, for boiling kills most if not all of the organisms originally present in the broth. Although boiling also kills organisms in Flask 2, nothing hinders the contents from acquiring new ones from the air.

- (3): This question should engender considerable discussion. Believers in abiogenesis argued that Spallanzani's sealed flask did not develop microbes because heating had destroyed the "power" of the air in the flask and there was no way for new air to enter. Anaerobic organisms were not known in their day. It is instructive to note that while Spallanzani failed to make his point theoretically, the practical import of his work followed rather quickly. Much of Napoleon's success has been attributed to his use of foods preserved by canning to feed his troops.

- (5): Pasteur needed to meet the argument made by Spallanzani's critics.

- (6): The curve in the tube forms a dust trap. Dust particles bearing spores of microorganisms do not get beyond this point even when air currents around the flask are rather strong. If the autoclaving has been properly done and the sealing has been done promptly and well, no living organisms are present in the broth; the tubing prevents new, living ones from entering; and therefore no turbidity develops. The single curve in Flask 6 has no such trap, but it is a rather effective barrier, and frequently no growth of microorganisms occurs in Flask 6 during the time of the experiment. Pasteur went one step further; he tilted a "swan-neck" flask until its contents flowed into the crook of the tube; soon thereafter a growth of microorganisms appeared in the flask.

- (7): Growth of microorganisms may appear almost simultaneously in Flasks 1, 2, and 4; but frequently it occurs slightly sooner in Flask 1. Presumably this results from an abundant supply of microorganisms in the broth at the beginning, while growth in Flasks 2 and 4 depends upon microorganisms arriving in the broth after heating.

- (8): Discussion can proceed in many directions. If results are not somewhat similar to those described above, the whole experiment may be inconclusive. Then the discussion should center on reasons for discrepancies between the class's data and results reported by Spallanzani and Pasteur (and many later investigators). If results are essentially similar to those described above, students should be led to see that the experiment discredits the idea that microorganisms can arise from matter that has no living organisms already within it. The ideas in the introduction may be put into a hypothesis expressed in negative terms: "Microorganisms cannot arise unless they have ancestors," or similar wording. You then have the opportunity to discuss the impossibility of prooving a negative proposition. The best that can be done is to amass evidence making the proposition more and more unlikely. This is what has happened to abiogenesis.

---

## GUIDE QUESTIONS (p. 212)

4. The best example and, perhaps, the oldest is the use of yeasts to make alcoholic beverages and later to leaven bread. Others: in making cheese, in making sauerkraut, in making silage, in retting flax, in curing tea and cacao, etc. See Rahn (reference: p. 213).

9. For more on this matter see Figure 11 · 2.

## PROBLEMS (p. 212)

1. This is a complex way to describe fission in combination with the principle of biogenesis.

2. We believe that the exact number is 2, 361, 183, 241, 434, 822, 606, 848 (if nothing has happened in the proofreading). At 12:00 noon the population is $2^0 = 1$ bacterium; at 12:20 it is $2^1 = 2$ bacteria; at 12:40 it is $2^2 = 4$ bacteria; at 1:00 P.M. it is $2^3 = 8$ bacteria; and so on to 12:00 noon the following day, when it is $2^{71}$. More importantly, have the student look at the magnifications in Figure 6 · 5 and then try to imagine what a population of the size he has calculated would look like. The idea of reproductive potential is a key idea in this course, culminating in Chapter 20 (p. 152, ¶ 3).

3. This can be discussed at several levels. Most students realize that cold storage does not kill microorganisms. The student is most likely to say that the microorganisms that bring about decay of food (by consuming it themselves) do not multiply at low temperatures. This is, however, a relative matter. Between 0°C and room temperature, molds generally thrive better than bacteria. Few students at this point are likely to point out the effect of lowering temperature on metabolic processes or to link this with rates of chemical reaction.

4. A good book to begin with is Frobisher (reference: p. T87), pp. 502–508. See also Morowitz and Tourtellotte (reference: p. 212).

5. This problem is anticipatory to Chapter 10. An interested student can be directed to Young and Ponnamperuma (reference: p. 375) or Oparin (reference: p. T151); the student can then serve as a resource person when the class arrives at Chapter 10.

## SUPPLEMENTARY MATERIALS

### Audiovisual Materials

The remarks concerning audiovisual materials for Chapter 4 (p. T72) apply equally well to Chapter 6.

**Phonograph records:** *The Scientists Speak: Biology.* Harcourt, Brace and Co. Includes a stimulating talk by René Dubos that weaves his personal experiences into the story of microbiology.

**Filmstrips:** *Great Names in Biology: Antony van Leeuwenhoek.* Encyclopaedia Britannica Filmstrips. Color. Good for biographical background.

*Bacteria.* Encyclopaedia Britannica Filmstrips. Color. A good visual survey of major bacterial groups.

**Motion-picture films:** *Bacteria.* Encyclopaedia Britannica Films. 16 mm. Color. Emphasizes the kinds of bacteria and their life processes.

*Bacteriological Techniques.* Thorne Films, Boulder, Colo. 16 mm. Color. 5 min. Produced by the BSCS; intended for the teacher who has not had a course in bacteriology. Techniques demonstrated include making cotton plugs, transferring cultures, preparing agar plates, spotting and streaking, forming a microculture chamber.

*The Protist Kingdom.* Film Associates of California. 16 mm. Color. 14 min. Excellent photography helps to acquaint students with these organisms. Uses the same groupings as our Chapter 6 except that it omits Cyanophyta.

*Bacteria.* McGraw-Hill Book Co., Inc. 16 mm. Color. 30 min. A good film for background, without too many excursions beyond the concerns of Chapter 6.

*Bacteriological Techniques.* A series of four film loops: *Preparing and Dispensing*, 3 min., 25 sec.; *Inoculating*, 3 min., 34 sec.; *Serial Dilution and Pour Plates*, 3 min., 53 sec.; *Staining*, 3 min., 20 sec. Super-8. Color. Ealing. An excellent series in lieu of the BSCS technique film if you have more time and a Super-8 cartridge projector.

## Teacher's References

BROCK, T. D. (ed.). *Milestones in Microbiology.* Englewood Cliffs, N.J.: Prentice-Hall, Inc., 1961. (Includes papers by Spallanzani, Pasteur, Koch, Stanley, Beijerinck.)

CARPENTER, P. L. *Microbiology.* 2nd ed. Philadelphia: W. B. Saunders Co., 1967. (A well-organized introduction to a wide variety of microbiological topics.)

CONANT, J. B., and L. K. NASH (eds.). *Harvard Case Histories in Experimental Science.* Cambridge, Mass.: Harvard University Press, 1957. (Contains accounts of Pasteur's and Tyndall's studies on spontaneous generation.)

DOBELL, C. *Antony van Leeuwenhoek and His Little Animals.* New York: Dover Publications, Inc., 1960. (The letters Leeuwenhoek sent to the Royal Society, in which he described his discoveries.)

DUBOS, R. J. *Louis Pasteur, Free Lance of Science.* Boston: Little, Brown & Co., 1950. (An illuminating biography by a man who has himself contributed to microbiology in many ways.)

FRASER, D. *Virus and Molecular Biology.* New York: The Macmillan Co., 1967. (A brief but comprehensive introduction to the viruses.)

KUDO, R. *Protozoology.* 4th ed. Springfield, Ill.: Charles C. Thomas, Publisher, 1954. (A standard handbook for information on the protozoa.)

LECHEVALIER, H. A., and M. SOLOTOROVSKY. *Three Centuries of Microbiology.* New York: McGraw-Hill Book Co., Inc., 1965. (A history of the development of microbiology, including extensive quotations from crucial research papers.)

MAXWELL, R. D. *Introduction to Protozoology.* New York: St. Martin's Press, 1961. (A general account of protozoa, with particular emphasis on their significance for man.)

STANIER, R. Y., M. DOUDEROFF, and E. G. ADELBERG. *The Microbial World.* 2nd ed. Englewood Cliffs, N.J.: Prentice-Hall, Inc., 1963. (This is particularly recommended for students carrying on individual research projects.)

STANLEY, W. M., and E. G. VALENS. *Viruses and the Nature of Life.* New York: E. P. Dutton & Co., Inc., 1961. (Stanley is the scientist who crystallized the tobacco virus. The contents apply directly to the question raised at the end of Chapter 6, p. 168.)

SUSSMAN, A. E. *Microbes—Their Growth, Nutrition and Interaction.* A BSCS Laboratory Block. Boston: D. C. Heath & Co., 1963. (An excellent source of ideas for microbial investigations feasible in a high school laboratory.)

WEDBERG, S. E. *Paramedical Microbiology.* New York: Reinhold Publishing Corp., 1963. (Especially good for the microbiology of sewage, soil, and atmosphere.)

# Section Three     PATTERNS
## IN THE
## BIOSPHERE

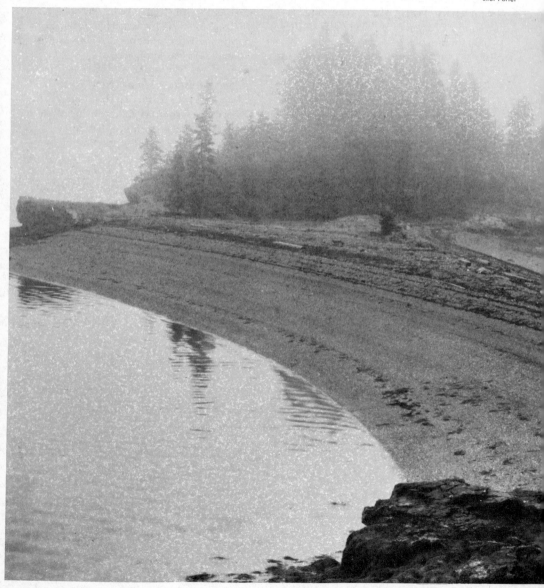

The break between Sections Two and Three is not a major one. The basic ideas of Section Two require no elaborate summation; moreover, work on Investigation 6.4 must extend beyond the time of transition. Emphasis on the diversity of organisms comes to an end with Chapter 6, but protists — viewed in their ecological settings — remain the center of attention in Chapter 7. Therefore, in the classroom the transition from section to section need not be conspicuous.

Reading the introduction to Section Three should be sufficient to establish in the student's mind the change in viewpoint that characterizes the return from taxonomic to ecological thinking. But some misunderstanding may arise from the use of the term "patterns" in the section title. The word can be ambiguous. If we think of it as denoting something *a priori*, then of course it can have no use in modern science. But this is not its meaning here. The Hinshelwood quotation points the way to the meaning that is proper: a mutable mental construct based on available data. A further quotation (from Henri Poincaré) may help you to guide the students' thinking: "Science is built up of facts as a house is built of bricks; but a collection of facts is no more a science than a heap of bricks is a house."

Section Illustration
The misty atmosphere blurs the distinction between aquatic and terrestrial ecosystems, emphasizing the continuity of the biosphere at the outset of the search for pattern in it.

# 7

# Patterns of Life
# in the
# Microscopic World

## MAJOR IDEAS

1. Microorganisms are found in all natural ecosystems; many have distributional patterns relatively unaffected by geographical features.

2. Disease is not a special curse of the human species, but a universal attribute of living things. An infectious disease is an ecological relationship between two organisms and therefore cannot be adequately understood except from an ecological viewpoint.

3. Virulence is a characteristic of pathogens; resistance is a characteristic of organisms that pathogens affect. The milieu in which pathogen and host meet is a third factor in the causation of disease.

4. Different diseases prevail in different parts of the world as a result of different ecological conditions. Among the ecological conditions necessary to the existence of some diseases is the presence of suitable vectors.

5. Soil is an ecosystem consisting of living organisms, organic remains, and inorganic substances. Although the larger organisms are more conspicuous, microscopic ones play important roles in soil life.

6. The community relationships discussed in Chapter 3 can be found in soil microcommunities.

7. Microorganisms are sensitive to the chemical nature of the ecosystems in which they occur. Ionization, especially that which results in pH of water, is a significant chemical process in soil environments.

8. The biogeochemical cycle of the element nitrogen is dependent on the activities of soil microorganisms.

9. Much of the return of other elements to the abiotic environment is also accomplished by soil microbes. The rate of decomposition varies with type of soil and nature of the substance being decomposed.

## PLANNING AHEAD

At this time of year in most parts of the country, seeds can probably be obtained only from biological supply companies. Investigation 8.1 requires radish, vetch, tomato, and lettuce; if these were not obtained previously, they should be ordered now.

Investigation 8.2 is facilitated if you can provide students with grids exactly like those used in the climatograms on pp. 256, 257, and 272—that is, having 12 divisions horizontally and 18 vertically. Such a grid can be drawn on a stencil and produced in quantity very cheaply.

To make the understanding of biomes vivid, assemble as much pictorial material as possible. Bulletin boards should receive heavy use during work on Chapter 8, and the displays should be changed frequently. Obtaining good ecological pictures is not easy; even the *National Geographic Magazine* tends to avoid natural landscapes. Some years may elapse before you have a really adequate file of pictures, but begin such a file now.

In many places it is already too late to collect the pond water and pond organisms needed for Investigations 9.1 and 9.2. If so, these should be ordered from a biological supply company.

## GUIDELINES

Investigation 7.1 provides motivation for an excursion into a long chapter containing few pictures and a rather large number of ideas. Moreover, these ideas are in some cases entirely unfamiliar to most students, or (and this is much harder to cope with) they are ideas involving unfamiliar ways of looking at superficially familiar things. All of this calls for a slowing of the rapid pace that should have characterized the work on Section Two.

The reading material is most logically broken into three assignments: pp. 217–231 (guide questions 1–11), 234–238 (guide questions 13–17), and 240–245 (guide questions 19–22).

Investigation 7.2 requires a long time to bring to completion, as does Investigation 7.4. Each one will run beyond the time needed for study of the chapter. Meanwhile, observations on Investigation 6.4 should be continuing. Because of this overlapping of several investigations, maintaining interest and preventing confusion require much attention from the teacher.

Curriculum-makers universally regard disease prevention and soil conservation as important topics. So do the writers of the *Green Version*. But at the tenth-grade level the time has passed for the building of terraces on the sand table and the morbid recital of disease symptoms. If the student is ever to progress beyond the rote repetition of "right" prescriptions for conservation of soil and prevention of disease, he must be induced to wrestle with the concepts embodied in the terms "soil" and "disease." Chapter 7 aims to bring the student to grips with the biological realities of these concepts.

There is, of course, need to apply the concepts in a local situation. Do you teach suburban students whose parents are struggling to make a lawn on subsoil hastily bulldozed into place by the departing "developer"? Do your students know soil only as a commodity that is sold in plastic bags at the variety store? Are the agriculturists of your region coping with drained muck soils, irrigated desert soils, acid soils, alkaline soils, sandy coastal soils lacking humus, upland clay soils, lateritic soils?

In many urban situations tuberculosis is still an important infectious disease; use it to point up the concepts of transmission, symptoms, virulence, resistance, epidemiology. In New Orleans, what has happened to yellow fever? In Charleston, what has happened to malaria? In Norfolk and Baltimore, what has happened to cholera? Even the most voluminous textbook cannot adequately treat such local or regional matters. Only an alert teacher can.

Appendix II of the student's book was frequently referred to during Section Two. Continue to call attention to it. As various groups of organisms are mentioned in Chapter 7, they should be placed in the framework of the classification scheme.

A final suggestion: Make the investigations central to the presentation of this chapter. Discussions of laboratory work will provide the "teachable moments" for most of the major concepts.

## TEACHING NOTES

### INVESTIGATION 7.1

#### MICROORGANISMS IN SCHOOL ENVIRONMENTS (pp. 216–217)

If the class did a thorough job on Investigation 6.2, then Investigation 7.1 can be done easily—especially if the corps of student assistants who learned the techniques of medium formulation and sterilization can be utilized again. This investigation often generates a considerable amount of interest outside biology classes and is desirable for intramural public relations.

#### Materials

Each plate should contain 15 ml of nutrient agar. The following quantities provide materials for 66 plates:

Water (preferably distilled), 1 liter
Peptone, 5 g
Beef extract, 3 g

Agar, 15 g

An incubation temperature of 37°C is desirable. The Temperature Gradient Box shown in Figure T–5 may be adapted as an incubator by taping cardboard over the open spaces at the bottom and setting it up in a place where an even room temperature is maintained.

#### Procedure

Ideally each student should expose a plate, but teams of any size can be used. If enough teams or individuals are involved, several plates may be exposed at each location. Then the results from each location can be averaged; this reduces chance variation.

Besides a total count of all colonies, the data may be classified into several categories: number of bacterial colonies, number of mold colonies, number of kinds of bacterial colonies, number of kinds of mold colonies, and number of colonies of each particular kind. Let the students decide how the different kinds of mold and bacterial colonies can be distinguished.

The type of medium and the temperature of incubation influence the development of colonies on the exposed plates. The medium used here is a general one on which many populations will grow. Certain specialized media (e.g., blood agar) are required to culture most pathogenic species.

CAUTION: Nevertheless, pathogenic organisms can be picked up and cultivated on plain nutrient agar. Therefore, after exposure the plates *must be taped closed.* Counting the colonies must be done without opening the dishes. Only *after dishes have been sterilized* should they be opened for washing. Disposable petri dishes are ideal for this experiment.

#### Discussion

• (2) and • (3): Results will vary from one school to another and even within one school from one year to the next.

• (6): This harks back to the idea of species diversity. In general, plates exposed in environments with small populations of many different kinds are more likely to pick up microorganisms of disease, because it takes only one or a few bacteria to start a colony —and the greater the number of kinds of bacteria in the environment, the greater is the probability of "trapping" a pathogen. In nature, human pathogens are rare among the total species of microorganisms. Of course, if you deliberately biased your sampling—by exposing plates in a sickroom, for example—the generalization would not hold.

• (1) and • (7)– • (9): These items all refer to methodology. It is important to standardize the duration of plate exposure to obtain a more uniform census. Secondly, it is important to have replicates from the several locations, so that the results will more reliably represent the populations available. The caution above answers • (9).

## MICROBES AND DISEASE
(pp. 218–231)

This section is an attempt to provide materials with which students can think about disease scientifically. Students are always eager to recount the symptoms of all their friends and relations and to testify to miraculous cures. To cut off *all* of this stifles interest; you must instead use it to guide students into discussions of principles. The section assumes that students already know something about many human diseases. To emphasize the biological universality of disease, try to mention animal and plant disease as often as possible.

**p. 220, Fig. 7 · 2:** For other examples of infectious plant disease, see Figures 3 · 10 and 7 · 7.

**p. 220, ¶ 5:** In some ways, allergies are similar to infections: in both, organisms react to the invasion of foreign substances. But in an allergy the foreign substance is not reproductive.

**pp. 221–224:** This is an opportunity to discuss venereal diseases in general —which, almost by definition, are contagious —if you wish. But emphasize that syphilis and malaria are extremes of a continuum; many diseases are neither as strictly contagious as syphilis nor as strictly vector-borne as malaria.

**p. 223, Fig. 7 · 5:** Eliminate the vector.

**p. 224, Fig. 7 · 6:** Each dot is a colony of bacteria or mold started from an individual organism that dropped from one of the fly's feet as it walked.

**p. 224, note 6:** *E. coli* is referred to as a commensal because it obtains its shelter and nourishment from the contents of a man's intestines (benefit) while it apparently does not harm man (neutral); thus we have a benefit-neutral, or commensal, relationship.

**p. 225, ¶ 6:** Note that virulence and resistance are both relative terms; to gauge either, the value of the other must be kept constant. This is a difficult idea for most students, who live in a simple world of "good" or "bad."

**p. 227, Fig. 7 · 8:** Use this cartoon as a catalyst for discussion or for student reports on other clashes between attitudes and innovation. The question in the caption is, of course, a matter of opinion.

**pp. 226–228:** The terminology for kinds of immunity is quite unsettled. That used here follows Frobisher, *Fundamentals of Microbiology,* 7th ed. (Philadelphia: W. B. Saunders Co., 1962) for the most part.

**p. 227, ¶ 2:** Note that cowpox is rather unspecific, occurring in both cattle and men. The story of vaccination is a good example of empiricism in science; the practice long preceded the modern theory of immunity and the germ theory.

**p. 231, Fig. 7 · 11:** Tsetse flies are tropical insects; they are most likely to spread to other tropical regions outside of Africa. Tropical South America is probably most endangered, because there is considerable air traffic across the South Atlantic.

## INVESTIGATION 7.2

### INVESTIGATING AN INFECTIOUS DISEASE (pp. 232–233)

The writers regard this as an extremely important investigation. It clearly demonstrates disease transmission, a topic that traditionally has been "talked to death" instead of demonstrated. Moreover, it applies the skills practiced by students in Investigations 6.2 and 6.3.

### Materials

*Agrobacterium tumefaciens* is not an animal pathogen. It is not dangerous to students. However, it should be handled carefully and with full attention to sterile technique, for it is dangerous to plants, and plants are also important. The bacilli are large enough to be studied under the 4-mm "high-dry" objective of the microscope. Cultures of *Agrobacterium* are available from biological supply houses, but permits for shipment are required. Application should be made on PQ-Form 26, obtainable from your state department of agriculture. You are obligated to *sterilize* all soil, pots, and plants at the conclusion of the work. Emphasis on careful handling of pathogens is an essential part of biological education.

Plants must be started at least a month before this exercise is set up. When ready for use, they should have three or four true leaves. Three-inch pots are large enough, or half-pint milk cartons may be used. Tomato is a good species to use. Pot labels are not essential; the pots themselves may be marked with a soft pencil.

For crystal-violet solution, see Investigation 6.3.

The scalpel must be quite sharp; a razor blade is preferable.

To prepare culture tubes of dextrose agar, you need:

| | |
|---|---|
| Peptone | 5 g |
| Beef extract | 3 g |
| Agar | 15 g |
| Glucose (dextrose) | 10 g |
| Distilled water | 1000 ml |

Heat water (just below boiling) and dissolve the agar in it; then add peptone, beef extract, and dextrose, stirring the mixture well. Pour 30 to 40 ml into cotton-plugged tubes. Sterilize tubes in autoclave or pressure cooker, and cool them at a slant of about 30 degrees.

### Procedure

Investigation 7.2 *can* be handled by one team from each class. Team members can then present their research report in seminar style.

Galls may be removed when about 5 mm in diameter.

Note that reference to data books as a place for recording laboratory observations is being dropped. Use of the data book should now be a habit.

Again, CAUTION: At the end of the work, be sure to sterilize in an autoclave or pressure cooker all plants, pots, and soil.

### Discussion

- (3): In an experimental procedure all setups must be treated exactly alike except for the variable under investigation. If the control plant (A) is not punctured with a needle, the way is open to ascribing the gall development to the needle wound rather than to the bacillus.

- (5): This leads to the idea that morphology alone is not sufficient for species identification in microorganisms (p. 193, ¶ 3). Biochemical characteristics and physiological reactions are used to distinguish among species of similar morphology.

- (6): This investigation merely associates in one instance a suspected pathogen with a particular symptom in the host. This is far from proof of causation. To carry out Koch's postulates, one should begin with extensive investigation of organisms in naturally occurring galls. The students have carried out only No. 3 and part of No. 4 of Koch's postulates.

## THE SOIL ECOSYSTEM (in part)
(pp. 234–238)

If any work was done with soil organisms during Investigation 3.1, be sure that students recall it now.

**p. 235, ¶'s 3 and 4:** It is not necessary to go deeply into the chemistry of ionization. But by all means use any knowledge that students may have gained in previous grades concerning atomic structure.

**p. 236, Fig. 7 · 14:** The left-hand photograph is of Brevard Loam. The numbers are in feet. The first 6 inches of this soil has an organic-matter content of 5%. The right-hand photograph is of Crete Silt Loam. Numbers are in feet. The first 6 inches has an organic-matter content of 2.2%.

**p. 237, note 4:** Since algae are photosynthetic, they require light for growth.

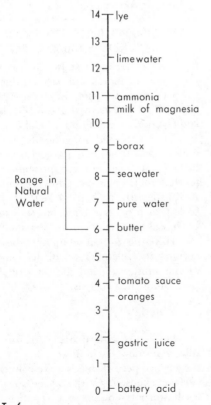

Figure T–6

**pH of some common substances.**

## INVESTIGATION 7.3

### A CHEMICAL CHARACTERISTIC OF SOILS (pp. 238–239)

This investigation provides encounters necessary for the meaningful assimilation of some basic ideas of acidity and alkalinity. Although some use of indicators is possible on a very simple basis (as, for example, Investigation 1.5), biological experimentation on any level must remain quite unsophisticated unless the student learns some method of measuring pH. Figure T–6 provides some examples of the range of pH in some substances with which students may be acquainted.

### Materials

Other indicators may be used. A chart of indicators and their pH ranges may be found in *Teaching High School Science: A Sourcebook for the Biological Sciences*, by E. Morholt, P. F. Brandwein, and A. Joseph (New York: Harcourt, Brace & World, 1968).

Hydrochloric acid and sodium hydroxide should be 0.1 N solutions.

A good brand of wide-range pH test paper is Hydrion. Paper with a pH range from 3 to 9 will cover most needs.

The greater the number of soil samples, the better. If many are available, different teams can measure different samples. However, several teams should measure each sample to obtain more than one reading. Samples should come from a variety of habitats, such as swamp areas, burned-over areas, beach, fence rows, and gardens.

The "10 g" of soil should be estimated, not weighed. (A nickel weighs 5 g.)

### Studying the Data

• (4): The ranges of the recommended indicators are as follows:

Methyl red . . . . . pH 4.2 (red) to pH 6.2 (yellow)

Bromthymol blue . . pH 6.0 (yellow) to pH 7.4 (blue)

Phenolphthalein . . pH 8.2 (colorless) to pH 10.0 (red)

- (6): Examples: bog soils are usually acid; many garden soils are close to neutral; soils from limestone and soils in arid regions may be alkaline.

- (7): Decomposing organic matter usually releases acids; therefore, soils with high humus content are often acid. For further discussion see Oosting (reference: p. 249).

- (8): Because the soil water is diluted in the procedure, the student is not measuring the true pH of the soil.

### For Further Investigation

If the pH of a soil is modified, composition of the microbial population of that soil may be modified. This can be demonstrated by plating a soil on agar adjusted for pH 5, 6, 7, and 8 and noting the differences in bacterial counts.

---

### THE SOIL ECOSYSTEM (cont.) (pp. 240–245)

**p. 240, ¶ 4, and p. 241, ¶ 2:** Students might be asked to fit these community relationships into the framework of Chapter 3. Antibiosis might be considered a negative-neutral relationship.

**p. 241, note 4:** Mutualism.

**p. 242, note 1:** The words "good" and "bad" are being used in the time-honored absolute sense that we are trying to avoid. If the insects attacked were honeybees, we would be inclined to label the nematodes "bad," especially if we were beekeepers. But the scientific questions remain: How much damage is done to bees compared with damage done to other insects? And how important are the bees compared with the other insects? Even from a strictly anthropocentric viewpoint, "good" and "bad" are terms that are relative ecologically.

**p. 243, Fig. 7·18:** Note that substances are printed in capitals, agents of change in lowercase. The diagram concerns the nitrogen cycle in the biosphere as a whole. In a particular place large amounts of nitrogen compounds may be lost from a soil by leaching, but they are not lost from the biosphere. Likewise, nitrogen compounds may accumulate and remain stationary in the cycle for long periods of time, as in the guano islands of Chile, but from a geological viewpoint these compounds are temporary. Students should compare this diagram with Figures 1·14, 1·15, and 1·16, which, however, are not as detailed as 7·18.

**p. 245, ¶'s 2 and 3:** In principle the *Rhizobium*-legume relationship is somewhat similar to the mycorrhizal situation.

**p. 245, Fig. 7·19:** In the situation depicted here, there is definite evidence that the vascular plant benefits; but in the situation of Figure 7·16, the evidence is clear that the vascular plant is harmed.

### INVESTIGATION 7.4

### DECOMPOSING ACTION OF SOIL MICROBES (pp. 246–247)

This experiment shows the decomposing power of molds and bacteria (including the actinomycetes) and also ties in with what the student has learned about the chemical composition of plant and animal structures. It is not expected to generate any great enthusiasm. It is neither colorful nor spectacular—and it may seem interminable to a tenth grader. Yet its purposes are important. And its length can help make the point that biological processes are often slow and the biological investigator must be patient.

Have the student set up hypotheses concerning the relative rates of decomposition of the substances and the rates of decomposition of the two soils.

### Materials

Lids of standard-size petri dishes fit snugly inside 4-inch flowerpots. In 5-inch flowerpots, petri-dish lids leave considerable surface exposed. Cans may be substituted for flowerpots—but be sure to punch several holes in the bottoms.

Obtain sharp builder's sand and wash it well; the fewer qualities of a true soil it has, the better. On the other hand, the garden soil should be a humus-rich loam.

Old stockings are good sources of nylon.

The aluminum dishes in which frozen potpies are packed make excellent substitutes for deep dishes if 4-inch flowerpots are used.

### Procedure

Not all members of the class need be involved in setting up the experiment. Two or three setups per class are quite sufficient for purposes of comparison; two to four students can work at each setup. However, the whole class should understand the procedure and participate in observing and recording the progress of decomposition.

The surfaces of the pots should not be watered; they must be kept moist by capillarity from the dishes in which the pots sit. Therefore the dishes must be kept filled with water. Since observations occur at infrequent intervals, one student from each team should be delegated to check the water each day.

The observation times listed on the chart (p. 246) may be varied.

### Discussion

• (1): Most of the substances have been mentioned in the text. A cotton string is mostly cellulose. Cellulose also occurs in a twig or a leaf; there is a small amount in rolled oats. The twig and the leaf contain considerable amounts of lignins, and the leaf also contains some pectins. The rolled oats are mostly starch, with small amounts of protein and fat. An insect, too, contains proteins and fat, but its exoskeleton is mostly chitin. Nylon is included as an example of a man-made material; the elements in it are similar to those in natural organic substances, but no microorganisms ever had a chance to use nylon as a food until man added it to the environment.

• (2) to • (6): The general rate of decomposition depends on temperature. Four weeks is scarcely enough time even in well-heated buildings; eight weeks is closer to the average. Probably the first evidence of decomposition will be mold hyphae on the oats. Later, molds may appear on other items. Still later, the typical earthy odor of actinomycetes and the putrid odor of bacterial decay may be detected.

• (8): Rates of decomposition on sand may or may not differ from rates on soil. Usually there are differences, decay of most items proceeding more slowly on the sand because of its smaller initial population of decomposers—but the facts should not be forced to fit the theory. In discussing results, stress the production of humus and the return of minerals to the soil, where they are used again as plant nutrients. In the economy of nature, the decay of food, fiber, and wood is no different from the decomposition of other plant and animal remains. "Desirable" decomposition and "undesirable" decomposition are only expressions of man's point of view.

### PROBLEMS (pp. 248–249)

1. (a) Disease causation is a complex interaction between host, parasite, and environment. A pathogen may or may not lead to disease, depending on its virulence, the degree of immunity of the host, and the nature of the environment. (b) No. A fly may carry typhoid bacilli mechanically on its body surface without being infected by the bacillus. (c) The lower the host-specificity of a disease, the wider the range of experimental organisms available to the researcher. (d) This is a straightforward library research question. Raise the further question whether the same immunizations are required for travel to all parts of the world.

2. A good resource for this question is: *Control of Communicable Diseases in Man,* 9th ed. (paperbound), 1960. The American Public Health Association, 1790 Broadway, New York 19, N.Y.

3. "Asian flu" involves strains of virus that may differ in virulence. An attack of the disease confers some immunity, although it is of short duration. The virus spreads from man to man by moisture droplets—probably both directly and indirectly.

4. One explanation of antibody formation is based on the idea of complementary molecular shapes. For example, gamma globulin is changed by contact with the active part of a toxin. These "template" gamma-globulin molecules combine with and inactivate other toxins of the type that produced the template.

5. The following is a partial list of pathogenic microorganisms that are most likely to be spread by sewage and of the diseases they produce: *Salmonella typhosa* (typhoid fever), *Salmonella paratyphi* (paratyphoid fever), *Salmonella schottmuelleri* (paratyphoid fever), *Salmonella enteritidis* (enteritis), *Shigella dysenteriae* (bacillary dysentery), *Vibrio comma* (Asiatic cholera), *Endameba histolytica* (amebic dysentery). Some infectious diseases with alternate hosts, such as typhus (fleas on rats), might also be favored. Obviously the incidence of noninfectious diseases would be little affected.

6. (*a*) Many aspects of this subquestion can be investigated. Soil texture influences air, water, and nutrient content, the nitrogen content, rate of decomposition, and rate of leaching. (*b*) Acid soil water may retard the work of nitrifying bacteria and of all forms of nitrogen-fixing bacteria. Acidity influences leaching of cations, many of which are important plant nutrients. Secondary effects, such as lowered aeration in clay soils with low pH, are numerous. (*c*) Very little leaching occurs

in desert soils, so inorganic nutrients are likely to be readily available. (*d*) The purpose of this subquestion is to evoke reasonable hypotheses from the students. There are many, for example, (1) destruction of root systems, (2) introduction into a soil of unfavorable pH, (3) lack of mycorrhizal fungi in the new soil. (*e*) For each decrease of 10°C in mean annual temperature, an increase in humus content of two to three times has been shown to occur; in warm, moist, well-aerated soil decomposition takes place at a very rapid rate.

7. During the first year the nutrients in field A were tied up in the rye, and therefore the potatoes in field B did better. However, the second year the nutrients were released from the rye, and the rye improved the drainage of the soils; and so potatoes in A did better.

8. Some biological examples are the practices relating to (*a*) immunization, (*b*) crop rotation, (*c*) pesticide control of insects, (*d*) animal and plant breeding. This problem emphasizes empiricism; a "scientific method" is not always necessary for technological advance.

## SUPPLEMENTARY MATERIALS

### Invitations to Enquiry

These materials are supplied in *The Biology Teacher's Handbook* (cited p. T35).

**Invitation 10 (pp. 78–83 of the Handbook).** The relationship between environment and disease is used to show the role of hypothesis in scientific investigations.

**Invitation 16 (pp. 103–105 of the Handbook).** The discovery of penicillin is used to illustrate serendipity in scientific investigation.

### Audiovisual Materials

**Phonograph record:** *The Scientists Speak: Biology.* Harcourt, Brace and Co., 1959. René Dubos speaks on microorganisms, referring to the work of Pasteur, to his own work with antibiotic-producing microbes, and to the interrelationships among the scientific disciplines. Now quite old, but still worthwhile.

**Motion-picture films:** *Microorganisms —Harmful Activities.* University of Indiana Audiovisual Center. 16 mm. Color. 18 min. A good film to back up this chapter. Discusses specificity of infection, types of immunity, antibodies, and Koch's postulates. Shows part of the technique used in Investigation 7.2.

*World at Your Feet.* National Film Board of Canada. 16 mm. Color. 23 min. Contains good material on soil structure and soil physics, but is inclined to place poetics above ecological principles.

*Nitrogen and Living Things.* United World Films. 16 mm. Color. 13 min. Links the nitrogen cycle to agriculture very well, but is somewhat superficial for many tenth-grade classes.

*Life in a Cubic Foot of Soil.* Coronet Films. 16 mm. Color. 11 min. A good introduction to the components of a soil.

## Teacher's References

ALEXANDER, M. *Introduction to Soil Microbiology.* New York: John Wiley & Sons, Inc., 1961. (A current standard textbook on the subject.)

BURNET, F. M. *Natural History of Infectious Disease.* 3rd ed. London: The Cambridge University Press, 1962. (Excellent background reading.)

NOTTINGHAM UNIVERSITY SCHOOL OF AGRICULTURE (Eng.). *Soil Zoology.* Ed. D. K. M. KEVAN. London: Butterworth & Co., Ltd., 1955. (Except for the economically important nematodes, the small animals that inhabit soils and often play an important role in the microcommunity have been much neglected. This book contributes to overcoming such neglect.)

RUSSELL, J. *The World of the Soil.* London: Longmans, Green & Co., Inc., 1950. (By the man who for thirty years headed Rothamstead, the British center for agricultural research. A cornerstone for any reading program on soils.)

# 8

# Patterns
# of Life
# on Land

## MAJOR IDEAS

1. In any given area the naturally occurring organisms are those that can survive and successfully reproduce under the environmental conditions (abiotic and biotic) prevailing there.

2. Over large areas of the earth, organisms and environment produce characteristic landscape patterns—biomes.

3. Rainfall and temperature (both ultimately determined by the global pattern of solar radiation) are the major abiotic environmental factors that determine the distribution of biomes.

4. In general, as one approaches the equator from the poles, one passes through biomes of increasing diversity of species, increasing complexity of community interrelationships, and increasing depth of vegetation.

5. In the low and middle latitudes an additional sequence of biomes may be distinguished along a gradient characterized by a diminishing availability of water.

6. The geographical distribution of many species cannot be explained on ecological grounds alone.

7. The present distribution of a species and the distribution of its fossils and of the fossils of its putative ancestors are keys to the distributional history of the species. A similar statement can be made concerning higher levels of classification—genera, families, orders, etc.

8. Organisms vary in ability to disperse; therefore, to explain the distribution of any species, one must consider its structural and physiological characteristics in relation to the nature of

the physical barriers that it may have had to cross in spreading from its area of origin.

9. Man has greatly influenced the distribution of many organisms by transporting them—sometimes deliberately, sometimes accidentally—across barriers that they had not themselves been able to surmount.

10. Man is an increasingly important element in determining the characteristics of landscapes. He has now succeeded in completely transforming large portions of some biomes. Most completely man-dominated are urban and suburban areas, where even the effects of climate are so highly modified that the eye of a trained geographer is needed to detect them, and where the major portion of biotic energy is derived from distant regions.

## PLANNING AHEAD

Pond water for Investigation 9.1 can be collected at any time up to the time ponds are frozen over. Water from a quietly flowing stream can be used. If collected more than a week before use, the unsterilized water should be kept in an aquarium rather than in a jug. In most parts of the United States, it is now too late to collect the larger organisms; if you have not already done so, order them immediately from a biological supply company. Order or collect the organisms to be used for Investigation 9.2 also.

The grid for Investigation 10.1 (Figure 10·26) should be drawn up on a stencil and duplicated.

Start onion-root growth for Investigation 11.3.

## GUIDELINES

The most logical division of this chapter for study is indicated by the positions of the investigations; the first assignment would be pp. 250–254 (guide questions 1–3); the second, pp. 256–282 (guide questions 4–18); the third, pp. 286–296 (guide questions 19–23). The second assignment is long, but most of its substance is descriptive.

Emphasis in this chapter should be placed upon the biome in which the student lives. However, one of the objectives of all true education is to broaden the student's view of his world, so other biomes should not be neglected. Direct experience with the local biome can be either assumed or secured, but experience with other biomes must usually be developed vicariously through audiovisual means. The clearer and more immediate the student's view of his local biome, the clearer will be his understanding of other biomes.

Even becoming familiar with the local biome may be somewhat difficult—especially in "inner city" schools. A field trip may be the best means of obtaining such familiarity. If the teacher himself is well acquainted with his region, he will undoubtedly be able to arrange an itinerary for a half- or full-day trip that will display the salient characteristics of the biome. Both municipal and state governments are becoming aware of the need for "wild" lands (not merely recreational areas studded with ball diamonds, tennis courts, and archery ranges) within easy reach of high-density human populations. Farseeing school systems cooperate in the development of these resources; administrators in such systems will welcome and facilitate the efforts of teachers to utilize the facilities.

Of course the pristine "climatic climax" of the local biome may long since have dis-

PATTERNS IN THE BIOSPHERE

appeared from any place within feasible traveling distance, but excellent examples of the influence of man on the biotic landscape, of successional stages, and of the "suburban forest" should be available. With a properly planned sequence of observations and a series of sharp, attention-fixing questions, the teacher can organize the immediate experiences of a field trip into an adequate acquaintance with the local biome. And do not forget that some acquaintance must have been acquired during Investigation 3.1.

Unlike that fieldwork, however, a field trip for Chapter 8 does not require growing-season conditions. The aspect of the landscape in early December is quite suitable for the study of biome characteristics unless deep snow prevails.

A biome is a biotic expression of a climate. To understand biomes, then, the student must have some knowledge of (1) the atmospheric factors that—when statistically summarized—constitute climate, and (2) the astronomical and geophysical phenomena that determine the distribution of climates. As in the case of distant biota, an understanding of distant climates is best developed against a background of familiarity with the local climate.

Many, if not most, of today's biology students already possess at least some background in climatology. However, for those teachers who wish to use it, some basic information concerning world distribution of climates is provided on pages T122–T130.

An excellent source of information about distant biomes and climates is often overlooked—students who have lived in other biomes. Such students often have photographs as well as an eagerness to talk about their former surroundings. Teachers in schools located near installations of the armed forces or near large industrial plants that frequently shift their personnel are usually aware of this resource, but other teachers might discover unsuspected possibilities by looking into their student records or by direct questioning.

## TEACHING NOTES

### MEETING THE ENVIRONMENT (pp. 250–254)

**p. 250, ¶ 1:** Inevitably this chapter must mention many kinds of organisms. But mere names are poor for arousing mental images. Therefore, almost all organisms mentioned have also been pictured. Marginal notes help to guide students to illustrations elsewhere in the book. The index should also be used.

**p. 251, Fig. 8 · 2:** Alligators have more rounded snouts than caimans, which come from Cuba and points south. Exportation of alligators from Florida is illegal.

**p. 251, ¶ 2:** Unlike the questions in paragraph 1, the questions in this paragraph are not entirely rhetorical. Some speculation on these points is in order.

**p. 251, ¶ 4:** The term "tolerance" was introduced incidentally in Chapter 7 (p. 237). It is further illustrated by Investigation 9.2. You may wish to use that investigation now, if you expect to omit Chapter 9.

**p. 253, ¶ 1:** If necessary, refer students to page 88 for review of competition.

**p. 253, note 1:** The design might indicate tests of tolerance to various degrees of flooding by (1) cypress alone, (2) pines, oak, or hickory alone, and (3) mixed species; also tests of survival of cypress with various upland species.

## INVESTIGATION 8.1

### A STUDY OF ENVIRONMENTAL TOLERANCE (pp. 254–255)

Seeds are a convenient form of organism to use for experiment. There is evidence that the distribution of bald cypress (p. 253) is at least partly a result of the intolerance of its seed for dry soil. Likewise, the absence of most other tree species from the swamps of the southeastern United States may be a result of the intolerance of their seeds for flooded soils. Moisture is, of course, a basic distributional factor, but it is difficult to maintain and measure in experimental situations. Effects of light and temperature are investigated more easily and are also important factors in distribution of organisms.

This investigation makes use of some technical skills developed in Investigation 1.2. If students are made aware of this, most will strive to show that they did indeed learn something.

Teams of 5 or 6 students each are suitable. These are not too large to provide each student with a task. One student may be assigned as a team leader. Extra students can distribute materials and coordinate the allocation of dishes to their proper environments.

## Materials

The plant species selected for this investigation provide a variety of responses to the conditions of the experiment. Other seeds may be substituted as follows:

For *tomato*—beet, pepper, carrot, sunflower, cotton.

For *radish*—tobacco, corn, bindweed, flax.

For *lettuce*—African violet, evening primrose, mullein, onion, fireweed, phacelia.

For *vetch*—celery, larkspur, columbine, henbit, plantain, shepherd's purse.

If sufficient petri dishes are not available, satisfactory substitute containers include: lids of large peanut-butter jars, small aluminum dishes from frozen potpies, cardboard milk cartons cut down to a depth of about 1.5 cm. Or dishes and covers may be made by molding circles of heavy aluminum foil around glass petri dishes.

The strips of cardboard used as dividers should be as wide as the petri dishes (or other containers) are deep. A good grade is that used in shirt boxes. The tabs at the ends of the dividers may be fastened to the dishes with rubber cement.

The plastic of which the bags are made should be thin (1 or 2 mils), to allow free diffusion of gases. Do not use Baggies. The plastic sheeting used by cleaners to protect clothing can be used in place of bags. The dishes should be wrapped in the plastic and the loose ends fastened with string or a rubber band.

For covering the seeds to be grown in darkness, coffee cans may be used in the place of cardboard boxes, or the dishes may be wrapped in aluminum foil.

A conventional refrigerator may be used to establish the cold environment. However, because the refrigerator light normally goes off when the door is closed, modification is necessary to insure continuous light. Such light can be provided quite simply by running an extension cord, with lamp attached, into the refrigerator. With this cord in place, the rubber gasket around the door will still permit normal opening and closing and at the same time prevent loss of cold air. An alternate method is to run a bypass wire across the light switch in the doorframe. This will allow the regular refrigerator light to burn continuously. It may be necessary to remove part of the frame in order to gain access to the switch. Because it produces heat, an incandescent lamp should not be used as the light source. Small fluorescent lamps (8 to 15 watts) and fixtures for them are available commercially. But even fluorescent lamps generate small amounts of heat, so it is wise to check the refrigerator a few days prior to the experiment to make sure that a temperature of $10°-12°C$ is maintained.

Teachers who have access to a commercial incubator need only make provision for a continuous source of light to provide the proper environment for Dishes 3 and 4. Use an extension cord, as in the case of the refrigerator. If the incubator door will not close when the cord is in place, it may be necessary to remove the thermometer and run the extension cord through the thermometer hole. As a safety measure, wrap tape around the cord at the point where it enters the incubator.

If an incubator is not available, a simple heat box can be made from the following:

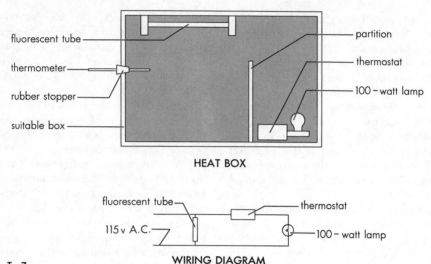

**HEAT BOX**

**WIRING DIAGRAM**

Figure T–7

Corrugated cardboard box or metal box of suitable size

Fluorescent light tube (same wattage as that used in refrigerator)

100-watt incandescent bulb

Small brooder thermostat rated at 23°–50°C

Thermometer

The equipment is to be assembled as shown in Figure T–7. A cardboard or metal partition separates the heat source from the petri dishes. Since the incandescent lamp serves as the heat source, it should be wired in series with the thermostat; the fluorescent light should be wired parallel. It might be necessary to experiment with a slightly higher or lower wattage to obtain the desired temperature.

Homemade or modified equipment is often better than none, but schools should be encouraged to provide standard laboratory equipment obtained from commercial supply houses. Care should be exercised in building or modifying equipment. *Before* constructing new electrical equipment or modifying existing equipment, check with your school principal concerning local fire codes and regulations.

Discussion

Tomato seeds germinate most rapidly in complete darkness at about 26°C. Lettuce (especially the Great Lakes variety) germinates best in light. Vetch requires a cool environment. Radish germinates well under a wide range of conditions.

• (1): Have the students discuss the hypotheses before performing the investigation. It is important that they are consciously trying to test their hypotheses throughout.

• (2): Refer students to Investigation 2.2, especially "Studying the Data," paragraph 2.

• (8): Students may have difficulty separating the influence of individual factors from combinations of factors. However, this is a very common experimental design; you should lend assistance when necessary.

• (11): Insist that the answer be consistent with the data.

• (12) and • (13): Both of these questions are speculative. The important thing to emphasize is the necessity in scientific reasoning that no conclusion be in conflict with evidence.

## ECOLOGICAL DISTRIBUTION OF LIFE ON LAND (pp. 256–282)

**p. 256, Fig. 8 · 7:** Students should notice the temperature relationships in these climatograms, which are arranged in order of decreasing latitude.

**p. 256, ¶ 3:** This paragraph echoes the quotation in the introduction to Section Three. It seems important to refer frequently to the relation between science, which is seeking for order, and nature, which may be—but is not *necessarily*—orderly.

**pp. 258–259, Fig. 8 · 8:** This map is based on one in Odum (reference: page 304 of the student's book). It is quite generalized. However, much of the world simply has not been studied sufficiently from the biome point of view to make a better map possible at present. Maps of *vegetation only* are many, and some are quite detailed. A good one is that by A. W. Küchler in *Goode's World Atlas* (reference: page 257, marginal note). For North America, Pitelka (*American Midland Naturalist* **25**: 113–137, 1941) compiled a fairly detailed biome map that has been widely reproduced.

**p. 260, ¶ 3:** Watch for a tendency to misread "man has modified the effects of climate." Modification of *climate* itself does not concern us here.

**p. 260, ¶ 5:** "No lack of water": Referring to Figure 8 · 7, students may be inclined to dispute this for tundra and taiga. If so, this is the place to introduce the idea of precipitation-evaporation ratio.

**p. 262, ¶ 1:** Something like tundra is found on the Palmer Peninsula of Antarctica. Life on polar ice is based on producers in the seas, so it is omitted from consideration here.

**p. 262, ¶ 2:** It may be desirable to demonstrate the relation between the angle of the sun's rays and the intensity of solar radiation. See p. T123.

**p. 262, Fig. 8 · 10:** Cold, dry winds constitute perhaps the chief factor in preventing woody plants from growing above the level of snow cover (thin in tundra) or protections such as the rock in this photograph.

**p. 263, Fig. 8 · 11:** This may only elicit the idea of protective coloration. You may wish to raise the question of how such conditions might have arisen, but do not try to pursue the idea too far at this point.

**p. 263, note 1:** Consider the lack of liquid moisture whenever the ground is frozen, and the short growing season. Throughout the biome descriptions, attempt to elicit explanations for adaptations. Marginal notes draw attention to some such ideas but by no means exhaust the possibilities.

**p. 264, note 2:** Snow acts as insulation against severe cold. Temperature under snow cover is usually several degrees higher than air temperature.

**p. 264, ¶ 5:** Of course any daily comparison must be of the same day of the year for both tundra and taiga.

**p. 265, note 2:** Bald cypress and larch lose all their needles each autumn.

**p. 265, ¶ 4:** Note that this is a brief description of an ecological succession.

**p. 266, ¶ 2:** Snowshoe hare and lynx are illustrated in Figures 2 · 19 and 3 · 16.

**p. 266, ¶ 3:** The title-page photo shows an aerial view of the deciduous forest in the Catskill Mountains. (Photo by Grant Heilman.)

**p. 267, ¶ 4:** The idea of community depth and the term "canopy" may have been encountered during work on Investigation 3.1.

**p. 267, note 3:** All of these birds are insectivores, but their niches do not overlap because each species obtains its food in a different way. *How* they hunt insects is an important part of the description of their niches.

**p. 268, Fig. 8 · 19:** Deer are browsers; buds and twigs are used throughout the year, but nourishment is more abundant when leaves are on woody plants. Snow can hinder travel.

**p. 270, Fig. 8 · 20:** In part, the general greenish tinge to the light at the floor of the tropical rain forest derives from the filtering out of other colors by foliage above.

**p. 270, note 3:** Much rainfall and high humidity are necessary conditions for the survival of epiphytes.

**p. 271, ¶ 2:** "Always green" may be equated by some students with "evergreen" and this in turn with "pines and spruces." Forestall this.

**p. 271, ¶ 3:** "Untold numbers" is quite literal; unknown thousands of species remain to be described.

**p. 272, note 1:** Vegetation on the forest floor is so sparse that little food exists for herbivores.

**p. 272, ¶ 2:** The idea of limiting factors may need to be reviewed from Investigation 2.2.

**p. 272, ¶ 3:** Refer to Figure 7 · 14. Have students speculate on the relationship between vegetation, amount of humus, and the abiotic environment.

**p. 273, note 2:** Production is a function of total annual radiant energy, given optimal water and nutrient supplies.

**p. 273, Fig. 8 · 24:** Several other first-order consumers (herbivores) are mentioned on p. 274. Seed-eating birds (granivores), mostly present in winter, are also first-order consumers.

**p. 274, Fig. 8 · 25:** In all biomes, local conditions may modify the biota characteristic of the overall climate. Here water available along a stream in a valley allows growth of trees in a grassland biome.

**p. 274, Fig. 8 · 26:** Early explorers described the voice of this ground squirrel as a "bark."

**p. 276, note 1:** The thorns and spines on desert plants probably are protection against first-order consumers in a land where their food is sparse. More clearly demonstrable is the relation between reduction in leaf surface and retardation of water loss.

**p. 276, Fig. 8 · 30:** Competition among root systems for water is probably the best explanation. But many desert plants are known to produce substances that are deleterious to other plants—a kind of antibiosis.

**p. 278, Fig. 8 · 34:** The dead leaves on the ground and the bare branches indicate the dry season. Dr. Küchler says the picture was taken in the spring of 1966 and shows forest partly in relatively good condition, partly damaged through cutting and burning, a characteristic of most tropical deciduous forests. Further, he states, "Speaking of deciduous forests, I should like to draw your attention to my discussion of deciduous and tropophyll in my book on *Vegetation Mapping* (1967, New York, Ronald Press, pp. 372 and 373). . . . Tropical trees just don't behave like those in our latitudes."

**p. 278, note 2:** Trees become less frequent, grass cover becomes discontinuous, and grass becomes mixed with scattered thorny shrubs.

**p. 279, Fig. 8 · 35:** The principal large predators are lions, leopards, and cheetahs.

**p. 280, ¶ 1:** Note that Figure 8 · 8 does not distinguish this biome from taiga. The cover photograph shows middle-latitude rain forest on the Olympic Peninsula, State of Washington. (Ruth Kirk, *The Olympic Rain Forest*, The University of Washington Press, Seattle. Photo by Johsel Namkung.)

**p. 280, ¶ 4:** This is termed "maquis" in parts of the Mediterranean and "broad-sclerophyll woodland" by some botanists.

**p. 280, Fig. 8 · 36:** Chaparral is most verdant in the season between the winter rains and the beginning of the summer drought.

**p. 281, Fig. 8·37:** The constant moisture favors dense growth of plants, especially epiphytes, mosses, and lycopods.

**p. 281, note 1:** Such leaves retain moisture well during the long, dry summers.

**p. 281, ¶ 2:** The first sentence may require some explanation if students have not yet grasped the relation between radiant energy and heat.

**p. 282, Fig. 8·38:** Note that no uniform scale is used in these diagrams. Even in the southern parts of the western United States, some mountains have sufficient altitude to exhibit the full range of zones. In the eastern states, however, an alpine zone occurs only in some of the higher mountains of New York and New England; the "balds" of the southern Appalachians are not comparable to tundra.

## INVESTIGATION 8.2

### TEMPERATURE, RAINFALL, AND BIOME DISTRIBUTION
(pp. 282–286)

Climatograms are common means of summarizing the two most important climatic variables; they are used especially by geographers. The representation (on page 272) of precipitation by vertical bars is a violation of the general principle that a continuous variable is best shown by a line, but it is justified by the need to distinguish easily between temperature and precipitation. This point is worth making in class discussion, because even those students who are familiar with the mechanics of graph-making often do not know how to select a form suitable for a given set of data.

### Materials

If the graphs are drawn on a variety of grids, comparisons are difficult. Therefore, it is well to furnish all students with graph paper of the same kind. The best practice is to duplicate grids that are exactly like those in the student's book — 12 blocks wide and 18 high. On this grid the April data for Moshi, Tanzania, go two blocks above the top, but these can easily be added.

Local climatic data can be obtained from the nearest United States Weather Bureau office. Conversion of Fahrenheit temperatures to Celsius can be done easily with the scale on page 781. Precipitation data in inches are converted to centimeters by multiplying by 2.54. Two or three students can be assigned the task of conversion; they should check each other's work before releasing the converted data for class use.

### Procedure

After some of the climatograms in the student's book have been studied, the graph-making phase of Investigation 8.2 may be assigned as homework. The number of graphs to be prepared by any one student is a matter of choice. The minimum would seem to be three: one based on local data, one on a set of data from Group 1, and one on a set from Group 2.

When added to the six graphs in the textbook, the four graphs drawn from the data in Group 1 provide the student with representative climatic data from ten major biomes.

### Studying the Data

Each graph should be discussed from the viewpoint of possible relationships between the climatic data and the characteristic features of the biome. Enlarged copies of the ten climatograms may be posted where they will be visible to all students. These and the discussion based on them may then serve as a background for making predictions from data in Group 2.

During discussion of the biome descriptions, attention should be focused on the relation of the climatic factors (as graphed in the climatograms) to the biota. For example, in the climatogram for the tundra (page 256), the graph indicates that the average monthly temperatures are above freezing—and not far above—only three months of the year; during most of the year the average monthly temperatures are far below freezing. Furthermore, the precipitation is quite low in all months of the year. From these facts we can conclude that the producers of the tundra biome are actively producing food during only a fraction of the year and that the density of consumers must be low. But the implications of the data presented by the climatogram need to be explored. The amplitude of the yearly cycle of monthly average temperatures implies a high latitude; this, in turn, assures a long daily period of sunlight during the season when temperatures are high. In addition, the low temperatures imply a low rate of evaporation. Thus conditions for plant growth during the brief summer season are not as unfavorable as they seem at first glance. The food-production conditions suggest that a large migratory summer population of consumers may be possible. Such reasoning should be applied to all the climatograms.

Students should be kept constantly aware of the limitations of the data with which they are working. Some significant variables not indicated in the climatograms are mentioned on page 285. It may also be well to discuss the way in which the data have been derived. The temperature data are means derived from "daily means," which are not really means in the usual statistical sense but, instead, are the midpoints in the range of hourly readings over a twenty-four hour period. The precipitation data, on the other hand, are true means for monthly precipitation over a period of years. The number of years of observation varies from station to station, of course. These data do not indicate the monthly *range* in precipitation and temperature. And the range of these variables is a significant factor for organisms, as are the extremes.

Having noted limitations in the climatic data, students must realize that a climatogram does not summarize precipitation and temperature for a biome as a whole. Any one climatogram merely shows the data for these variables at one station within a biome. The stations have, of course, been chosen as carefully as possible to provide data that are representative—"typical"—for each biome.

The stations from which the data in Group 2 were obtained are as follows:

- *a.* Washington, D.C. (middle-latitude deciduous forest)
- *b.* Lisbon, Portugal (chaparral)
- *c.* Iquitos, Peru (tropical rain forest)
- *d.* Yuma, Arizona (desert)
- *e.* Odessa, U.S.S.R. (middle-latitude grassland: steppes)
- *f.* Valparaíso, Chile (chaparral)
- *g.* Upernavik, Greenland (tundra)
- *h.* San Antonio, Texas (middle-latitude grassland: mesquite-grass savanna)
- *i.* Bahía Blanca, Argentina (middle-latitude grassland)
- *j.* Oaxaca, Mexico (tropical deciduous forest)
- *k.* Moose Factory, Ontario, Canada (taiga)
- *l.* Fallon, Nevada (middle-latitude desert)

## For Further Investigation

The first set of data illustrates a cline of decreasing precipitation along a level of latitude. Dubuque is in tall-grass prairie; Kearney is in mid-grass prairie; and Laramie is in short-grass plains. The second set of data illustrates the reciprocal effect of increasing precipitation and decreasing latitude. At Galveston the solar radiation, with its consequent evaporation, is so high that the effectiveness of the large amount of precipitation (compared with that of Winnipeg) produces a precipitation-evaporation ratio insufficient to support tree growth.

Figure T–8 shows another kind of climatogram. Some students may like to replot some of their data on such a grid and attempt to associate shapes with biome characteristics.

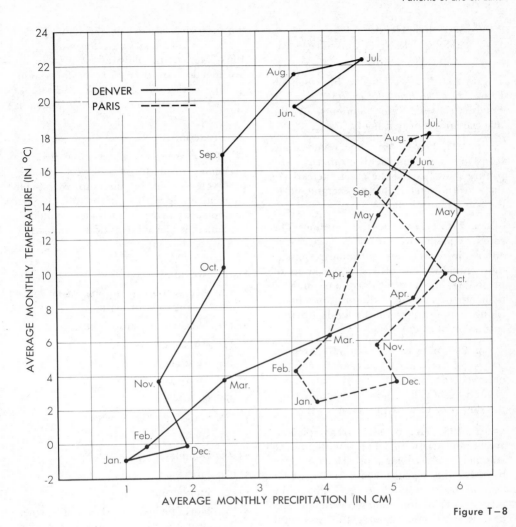

Figure T—8

## EARTH HISTORY AND DISTRIBUTION (pp. 286—290)

**p. 286, ¶ 1:** Penguins do cross the equator, but only in the cold waters of the Humboldt Current on the west coast of South America.

**p. 288, Fig. 8·41:** Any ideas that the students have about this situation must be judged entirely on the basis of logic, since there is no accepted explanation. See note on Item 16, Investigation 8.3 (p. T120).

**p. 288, note 1:** The Atlantic Ocean. See note about Figure 7·11 on p. T103.

**p. 289, ¶ 2:** Note that this conclusion does not *necessarily* imply evolution.

## MAN'S INFLUENCE ON TERRESTRIAL ECOSYSTEMS
### (pp. 290–296)

**p. 293, ¶ 2:** In many high schools Paton's *Cry, the Beloved Country* is used in English classes. Refer students to the first paragraph of that book.

**p. 293, Fig. 8·46:** The water comes from mountain snowfields primarily. The picture shows part of the great ditch system that diverts water from the Sacramento to the San Joaquin Valley.

**p. 294, ¶ 2:** Note the wording. The seeds of plants are not likely to arrive in an area in serial order, but some germinate more rapidly than others, some kinds of plants become conspicuous more quickly than others, and some die out after flourishing temporarily. All this adds up to a succession of *adult forms*.

**p. 294, note 1:** Even in mid-city some stages of secondary succession can be observed on recently bared patches of ground — especially those resulting from the slow pace of urban renewal.

**p. 295, Fig. 8·48:** Urban pigeons are commensals of man. Without the voluntary or accidental provision of food by man, the pigeons could not exist. If anyone really wanted to get rid of the pigeons of Boston Common or of San Francisco's Union Square, the ecological procedure would be clear.

## INVESTIGATION 8.3

### EFFECTS OF FIRE ON BIOMES
### (pp. 296–301)

This investigation can be worked through in a class session, without previous assignment. Or it can be assigned as homework and then discussed briefly in class. Or it can be assigned to certain of the better students for independent work, followed by a report to the class.

It is advantageous, though not essential, for the teacher to read the article on which the exercise is based: "The Ecology of Fire," by C. F. Cooper, *Scientific American*, April, 1961. Most of the illustrations used in the investigation are derived from illustrations in that article, through the courtesy of Gerard Piel, publisher of *Scientific American*.

### Procedure

The answers suggested below carry the reasoning through in a logical manner. But you should be alert to reasonable alternative ideas that bright and original students may provide. Such ideas should be welcomed, subjected to critical examination, and, if tenable, nurtured.

- (1): Mesquite.
- (2): Access to deep supplies of moisture during long droughts.
- (3): Mesquite brush with little grass.
- (4): Both survive.
- (5): Mesquite.
- (6): Mesquite.
- (7): Grass.
- (8): Somewhat like A or B.
- (9): See (3).
- (10): Dominantly grassland.
- (11): Fire.
- (12): Lumbering.
- (13): More people; brush piles; further clearing by fire in attempts at agriculture.
- (14): Eventually much like A. Deciduous woody plants at first would be favored, because they spring up as sprouts from stumps.
- (15): Small fires cause the cones of jack pine to open; otherwise, seeds may be held in the cones many years.
- (16): An area dominated by young jack pine. It is such areas that form the breeding habitat of Kirtland's warbler (Figure 8 · 41).
- (17): Jack pine would become rare, and other trees would take their place.

- (18): Dominated by jack pine.
- (19): Fire damages only the needles of the longleaf pine.
- (20): Fire usually kills young deciduous plants.
- (21): Longleaf pine.
- (22): Ground fires kill the lower branches, but not the tops or the trunks.
- (23): Deciduous trees in the absence of fires grow faster than the pines and eventually shade them out.
- (24): Fire.

Discussion

- (25): Advantage because it maintains grass.
- (26): Disadvantage because it favors growth of jack pine.
- (27): Advantage because it maintains longleaf pine in competition with deciduous trees.
- (28): Burning would have to be done at a season when bobwhites were not nesting.
- (29): First, of course, the landowner must decide what he wants. Even so, it is impossible to predict the effects of fire without prior empirical evidence, because in all cases the variables are very numerous. For example, periodic fires in certain tall-grass prairies tend to increase productivity of cattle; fires in the mid-grass prairies tend to have the opposite effect. Some ecologists suggest that the depth of mulch is the important variable in this case.

To some degree, fire is used as a management tool in all regions. Indeed, it is perhaps the most ancient tool that man has employed to change the landscape. What is not stated either here or in Cooper's article is that today there are many other such means—fertilizing, employing herbicides and the saw and ax, disking, and bull-dozing—and that these usually can be used more selectively than fire. Thus, though fire may have played a major part in shaping grasslands and forests in the past, ecologists are by no means agreed that fire should continue to have a large role in land management today. It would be well to draw out these points during class discussion.

GUIDE QUESTIONS (p. 302)

4. Students should realize that a biome is a relative unit in a system of classifying ecosystems according to magnitude.

10. This question seeks only a superficial matching of habitat with organism, not an evolutionary or zoogeographical treatise.

PROBLEMS (pp. 302–303)

1. Some organisms that might be found on these lists are: apple, grapes, orange, plum, cherry, melons, potato, tomato, beans, squash, corn, barley, wheat, rice, sorghum, house mice, Norway rats, cockroach, bedbug, house sparrow, starling, pheasant. Whether or not each of these could survive in your locality without man depends in part on the climate of your region. However, some, such as corn and perhaps bedbugs, could probably not flourish anywhere without man.

2. (a) Havana, New Orleans, Caracas, Boston, Winnipeg, Anchorage, Rio de Janeiro. (b) Brisbane, Hobart, Singapore, Manila, Little America, Tokyo, Vladivostok. (c) Nairobi, Tananarive, Cairo, Cape Town, Madrid, Copenhagen, Murmansk. (d) Day length and cloud cover particularly.

3. (b) Consider the influence of permafrost. (c) Estivation is usually in response to dryness. (d) An ecotone is a transition zone between two ecosystems. See Kendeigh, *Animal Ecology* (reference: page 304). (e) The most important relationship is between precipitation and evaporation: the hotter the climate, the greater the evaporation. Therefore, in two regions with equal precipitation, the

hotter one is the more arid. Tundra introduces a special factor: there the permafrost prevents loss of moisture from the surface by the downward percolation that occurs elsewhere.

4. This is often explained on the basis of a climate warming trend. But increased sources of food from the presence of man may also be involved. Students may evolve explanations that have equal intellectual validity.

5. This problem will test the student's reference-using skills as well as his ecological thinking. No one reference will serve for all parts; perhaps the best single one would be that much-abused tool, the encyclopedia.

   Clues that may aid in assessing the student's success: (a) cattle; (b) (steppes of Asia): old world bison, horses, wild ass; (pampa of Argentina): guanaco, pampas deer; (veldt of South Africa): gnu and other large antelopes; (c) reindeer, caribou, musk ox; (d) the euphorbias, which have succulent stems, are thorny, and live in arid climates of South Africa; (e) the sunbirds, which are small, have long bills, and feed on nectar.

6. Contraction of geographic ranges might be due to: (a) climatic changes, (b) evolution of tolerances toward a more spe-

cific or limited range, or (c) results of species interactions (e.g., predation, parasitism, competition).

7. Some good evidence now exists for this theory. See Runcorn, *Continental Drift* (reference: p. T132). The filmstrip *Geological Oceanography*, by Encyclopaedia Britannica Films, gives an excellent presentation of it.

8. Work on this problem is similar to that for Problem 5. Both should be voluntary undertakings unless you have personally checked the availability of pertinent references.

10. The answer to this question can become extremely sophisticated if the students consider effects of gravity, various types of solar radiation, temperature, lack of air, etc. See Darlington, *Zoogeography* (reference: p. T131).

## SUPPLEMENTARY MATERIALS

### Materials on Climate

The background material presented below may be used in any way you wish. Two suggestions: Use it as background for a lecture illustrated with a globe and maps and with charts presented on an overhead projector. Or duplicate the material and distribute it to students for reading.

### CLIMATES

Because climate has such an overwhelming effect upon the organisms in any landscape, we should understand something of the way in which it varies from place to place on the surface of the earth. If you already understand the distribution of climates, you may treat this topic as a review. If the topic is new to you, it forms a necessary background in physical science for your biological study.

### DISTRIBUTION OF RADIANT ENERGY

Energy enters the biosphere in the form of radiation from the sun. This energy is changed into chemical form through the process of photosynthesis. From the organic

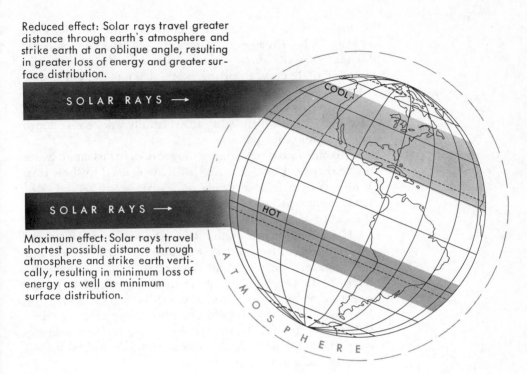

Reduced effect: Solar rays travel greater distance through earth's atmosphere and strike earth at an oblique angle, resulting in greater loss of energy and greater surface distribution.

SOLAR RAYS →

SOLAR RAYS →

Maximum effect: Solar rays travel shortest possible distance through atmosphere and strike earth vertically, resulting in minimum loss of energy as well as minimum surface distribution.

COOL

HOT

ATMOSPHERE

Figure T–9

Showing how the earth's atmosphere and the angle of contact affect the amount of solar radiation received on the earth's surface—here, during a period of seasonal extremes.

substances thus produced, the energy for all the activities of living things is derived. The amount of solar energy received on any particular part of the earth's surface is therefore a most important environmental factor for organisms.

The shape of the earth and its position in relation to the solar system affect the distribution of solar radiation on the earth's surface. Different places receive different amounts of radiation. Through the year the regions near the equator receive most; the polar regions—north and south—receive least.

This situation results from two factors. (As you read on, refer to Figure T–9.) First, to reach the earth's surface, solar energy must, of course, pass through the earth's atmosphere. The atmosphere absorbs some of the solar energy. The greater the thickness of the atmospheric blanket that the energy passes through, the greater the amount of energy absorbed. Rays striking the earth at a right angle (vertically) travel through less atmosphere than do those striking the earth at an acute angle. Hence parts of the earth on which light falls vertically will receive more energy than other parts.

Second, radiation striking the earth's surface at an acute angle is spread out. A flashlight may be used to show this. When its light falls vertically on a surface, we see a bright circle. When its light falls at a slant, we see a dimmer oval; the light is dimmer because it is spread over a greater area.

If we look at the matter from the viewpoint of an observer on earth (where the organisms are) instead of from outer space, we can see that the higher the sun is above the horizon, the greater the amount of energy received. In any one day at any one place, the sun is highest above the horizon at noon (noon local time, not "zone time" or "daylight saving time"). And any place where the sun is *directly* overhead at noon will receive the maximum possible amount of solar radiation.

As the earth revolves around the sun, the tilt of its axis causes a shift in the latitude at which a ray falls vertically at noon (Figure T – 10). At noon on June 21 the vertical ray will strike the earth 23°30' (23 degrees and 30 minutes, or 23.5 degrees) north of the equator (along a line called the *Tropic of Cancer*), and on December 21, 23°30' south of the equator (along the *Tropic of Capricorn*). The sun is never directly overhead at any point north or south of these latitudes; at the poles it is never more than 23°30' above the horizon. In general, then, the solar radiation received by the earth is greatest between the tropics and decreases rapidly toward the poles.

Thus far we have been considering solar radiation received in an "instant" of time—the *intensity* of radiation. But the time unit most important from the point of view of a photosynthesizing plant is probably twenty-four hours—a day. Thus we must consider not only the intensity of the solar radiation but also its *duration* on the basis of a twenty-four hour period.

Duration is another result of the tilt of the earth in relation to the sun. By examining Figure T – 11 carefully, we can see that the parts of the earth beyond 66°30' north or south will have at least one twenty-four hour period during the year without any sunlight. We also can see that the

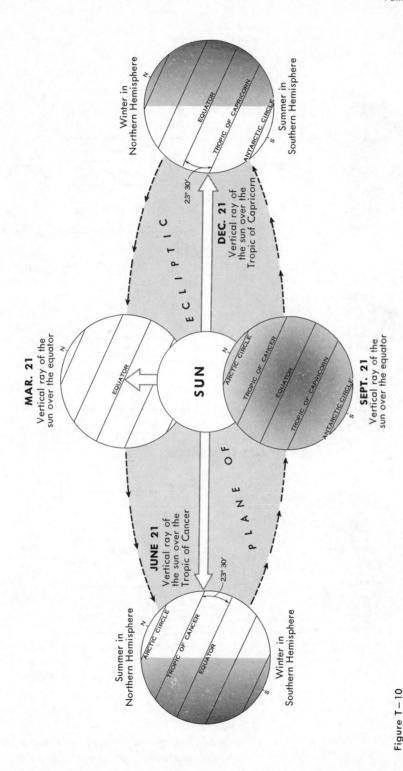

Figure T–10

Showing relation between the earth and the sun during the annual cycle.

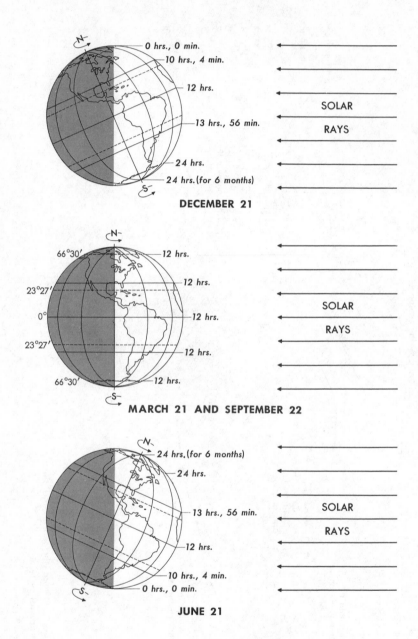

DECEMBER 21

MARCH 21 AND SEPTEMBER 22

JUNE 21

Figure T–11
Showing distribution of daily solar radiation
in the annual cycle.

period between sunrise and sunset is always twelve hours long at the equator, and it does not vary greatly within the tropics. On the other hand, at the poles the sun shines for six months at a stretch; twilight is measured in weeks, and night lasts until dawning begins, about five months later.

Thus there is great variation over the earth's surface both in the duration of daily solar radiation and in its intensity. At the poles, the sun shines for six months, but the intensity is always low; within the tropics, days are never greatly prolonged, but the intensity of radiation is high. We can conclude that the rate of photosynthesis over the surface of the earth will vary according to geographical position and time of year, with corresponding effects on the whole biotic community.

## DISTRIBUTION OF HEAT

Up to this point we have discussed solar radiation as if it were only light. Actually it contains many wavelengths besides those we see (student's book Figure 1 · 10). But it does not contain the energy we call heat. The warmth of the sun's rays, which we feel on a summer's day, is solar radiation transformed into heat as the light strikes our bodies, the air around us, or other material things. (Thus, in interplanetary space, where radiation is plentiful but matter is not, there is very little heat.) Light is the source of energy for photosynthesis, but heat—some degree of it—is important for *all* biochemical processes.

The fact that the sun's "warmth" comes only from the interaction of solar energy with matter leads to a remarkable conclusion: The earth's atmosphere is heated mainly from *below*. When solar radiation strikes the upper atmosphere, very little heat results, because the molecules that compose the upper atmosphere are few and far apart. At lower levels, where the air is denser, more solar energy is changed to heat. But the greatest change occurs when the light hits land and water. Therefore, despite the fact that the sun shines above us, its heating effect comes from below.

When a fluid (liquid or gas) is heated from below, the warmer molecules rise. The warmer fluid spreads up and over the cooler portion. In this way heat is distributed throughout a container of water over a fire. Air is a fluid, and over the year it receives more heat in the region of the equator than anywhere else. A basic pattern of atmospheric circulation results.

This massive circulation is brought about by the unequal distribution of solar radiation; it transports heated air over

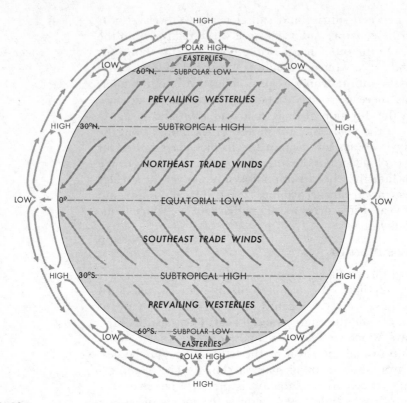

Figure T–12

Showing basic pattern of atmospheric circulation on the earth's surface.

the earth's surface, as shown in Figure T–11. Solar energy supplies the force, but gravity also plays a part. Cool air is denser—that is, heavier per unit of volume—than warm air. As a result, air descends over cooler regions and rises over warmer regions. Since the air near the equator is, in general, warmer and lighter than elsewhere on the globe, the air movement there is upward. As the warm air rises, it is replaced by cooler air from both the Northern and the Southern hemispheres. This horizontal movement of air results in constant winds, the *trade winds*. The entire wind pattern shifts with the seasonal movement of the vertical ray of the sun—northward in the period from January to June, southward from July to December.

Another factor affects winds—the rotation of the earth. Because of this rotation, cooler air moving into the region of the *equatorial low* (the "doldrums" of mariners) does not move directly from the north in the Northern Hemisphere or from the south in the Southern Hemisphere (see Figure T – 12). Instead, in the Northern Hemisphere the currents flowing toward the equator are turned to the right, resulting in winds that blow from the northeast; in the Southern Hemisphere there is an opposite deflection, to the left, resulting in winds from the southeast.

The circulation of warm air is away from the tropics; cooler air from the *subtropical highs* (the "horse latitudes" of mariners), two regions of descending air, is constantly being brought back for reheating. This means that the equatorial regions of the earth are cooler and the middle latitudes warmer than they would be otherwise. In other words, the region between the tropics exports heat. The air that sinks in the regions of the subtropical highs does not lose all its heat there, however. Some of it swirls out into the higher latitudes — northward in the Northern Hemisphere, southward in the Southern — and mixes with cold air moving toward the equator from the poles. These movements spread heat still farther toward the poles, so that even those extreme regions are warmer than would be expected from the small amount of radiation they receive.

## DISTRIBUTION OF MOISTURE

The oceans are the principal sources of moisture for the land. Moisture is carried to the land by circulating air. Therefore our understanding of atmospheric circulation is basic to our understanding of both temperature and moisture conditions on the earth — and these are, in turn, the two most important factors in understanding the distribution of organisms.

Warm water evaporates faster than cold water. Warm air holds more water vapor than cold air. When air passes over warm ocean water, it picks up much water vapor. When the air is cooled, the water vapor precipitates as rain or snow. It may precipitate by passing from a warmer ocean area to a cooler land area. This accounts for the relatively humid (moist) climate of western Europe and for the winter rains in California. Water vapor may precipitate if it meets a cooler air mass. This accounts for the summer rains in the eastern United States. Although warm, moist air from the Gulf of Mexico passes over land that is even warmer, it often meets cool air from Canada, and precipitation results.

On the other hand, along the northern coast of Chile air passes from a cool ocean, where it picks up rather little water, to a warm land, where there are no cool air masses.

The result is one of the driest deserts in the world (Figure 8 · 8). But there is another way that air may lose its moisture. We have already seen that the higher atmosphere is cooler. An air mass that is blown against a mountain will rise and, becoming cooler, lose its moisture. In this way the high Andes in Chile receive the moisture that fails to precipitate on the coast.

## Audiovisual Materials

There is an abundance of visual materials generally related to the content of this chapter, but by and large they tend to be quite elementary. We regret that the situation noted in 1963 still exists: a great need for new materials pitched on the senior high school level, materials that feature biological principles and that avoid anthropomorphism, teleology, and moralizing. The items cited below are among the better ones now available.

**Phonograph records:** *Sounds of the South American Rain Forest.* Folkways Records. Produced for the American Museum of Natural History, this record provides sounds of weather, of mammals, and of birds.

*Prairie Spring.* Houghton Mifflin Co. Principally bird voices of the Canadian prairie.

*Sounds of the American Southwest.* Folkways Records. Sounds of weather, insects, reptiles, birds, and mammals of the desert.

*A Day in Algonquin Park.* Houghton Mifflin Co. Birds, animals, and wilderness sounds in taiga.

**Filmstrips:** *The World We Live In: The Tundra.* LIFE Filmstrips. Color. Excellent pictures, a good organization, some attention to ecological principles—and an unfortunate abundance of anthropomorphism and teleology.

*The World We Live In: The Woods of Home.* LIFE Filmstrips. The title refers to middle-latitude deciduous forest. See comments for the filmstrip above.

*The World We Live In: The Rain Forest.* LIFE Filmstrips. Concentrates on the tropical rain forest of South America. See comments for first filmstrip.

**Slides:** Perhaps the best method of illustrating this chapter—at least for the teacher with a good background—is with slides. These can be placed in any desired sequence, and the "captions" can be supplied by the teacher—largely in the form of questions directed to the students. The quantity of good ecological slides is small compared with the number of taxonomic ones, but all of the following suppliers have ecological lists: CCM: General Biological, Inc., 8200 S. Hoyne Ave., Chicago, Ill. 60620; Carolina Biological Supply Co., Burlington, N.C. 27216; and Ward's Natural Science Establishment, P.O. Box 1712, Rochester 3, N.Y. (or Ward's of California, P.O. Box 1749, Monterey, Calif.).

**Motion-picture films:** *Prairies and Deciduous Forests.* BSCS Inquiry Film Loop. (Rand McNally #11–2978, 1968). This film provides an opportunity to analyze the factors determining distribution of two large biomes.

*Water and Desert Plants.* BSCS Inquiry Film Loop. (Rand McNally #11–2979, 1968). Through discussion the students can use the data in this film to discover some of the anatomical and physiological adaptations to the desert biome.

*Water and Desert Animals.* BSCS Inquiry Film Loop. (Rand McNally #11–2967, 1968). The physiological adaptations and responses of desert animals to the limiting factor of water can be easily observed in this film.

*Mountain Trees—An Ecological Study.* BSCS Inquiry Film Loop. (Rand McNally #11–2970, 1968). An excellent opportunity for students to apply their knowledge of ecological principles to the problems of plant distribution.

*High Arctic: Life on the Land.* Encyclopaedia Britannica Films. 16 mm. Color. 22 min. A film on a specific location in the tundra—Queen Elizabeth Islands, Canada.

*The Spruce Bog.* National Film Board of Canada. 16 mm. Color. 20 min. Primarily concerned with pond succession, but provides a good view of the taiga. However, it is short on ecological principles.

*The Boreal Forest.* International Film Bureau. 16 mm. Color. 19 min. Community structure in the taiga is based on an analysis of the vegetation. This is followed by a portrayal of insects, birds, and mammals, with particular reference to food sources.

*The Prairie.* International Film Bureau. 16 mm. Color. 18 min. The community structure of the middle-latitude grasslands of North America is shown (with special reference to the short-grass plains). This and the preceding film include natural sounds of the biome on the sound track.

*Distribution of Plants and Animals.* Encyclopaedia Britannica Films. 16 mm. Color. 16 min. The various factors that influence the distribution and survival of selected organisms in a given geographic area are discussed.

*The Temperate Deciduous Forest.* Encyclopaedia Britannica Films. 16 mm. Color. 17 min. The annual cycle of changes in the middle-latitude deciduous forest of North America is well depicted.

*The Desert.* Encyclopaedia Britannica Films. 16 mm. Color. 22 min. Adaptive mechanisms rather than community relationships are featured in this film about deserts in general.

*The Tropical Rain Forest.* Encyclopaedia Britannica Films. 16 mm. Color. 17 min. A good integration of abiotic and biotic factors in this biome.

## Teacher's References

ALLEN, D. L. *The Life of the Prairies and Plains.* New York: McGraw-Hill Book Co., Inc., 1967. (Well-illustrated book written on the high school level.)

AUBERT DE LA RUE, E., F. BOURLIERE, and J. P. HARRAY. *The Tropics.* New York: Alfred A. Knopf, Inc., 1957. (Magnificently illustrated.)

BATES, M. *Animal Worlds.* New York: Random House, Inc., 1963. (Reviews the zoological aspects of both terrestrial and aquatic biomes, with a good selection of pictures.)

———. *Where Winter Never Comes.* New York: Charles Scribner's Sons, 1952. (Mostly about the tropical rain forest. Describes the conditions of life in the tropics and explores man's place there.

BRAUN, E. L. *Deciduous Forests of Eastern North America.* New York: The Blakiston Co., 1950. (Does not describe an entire biome; devoted exclusively to macroscopic vegetation; covers the subject excellently.)

BROOKS, M. *The Life of the Mountains.* New York: McGraw-Hill Book Co., Inc., 1967. (Contains an abundance of illustrations but also an excellent text stressing ecological principles.)

BURNS, W. A. (ed.). *The Natural History of the Southwest.* New York: Franklin Watts, Inc., 1960.

CAIN, S. A. *Foundations of Plant Geography.* New York: Harper & Brothers, 1944. (Rather old, but it illustrates well the synthetic nature of biogeographical study.)

CLEMENTS, F. E., and V. E. SHELFORD. *Bioecology.* New York: John Wiley and Sons, Inc., 1939. (Now rather old, but still a good reference for descriptions of biomes in North America.)

DARLINGTON, P. J. *Zoogeography.* New York: John Wiley & Sons, Inc., 1957. (The standard current American reference, concerned principally with terrestrial vertebrates.)

FARB, P. *The Forest.* New York: Time, Inc., Book Division, 1961. (Treats forests in general — as distinguished from grasslands, deserts, and tundra — and does not describe biomes specifically. Animals enter the picture only incidentally. Some good illustrations.)

GEORGE, W. B. *Animal Geography.* London: William Heinemann, Ltd., 1962. (More recent than Darlington.)

GOOD, R. D. *The Geography of the Flowering Plants.* London: Longmans, Green & Co., Ltd., 1953. (As the vertebrates have been the principal, though by no means the exclusive, source of evidence for zoogeographers, so the angiosperms have been for phytogeographers. This is a standard reference.)

RICHARDS, P. W. *The Tropical Rain Forest.* London: Cambridge University Press, 1955. (An excellent description of the tropical rain-forest biome by a perceptive naturalist.)

RUNCORN, S. K. (ed.). *Continental Drift.* New York: Academic Press, Inc., 1962. (The geological theory of continental drift has a direct bearing on biogeography. Useful background for Problem 7.)

SUTTON, A., and M. SUTTON. *The Life of the Desert.* New York: McGraw-Hill Book Co., Inc., 1967. (Well-illustrated account stressing some important ecological principles.)

THOMAS, W. L. (ed.). *Man's Role in Changing the Face of the Earth.* Chicago: University of Chicago Press, 1956. (Fine review: historical, contemporary, projective.)

WEAVER, J. E. *North American Prairie.* Lincoln, Neb.: Johnsen Publishing Co., 1954. (For a long time this summary of results from a lifetime of study will be a source of reference and inspiration.)

# 9

# Patterns
# of Life
# in the
# Water

## MAJOR IDEAS

1. Aquatic environments encompass almost three-fourths of the total biosphere — and in some past geological periods the proportion was even greater.

2. Current, translucency, turnover, and chemical characteristics are the most important abiotic factors in the classification of inland-water ecosystems.

3. In aquatic communities the greatest proportion of food production is accomplished by microscopic plants and protists. The diversity and abundance of aquatic consumers are indications of the vast amounts of energy made available by the aquatic-producer system.

4. The chemical characteristics of the sea are to a considerable degree the result of the activities of marine organisms, just as the chemical characteristics of the atmosphere are to some extent the result of the activities of terrestrial organisms.

5. Recent explorations have revealed that life occurs even on the abyssal floor of the oceans.

6. Man has influenced inland-water ecosystems almost as much as he has influenced the surface of the land. However, except for slight disturbance of the margin, man has as yet had little effect upon the seas. Indeed, the ocean depths are a frontier of exploration at least as rich in possibilities as the depths of solar space.

## PLANNING AHEAD

If you have not yet duplicated grids for Investigation 10.1, do this at once.

For Investigation 11.1 you will need a few living frogs. If you do not keep frogs over winter in your laboratory, better order some now. The same investigation (and also Investigation 12.5) requires elodea. This should be always available in your classroom aquarium; if it is not, order it, also. Elodea, however, is frequently obtainable locally from pet shops and even variety stores. If you intend to demonstrate slime molds, order sclerotia.

The nonliving materials and the equipment required by the investigations in Chapters 11 and 12 are probably to be found in most school laboratories. However, it would be well to check through the lists now. Note particularly: cellulose tubing and Tes-tape (Investigation 11.2); Carnoy's fluid, aceto-orcein solution, slides of onion-root tip (Investigation 11.3); pea seeds, glass beads, Ascarite, volumeters (Investigation 12.1); vacuum bottles (Investigation 12.3); acetone, petroleum ether (Investigation 12.4).

## GUIDELINES

In Chapter 8 principles of tolerance, limiting factors, biogeography, biomes (and man's influence on them), are treated in the context of terrestrial life. These principles are further exemplified in Chapter 9. Additional concepts in Chapter 9 are those pertaining specifically to aquatic life. These involve only a few new terms, however, so the vocabulary load is quite light.

It is undeniable that aquatic biology is important, but in view of the overlap of concepts in Chapters 8 and 9, the latter may be considered for omission. But even if a class skips it, some students who have interests in aquatic biology or who complete their work rapidly might undertake it. Such individual or small-group efforts might include the setting up of Investigation 9.1 as a demonstration for a class. Further, it may be desirable to have all students read "The Ocean Environment" (pages 323–325)

when the subject of the origin of life arises in Chapter 10.

Some teachers do not want to omit Chapter 9 but find that in the regular sequence of chapters it comes at a season inconvenient for fieldwork. If this problem arises, the chapter may be shifted to the spring semester. Quite logically it may be inserted as an interlude between Sections Five and Six, where it can serve as a summary experience for the whole course up to this point. A field trip can focus the students' attention once again upon the individual organism and its adaptations, upon species populations, and upon the interaction of both with environment. A study of man's involvement with aquatic ecosystems serves as a bridge to Section Six. If the chapter is studied any time after Section Four has been completed, it is possible to introduce many ideas that are unsuitable earlier in the year — for example, differences between freshwater and saltwater environments in conditions for water diffusion.

The chapter easily divides into three assignments: pages 305–313 (guide questions 1–4), 314–322 (guide questions 5–10), and 322–334 (guide questions 12–16).

## TEACHING NOTES

### INLAND WATERS (in part)

(pp. 306–312)

**p. 306:** If the ideal introduction to this chapter—a field trip—is impossible, a good beginning is to show slides illustrating the description of a pond. A dramatic reading of the text may accompany the slides.

**pp. 307–312:** Remind students to use Section Two and Appendix II. Practically all organisms mentioned in the pond description are illustrated somewhere in the student's book.

**p. 310, Fig. 9 · 3:** Students should be able to recognize these as arthropods.

**p. 313, Fig. 9 · 8:** This is an integral part of the consideration of pond ecology. Do not allow it to be overlooked.

## INVESTIGATION 9.1

### SUCCESSION IN A FRESHWATER ECOSYSTEM (pp. 312–314)

This investigation, which may be carried on during the winter months, allows some insight into freshwater biology without a trip outside the classroom. It is particularly concerned with succession and provides means for deepening an understanding of that concept.

Spend at least half a period considering the "Introduction and Purpose" through discussion and audiovisual aids. Have the students suggest hypotheses for the two stated purposes. Then remember during the post-laboratory discussions to have the students relate their experimental data to their hypotheses.

### Materials

For wide-mouth jars use one-gallon pickle, relish, or mayonnaise jars, obtainable from the school cafeteria or from a restaurant. Clean the jars thoroughly. Rinse them a number of times to remove all traces of soap or detergent; mere traces of these kill many aquatic organisms.

Pond water may be sterilized in an autoclave, but boiling is sufficient. Rainwater may be collected and used in place of pond water. If nothing but tap water is available, condition it before using. This is done by allowing the water to stand for at least forty-eight hours in shallow glass vessels. (Large baking dishes are good.) Distilled water should, if possible, be obtained from a *glass* still; some organisms are quite sensitive to traces of metallic ions, especially copper.

### Procedure

It is desirable that the setups be replicated. But having even one setup for each class may present space problems—especially since the investigation should be continued for six weeks. If laboratory space is inadequate, selected students may set up the jars at home and bring samples of the water to the laboratory for occasional microscopic examination. The teacher must urge cau-

tion in the transportation of glass containers. If possible, use plastic ones.

Jars should not be placed in direct sunlight for more than an hour at a time, especially around noon.

### Discussion

- (1): Jar C.
- (2): Jar A.
- (3): Jar B.
- (5): Mostly from the twigs, stones, etc.
- (7): From dust in the air. Cf. Investigation 6.4.
- (8): Organisms usually do disappear, but it is difficult to generalize on causation. Logical speculation by students should be encouraged.
- (10): Succession should be most evident in Jar A.
- (11): Most rapid succession would probably occur in a "new" body of non-flowing fresh water that formed where debris from a previous body of water existed.

Additional questions for discussion: Why is pond water preferable to distilled water for this investigation? [*Sterilization kills organisms but does not remove minerals and possibly organic substances important to organisms.*] Why is distilled water used to replace water lost by evaporation? [*Since quantities replaced may differ among setups, distilled water provides the least change among setups.*] What is the source of energy in the three jars? [*Some may be in organic materials dissolved in the water, some in the debris (Jar A), some in the organisms (Jar C), but most in light.*]

### INLAND WATERS (cont.) (pp. 314–322)

**p. 315, note 1:** Salt concentration is an obvious variable. Temperature and light are others. Some students may bring up the matter of kinds of salts; both anions and cations should be considered.

**p. 315, ¶ 5:** Oceanic mixing is also brought about by the great current systems which are powered, as is atmospheric circulation, by differential interception of solar radiation. Cf. material on climates, pp. T122–T130.

**p. 315, ¶'s 4–6:** The problem of Lake Baikal and Lake Tanganyika can be treated as an invitation to inquiry before students have read the section "Lakes." They can then evaluate their hypotheses as they read.

**p. 316, note 1:** The larger and deeper the lake, the less, proportionally, can rooted, shallow-water plants contribute to the big energy budget of the ecosystem.

**p. 316, note 3:** In flowing waters un-attached or nonmotile organisms (plankters are both) are swept away.

**p. 317, Fig. 9·9:** Note the melting snow in the background.

**p. 318, note 4:** Consider the Nile Valley. Students should suggest irrigation possibilities in addition to soil building that results from annual floods.

**p. 319, ¶ 3:** You might discuss water tables and the effect of drainage on them.

**p. 319, Fig. 9·11:** The band of light rock on the left shore (obscured by shadow on the right) indicates great fluctuation of the water level in this reservoir. Rapid and irregular changes of water level in such reservoirs fatally expose shoreline aquatics to the air, while plants that invade mud flats are drowned when the level rises again.

**p. 320, Fig. 9·12:** In many farm ponds, as in this one, the development of emergent vegetation is prevented by cattle. Farmers who wish to exploit the potentialities of ponds for fish production fence their ponds or allow access for watering of stock at one point only.

**p. 320, Fig. 9·13:** Many miles of river course are compressed into this diagram.

**p. 321, ¶ 1:** Some discussion of balancing values of drainage *v.* impoundment could be encouraged, but this might better occur in connection with Chapter 20.

**p. 321, note 1:** Relate this question to the food-web concept, to the loss of energy through trophic levels (Figure 1·12, p. 22), and to the effects of overcrowding.

**p. 322, ¶ 3:** No mention of health hazards in pollution occurs because this receives adequate attention in news media. But you should be sure the students are aware of it.

## THE OCEANS (pp. 322–334)

**p. 322, Fig. 9·14:** Students may require some assistance in interpreting this graph. The percentages on the horizontal axis are cumulative.

**p. 324, Fig. 9·15:** Unlike the major constituents ($Na^+$, $Ca^{++}$, $K^+$, $Mg^{++}$, $SO_4^{--}$, $Cl^-$, and $CO_3^{--}$), the trace elements vary greatly in concentration from place to place and from time to time.

**p. 324, note 1:** Both calcium carbonate and silica are removed from the dissolved reservoir in the sea by marine organisms. Once removed, they may remain in the accumulated skeletons for long periods of geological time. Refer to Figure 1·16.

**p. 326, note 1:** The location of most fisheries is correlated with the location of oceanic areas rich in phytoplankton, the basis for food chains that lead to fish useful as food for man.

**p. 328, Fig. 9·19:** The U.S. Navy's *Sealab* project has shown that man can live and work on the continental shelf at depths of from 60 to 120 meters. A film concerning the *Sealab* project is available from the navy.

**p. 329, note 1:** Gases within the bodies of these fishes are adjusted to the great external pressure of the ocean depths. When pressure is reduced as such fishes are hauled to the surface, the pressure of the internal gases is no longer balanced from without; the gases expand and may rupture membranes within the fish.

**p. 330, ¶ 1:** Some further comparison of the ecology of caves and ocean depths should be undertaken in class discussions.

**p. 330, Fig. 9·23:** This photograph merely calls attention to the existence of estuarine biology. If your school is near an estuary, you may wish to pursue the topic further. A good reference is Lauff, G. H. (ed.), *Estuaries.* Publication 83, American Association for the Advancement of Science. Washington, D.C., 1967.

**p. 331, note 3:** Except for phytoplankton, plants cling by roots (or by holdfasts in the larger algae), and so they require a stable substrate. Thus shifting sands—either above high tide (on dunes) or below—have few plants.

## INVESTIGATION 9.2

### EFFECTS OF SALINITY ON AQUATIC ORGANISMS (pp. 334–335)

This investigation is concerned with the idea of tolerance, which was discussed in Chapter 8. Tolerance to variations in concentration of dissolved substances is of basic importance to all aquatic organisms. In a more general view, the investigation is concerned with osmoregulation. When the concept of diffusion is encountered in Chapter 11, reference to the observations in this investigation will help to make the abstract molecular process more vivid.

Devote some time to a pre-laboratory discussion. Be sure that each student has developed a hypothesis and understands how to use it in directing his experimental procedure.

### Procedure

Each pair of students should test the effects of all concentrations of sodium chloride on a particular organism. Many different aquatic organisms may be used. The following are suggested largely on the basis of availability:

| | |
|---|---|
| *Amoeba* | *Artemia* (brine shrimp) |
| *Vorticella* | *Spirogyra* or other filamentous algae |
| *Euglena* | *Daphnia* or *Cyclops* |
| *Hydra* | rotifers |

If students have forgotten the method for drawing a liquid beneath a cover slip, refer them to Figure 1·9.

You can provide a basis for comparison by having all students observe the effect of a 5% salt solution on elodea cells. The "shrinking" of the cytoplast away from the wall is very dramatic and easily observed.

- (1): Several assumptions could be suggested, but the principal one is that the technique actually replaces the salt solution with relatively salt-free water. This is not likely on a single try; the salt must be flushed out with several applications of culture water.

### Discussion

All the questions asked in this investigation depend upon the observations made during the Procedure. A great deal of variation is to be expected. Students should always be kept aware of the sources of observational variation, and this investigation is a good point at which to renew this concern. In addition, there are variations in the ways that students carry out the Procedure—especially with respect to timing—and variations in tolerance among different individual organisms. For microscopic freshwater organisms, individual variation may be greater than variation between species. However, if *Artemia* is used, it should provide marked contrast to most other species in its ability to tolerate even a 5% salt solution.

- (4): Failure to recover may be merely the result of failure to extend the period of observation far enough to note recovery.

- (5): Of the organisms listed above, *Artemia* is most tolerant to high salt concentration.

### For Further Investigation

If marine species are used, it is appropriate to vary the concentrations *downward* from about 3.5%.

GUIDE QUESTIONS (p. 336)

11. A student should state the type of small organism he is referring to when answering this question. A general statement covering all small organisms is hardly possible.

PROBLEMS (pp. 336–337)

1. Students should compare such things as origin, size, depth, organisms, food webs, stage of succession.

2. Cloudiness, by reducing intensity of radiant energy, decreases photosynthesis. But windy conditions circulate phytoplankton, gases, and nutrients; this increases photosynthesis because more phytoplankton is exposed to sunlight, the nutrient supply near the surface is augmented, and a rough water surface reduces reflection of light.

3. When a pond with a favorable food supply is stocked with a single species of fish, such as bluegills, rapid reproduction results in a dense population (cf. Investigation 2.1); but because of intraspecific competition, individuals are stunted. If at least one prey-predator combination is included, the predator tends to consume excessive prey offspring, and the average size of remaining fish increases.

4. Acid water is associated with bogs, swamps, and many streams emptying such places. Streams draining areas having abandoned coal mines (e.g., in Pennsylvania) are often intensely acid. In waters of low pH, plankton, bottom organisms, and fish are usually scarce.

Alkaline water is characteristic of areas having limestone or marl substrates. Alkaline waters generally have a greater diversity of species and greater productivity. But desert alkali lakes such as Pyramid Lake, Nevada, have a very high pH and few animal species. Most large lakes vary in pH between 6.0 and 9.0, but extreme values of 1.7 and 12.0 have been observed.

5. Answers to these questions are all related to the idea that the density of water is greater than that of air. (a) Resistance in water is greater than in air and increases at a greater rate with increased rate of movement. (b), (c) Birds that catch their food by pursuit in air correspond to fish that catch their food by pursuit in water. In both, streamlining is associated with predation niches. (d) Plankton organisms, being drifters, encounter no resistance in moving. (e) More energy must be expended to walk in water due to the increased resistance, but less energy is required to support the body because of greater buoyancy of water than air.

6. The essence of the matter is: Estuaries contain a gradient from salt water to brackish water to fresh water. This fluctuates back and forth with the tides. Hence organisms must have wide tolerances for salinity. See Reid (reference: p. T141) for a full discussion that your good readers can use.

7. (a) Among nations Japan has perhaps made the greatest use of marine resources. (b) Food from the sea includes whales, fish, crustaceans (shrimps, lobsters), mollusks (scallops, squid, octopuses, snails, clams, oysters), and the larger algae ("seaweeds"). (c) It is difficult to harvest marine producers, for they are mostly microscopic, planktonic forms. (d) Some marine biologists believe that man is even now harvesting nearly the maximum that can be obtained on sustained yield from the sea. The supply of minerals such as nitrates and phosphates appears to limit production in much of the sea. (e) By the time we get organisms in edible sizes, the materials have gone through several food levels with great loss of energy (Figure 1·12).

8. Here the focus is upon large areas of the seas, such as the Sargasso Sea, which are deficient in nitrates and phosphates and therefore produce very little. This is in contrast to areas with upwelling

currents (such as the western coasts of North and South America), which circulate minerals from the depths to the surface, and to areas of rather shallow waters near the mouths of streams that contribute runoff minerals from the land. In those areas, marine fisheries are extensive, and the fishing fleets of many nations may congregate there.

9. Pollution of the seas can occur through dumping of garbage, oil (cf. Figure 20·21), and radioactive wastes. The major argument for the use of seas as dumping grounds is that of dilution, but care must be taken with the effects of currents, stagnation in basins, and ecological concentration of materials in food webs.

## ADDITIONAL PROBLEMS

1. Measurements of oxygen in a Wisconsin lake produced the following data:

| DEPTH (IN METERS) | OXYGEN (CC PER LITER) | | |
|---|---|---|---|
| | *Aug. 24* | *Oct. 11* | *Nov. 10* |
| 0 | 5.5 | 4.8 | 6.0 |
| 5 | 5.3 | 4.3 | 6.0 |
| 10 | 0 | 4.3 | 5.2 |
| 15 | 0 | 4.8 | 4.0 |
| 20 | 0 | 5.0 | 2.0 |

Write a short paragraph that describes the major principle illustrated by these data. How does this phenomenon influence mineral cycling? Characterize the environmental demands placed on organisms living at 20 meters. Where should the proportion of saprovores be greatest? Producers? Would the measurements of oxygen in April be most like those of August, October, or November? [*The data illustrate seasonal water turnover in middle-latitude lakes. Turnover tends to circulate minerals as well as oxygen. Any organism living permanently at a 20-m depth must be a facultative anaerobe, and many of these are saprovores. Producers must be at depths to which light sufficient for photosynthesis can penetrate. In April the spring turnover produces oxygen distribution similar to that of early fall.*]

2. At a meeting of limnologists in the summer of 1962, Dr. Ruth Patrick of the Philadelphia Academy of Natural Sciences reported that she had found that many of the microscopic organisms in the small streams of tropical South America were the same as those in the small streams of middle-latitude North America. How can this be explained? [*Small aquatic organisms in their dormant stages are easily transported from one body of water to another in mud dried on the feet and plumage of water and marsh birds. Also, many dormant microscopic organisms are blown through the air on dust particles when temporary bodies of water dry up.*]

3. How does temperature affect the species composition of a stream? [*See Reid (reference: p. T141).*]

4. Current is one of the most important limiting factors in a stream ecosystem. Stream organisms must be adapted for maintaining a constant position. Cite at least five specific organisms showing five different adaptations to stream currents. [*See Reid and Morgan (references: p. T141).*]

5. Why does the introduction of small quantities of organic wastes into bodies of water sometimes increase the size and productivity of the animal populations? Why is this not a good argument for putting wastes into streams? [*Organic wastes provide food for saprovores and nutrients for photosynthetic organisms, but in large quantities they upset the stream ecosystem by encouraging the growth of large populations of such organisms. Often the result is conditions undesirable from a human viewpoint, such as the production of undesirable odors and the decrease of fish populations.*]

6. Why do lake organisms sink to the bottom when they die? How would a lake ecosystem be changed if this sinking did not occur? [*In general, organic matter is slightly more dense than water. The second part of the problem is a matter for student imagination.*]

7. How does the amount of nitrogen fixation in aquatic ecosystems compare with the amount of nitrogen fixed on land? [*This problem can test the student's research and reasoning abilities. Measurements of nitrogen fixation are many, but no overall estimates exist.*]

T 140

PATTERNS IN THE BIOSPHERE

## SUPPLEMENTARY MATERIALS

### Audiovisual Materials

**Phonograph record:** *Sounds of Sea Animals.* Folkway Records, FX6125. Sounds made by crustaceans, by various fishes, and especially by porpoises. Too long, but, used in part, this is a good interest-arouser.

**Filmstrips:** *Oceanography: Understanding Our Deep Frontier.* Prepared under the auspices of the Committee on Oceanography, National Academy of Sciences. Encyclopaedia Britannica Educational Corp., 1966, EB 6416 – nine filmstrips in color (average, 70 frames each) and five phonodiscs; 12 in., 33 rpm. Includes nine booklets to accompany the filmstrips. This set contains the following titles: *Physical Oceanography; Geological Oceanography; Chemical Oceanography; Biological Oceanography; Marine Resources; Air-Sea Interaction; Ocean Engineering; Careers in Oceanography; An Introduction to Oceanography.* Probably the finest set of materials on oceanography available. All frames are masterfully done artwork.

*The Miracle of the Sea.* ("The World We Live In," Part II). Color. New York: LIFE Filmstrips, 1954. Contains little about living things, but is useful for establishing the dimensions of the seas and the physical processes that are important factors in the abiotic environment of marine organisms.

*Creatures of the Sea.* ("The World We Live In," Part VII). Color. New York: LIFE Filmstrips, 1955. Excellent photographs and better-than-average paintings.

*The Coral Reef.* ("The World We Live In," Part VIII). Color. New York: LIFE Filmstrips, 1955. Contains a good collection of photographs.

*Animal and Plant Communities: the Pond.* (Interdependence of Living Things Series). Color. New York: McGraw-Hill Book Co., Inc., 1961. Descriptive rather than analytical. Good pictures. Text fairly accurate and not marred by excessive teleology.

**Motion-picture films:** *The Intertidal Region.* BSCS Inquiry Film Loop. (Rand McNally #11–2972, 1968.) The concept of

zonation is presented and the problem of zonation on various substrates is explored.

*Life in the Intertidal Region.* BSCS Inquiry Film Loop. (Rand McNally #11–2974, 1968.) Primarily concerned with the structural, physiological, and behavioral adaptations to the intertidal region. Students have an opportunity to evaluate a controlled experiment dealing with a behavioral adaptation.

*Predation and Protection in the Ocean.* BSCS Inquiry Film Loop. (Rand McNally #11–2982, 1968.) An investigation into the evolutionary significance of various adaptations to specific niches.

*The Pond.* International Film Bureau. 16 mm. Color. 20 min. Parallels the pond description in the student's book.

*The Stream.* International Film Bureau. 16 mm. Color. 15 min. An excellent visualization of the "Flowing Waters" section of the student's book.

*Life in the Ocean.* Film Associates of California. 16 mm. Color. 13 min. Contains little about oceanographic principles, but its beautiful photography will give students far from the sea some close aquaintance with marine animals—and simultaneously it offers a chance to review some animal phyla.

*The Sea.* Encyclopaedia Britannica Films. 16 mm. Color. 26 min. Interrelationships among marine organisms are shown against the background of conditions in the environment.

*Plankton and the Open Sea.* Encyclopaedia Britannica Films. 16 mm. Color. 19 min. Uses photomicrography to show many plankton organisms. Also develops the importance of plankton in marine food chains.

*World in a Marsh.* National Film Board of Canada. 16 mm. Color. 22 min. Ecological relationships in a marsh. The organisms are chiefly those of eastern North America.

*Survival in the Sea.* University of Indiana Audiovisual Center. 16 mm. Color. This is a series of four films, 30 min. each: (1) *Life Cycle of the Sea*—a general survey of marine ecology; the basic film in the series. (2) *Life on the Coral Reef*—contains some fine underwater photography. (3) *On the Rocks*— stresses organisms that are adapted to life on rocky bottoms and shores. (4) *Where Land and Water Meet*— habitats along the sea's margins.

## Teacher's References

BENNETT, G. W. *Management of Artificial Lakes and Ponds.* New York: Reinhold Publishing Corp., 1962. (Excellent for relating principles of aquatic ecology to the practical techniques of managing impoundments for fish production.)

BERRILL, N. J. *The Living Tide.* New York: Fawcett World Library, 1964. (Weaves ecological principles into clear description of seashore life.)

FREY, D. G. (ed.). *Limnology in North America.* Madison: University of Wisconsin Press, 1963. (Thirty-two contributors survey the limnology of the continent by regions.)

HARDY, A. C. *The Open Sea; Its Natural History.* Part I, "The World of Plankton." Boston: Houghton Mifflin Co., 1957. (This British book beautifully describes the life and environment of plankton.)

MORGAN, A. H. *Field Book of Ponds and Streams.* New York: G. P. Putnam's Sons, 1930. (Intended as a field guide for identification of organisms, but contains a great deal of general information on freshwater life.)

NEEDHAM, J. G., and P. R. NEEDHAM. *A Guide to the Study of Freshwater Biology.* 5th ed. San Francisco: Holden Day, Inc., 1962. (Small but of great value to the teacher — especially when he is called upon to guide students who have a special interest in aquatic biology.)

POPHAM, E. J. *Some Aspects of Life in Fresh Water.* 2nd ed. Cambridge, Mass.: Harvard University Press, 1961. (A good, readable introduction for the teacher. Also good for the better student.)

REID, G. K. *Ecology of Inland Waters and Estuaries.* New York: Reinhold Publishing Corp., 1961. (Deserves a place in in this list for its attention to estuaries, much neglected bodies of water that present the reader with some interesting special problems.)

RICKETTS, E. F., and J. CALVIN. *Between Pacific Tides.* 3rd ed., rev. by J. W. HEDGPETH. Stanford University Press, 1962.

SEARS, M. (ed.). *Oceanography.* Washington, D.C.: American Association for the Advancement of Science, 1961 — Publication No. 67. (A symposium volume that covers the whole range of the subject and provides one of the best available views of the purposes, requirements, and opportunities of the discipline.)

SOUTHARD, A. J. *Life on the Seashore.* Cambridge, Mass.: Harvard University Press, 1965. (Not a guidebook, but a handbook of procedures for studying what goes on at the seashore.)

SVERDRUP, H. U., M. W. JOHNSON, and R. H. FLEMING. *The Oceans; Their Physics, Chemistry, and General Biology.* Englewood Cliffs, N. J.: Prentice-Hall, Inc., 1942. (Now quite old, but still a mine of information.)

# 10

# Patterns
# of Life
# in the
# Past

## MAJOR IDEAS

1. Fossils are the tangible evidence for the existence of organisms in the past.

2. From this evidence paleontologists have been able to piece together a sketchy history of life on earth. But this history is more than a mere recital of names and descriptions of extinct organisms; it includes reconstructions of biotic communities, of climates, and even of whole ecosystems.

3. To reconstruct the past from the scattered and fragmentary fossil evidence, paleontologists begin with a thorough knowledge of the organisms and ecosystems of the present. Then, by inference and logical analysis, they extrapolate this knowledge into the past—guided by the fossils. "The present is the key to the past."

4. Though man's understanding of the history of the earth is, and probably always will be, meager, it increases as more fossils are discovered. And almost every year discoveries push the antiquity of life on earth farther back in time.

5. In successive layers of rock, the presence of certain fossils and the absence of others enable paleontologists to construct a geological time sequence. In recent years, measurements of the products of radioactive decay have helped to tie geological time more firmly to an absolute time scale.

6. While it seems likely that life on this planet originated in the primordial oceans, paleontologists have no direct evidence of how it originated. Some biologists have been willing to speculate about the origin of complex carbon compounds that could have been biochemical forerunners of simple living systems, and recent laboratory experimentation has lent support to some of these speculations.

7. The fossil record indicates that throughout the biological history of the earth, as environments changed, once-abundant kinds of organisms became extinct and new kinds of organisms appeared. On the other hand, in ecosystems which have shown little change through time (certain marine situations, for example), many organisms have shown great stability.

8. The fossil record indicates that through time many groups of related organisms have exhibited the phenomenon of adaptive radiation (the occupation of diverse niches by members of a taxonomic group) as well as adaptive convergence (the pursuit of a particular way of life by unrelated organisms).

9. The fossil record not only indicates the past distribution of organisms but also helps to explain present distribution. "The past sheds light upon the present."

## PLANNING AHEAD

Because time devoted to Chapter 10 should be short, all preparations for Chapter 11 should be quickly completed and those required for Chapter 12 should be pushed forward. See advice on p. T134. In addition, if you plan to use the demonstrations in Chapter 11, prepare the mitosis models and start the slime-mold cultures (pp. T165–167).

Have you decided what plant material to use in Investigation 13.1? It is probably now too late to start tomato plants from seed. Although not ideal, geranium plants can be used, and they are easy to obtain. You need rather long, unbranched stems. Plants grown on window ledges in winter naturally acquire this "leggy" form. Evergreen woody plants are unsuitable, but in the South some deciduous plants may already have leafed out when you arrive at Chapter 13.

Geranium or coleus may be used for Investigation 13.2. You will need a number of potted specimens. If you are not growing these plants routinely in your laboratory or greenhouse, obtain them several weeks before they are needed so that they may adjust to the laboratory environment.

## GUIDELINES

Telling the story of our present knowledge of the past requires considerable space, and the mere recounting of facts is not enough in a course that attempts to stress the investigative nature of biology. But the very nature of paleontological research makes difficult student laboratory investigations of a paleontological type. An attempt must be made to accomplish, by means of the textbook, some goals that might preferably be accomplished in investigations.

Early in the study of Chapter 10, students should have some firsthand experience with fossils. If the school is near good fossil-bearing strata, this is preeminently an occasion for a field trip; at least, you can lead a Saturday expedition of volunteers. Check the references for Problem No. 1 (p. T149) for fossil localities near you. But regardless of your school's location, fossils should be in the classroom. The fossil collector is a breed of hobbyist that may occur anywhere, and donations from one can usually be arranged. In your own journeyings, be alert to opportunities for acquiring specimens. Finally, there are the biological supply companies, among which Ward's Natural Science Establishment, Inc. (P.O. Box 1712, Rochester, New York 14603, or P.O. Box 1749, Monterey, California 93940) is particularly noted for fossils.

Chapter 10 logically breaks into three sections: "Evidence of the Past" (the nature of fossils and the geological record); "The History of Life" (the origin of life, antiquity of life, and descriptions of paleoecosystems during Cambrian, Carboniferous, Triassic, and Eocene times); and "The Work of the Paleontologist" (studying the fossil evidence, interpreting the evidence, with some concepts which have developed out of this work). The first two sections, however, can be handled as one reading assignment (pp. 339–358, guide questions 1–13) and the third as a second assignment (pp. 358–371, guide questions 14–20). The one investigation is in the latter section. In this chapter — as in Chapters 8 and 9 — much stress needs to be placed upon illustrations.

Just as we cannot bodily transport students to distant biomes, so we cannot take them to the distant past. But vivid illustration can partially overcome the difficulty. There is, however, a complicating factor in illustrating Chapter 10, a factor often overlooked but crucial to the teaching of biology as a science. When we present a photograph of a scene in a distant biome, we are presenting evidence subject only to a *narrow* margin of error imposed by the limitations of photography. But when we present a painting of a scene in the distant past, we are presenting an artifact subject to myriad errors in trans-

lation from fossil evidence. Students must realize this. You yourself must keep in mind that in general the more vivid the portrayal of a scene from the geological past, the further the artist has probably departed from the strict fossil evidence.

Mindful of the caution in the last paragraph, the authors have tried to balance illustrations showing restorations with illustrations of the fossils themselves. Likewise an attempt has been made to distinguish between statements that are facts concerning the occurrence of fossils and statements that are interpretations of such occurrences. You are urged to carry through and strengthen this distinction during class discussions.

Remind students to frequently refer to Section Two and to Appendix II. Neither of these treats extinct groups of organisms, but the task of fitting extinct groups into the assemblage of modern organisms is instructive. And, of course, most of the groups on the higher levels of classification have had long histories, so that mention of them recurs frequently in Chapter 10. But perhaps the chief reason for referring students to Appendix II is to give you an opportunity to show how the arrangement of taxonomic groups reflects the attempts of taxonomists to portray phylogeny — a matter briefly discussed at the end of Chapter 4 in the text. And Chapter 10 is, of course, an exhibit of one major sector of the evidence for evolution.

Chapter 10 also provides evidence for the field of biogeography. In the 1963 edition, an entire chapter was devoted to biogeography. In this edition, biogeographical topics have been dispersed throughout the textbook where pertinent. And thus Chapter 10 ends with a brief discussion of "light on the present from the past."

## TEACHING NOTES

### EVIDENCE OF THE PAST
(pp. 339–345)

**p. 340, ¶ 2:** Not all objects that resemble organisms and that may be dug from the earth are fossils. Some are mere chance resemblances. Often it takes an expert to distinguish true fossils.

**p. 342, ¶ 3:** For examples of such "indications," refer to Figure 10 · 8 (fossil casts or tubes made by wormlike organisms) and Figure 10 · 15 (fossil footprints left by a dinosaur).

**pp. 343–345:** For methods of dating, see *The Biology Teacher's Handbook* (reference: see p. T35), Chapter 11.

**p. 344, Fig. 10 · 4:** The absolute time scale in the right-hand column is recorded in figures that have been widely published. It is perhaps too much to say that they are generally accepted. The student can no doubt find others in various reference works. And as more dating is done by means of radioactive isotopes, still other figures will come into use.

**p. 344, Fig. 10 · 5:** The dark gorge at the canyon bottom (*right foreground*) in which the Colorado River lies (out of sight) is cut into pre-Cambrian schist and granite, while the rimrock is Permian in age and sedimentary in nature. Like many "geological books," this one has many missing pages, including the middle of the Paleozoic (Ordovician, Silurian, and most of the Devonian) and everything more recent than Permian. Thus, from the standpoint of life in the past, Grand Canyon rocks in this figure do not represent the "Age of Reptiles" or the "Age of Mammals." Students might guess that the "missing pages" either were not deposited or have been eroded away.

## THE HISTORY OF LIFE
(pp. 345–358)

**p. 346, ¶ 1:** Oparin's *The Origin of Life* is available in paperback (complete reference: see p. T151).

**p. 346, ¶ 3:** For amino acids refer students to p. 424.

**p. 347, ¶ 1:** Research on the synthesis of complex organic molecules is continuing. Late in 1967 Arthur Kornberg and Mehran Goulian, of the Stanford University Medical School, were successful in synthesizing biologically active molecules of DNA. This DNA, made up of some 5500 nucleotides, represented the core of a bacterial virus (X174) which normally occurs within *Escherichia coli*. It exhibited biological activities, including the abilities to infect and replicate. At this point the student is probably not in a position to appreciate all this, but you may want to refer to it later during work on Chapter 12 or Chapter 17.

**p. 348, note 1:** The fossil evidence supports Oparin's idea that consumers preceded producers. An abundance of free organic molecules (synthesized by the same processes which resulted in the earliest organisms themselves) may well have been a source of energy for such consumers. Presumably, by the time this energy source became inadequate, producers were evolving. Of course, some early organisms may have been chemotrophic, as the iron and sulfur bacteria are today.

**p. 350, ¶ 3:** The diversification of the trilobites is a fine early example of adaptive radiation, discussed on pp. 368–369.

**p. 351, Fig. 10 · 11:** The large shovel-nosed "fish" in the foreground is an ostracoderm, a distant relative of the modern chordate class Agnatha, characterized by having neither paired appendages nor jaws. In the upper-right background the organism that has many evident appendages is a eurypterid, an ancestor of the modern horseshoe crab (an arthropod). The finned "fish" in the middle background (a placoderm) is an extinct distant relative of modern sharks. The palmlike stalked organisms on the left are crinoids, relatives of starfish, while at their base are spiny sea urchins, also related to starfish. Trilobites, now extinct, occur in the middle foreground, while in the right foreground is a brittle star, a member of a group related to starfish and still in existence today. Above the brittle star are brachiopods, which look superficially like clams but are in a quite different phylum. Several hundred species of brachiopods still exist in the oceans today, but this is a small number in comparison with the thirty thousand or more that occurred in the past.

**p. 352, Fig. 10 · 12:** This map may be overlooked by many students. However, you may find it useful for relating past geography to present. Consider, too, the question: On what kind of evidence is such a map based? The geological evidence of evolution in land masses led Darwin's thinking toward the idea of organic evolution. For a number of maps showing past geography, see the book by Simak (reference: see p. T152).

**p. 353, note 1:** If decay is rapid, saprovores reduce organic matter to $H_2O$ and $CO_2$. Slow decay is likely to occur under anaerobic conditions.

**p. 354, Fig. 10 · 15:** These tracks were made by a bipedal dinosaur.

**p. 355, Fig. 10 · 16:** The crocodile-like animal on the left is actually a phytosaur (the name means "plant lizard" but is incorrect because the reptile was a carnivore). This "false crocodile" was a primitive thecodont reptile in a group that became extinct, though very distant relatives eventually gave rise to modern crocodiles (see Figure 10 · 31). To a degree, the similarity of crocodiles and false crocodiles is an example of adaptive convergence (pp. 369–370), in which two different taxonomic groups exhibit similar characteristics and occupy similar niches. The large organism in the water is one of the most primitive amphibians (*Eupelor*); in the far background on the right are two dinosaurs, descendants of thecodont stock. A different type of thecodont is in the background behind *Phytosaurus*, and still another is standing on its hind legs in the right foreground beside the pond. The thecodont group exhibited adaptive radiation (pp. 368–369), giving rise to phytosaurs, crocodiles, reptiles with wings, and several types of dinosaurs (again see Figure 10 · 31). Vegetation along the shore is made up of ancestors of our modern horsetails or scouring rushes, and on the shore at the right are tree ferns. The large trees in the background are araucarian trees, true conifers related to our modern monkey-puzzle pine. Unlikely as it seems, this ecosystem occurred in our present semiarid Southwest (New Mexico and Arizona). By the way, Figure 1 · 19 shows a food web for a late Mesozoic ecosystem somewhat like this Triassic one.

**p. 356, Fig. 10 · 17:** This is probably very similar to the Geisel Valley ecosystem described on p. 358.

**p. 357, ¶ 6 and note 2:** There is, of course, a possibility that most of these bacteria were saprovores. Sometimes, however, fossil remains show abnormalities which must have been caused by pathogens. An interesting aspect of this, related to early man, can be found in Calvin Wells' book *Bones, Bodies and Disease* (London: Thames and Hudson, 1964).

## THE WORK OF THE PALEONTOLOGIST (in part)
(pp. 358–359)

**p. 358, ¶ 5:** The work of some paleontologists has proved high adventure. Students might especially enjoy reading Roy Chapman Andrews' account of his life and experiences, including his discovery of fossil dinosaur eggs in Asia (*Under a Lucky Star*. Garden City, N.Y.: Blue Ribbon Books, 1945). Some of the controversial and personal aspects of two famous dinosaur hunters' activities have been delineated in a readable manner in Robert Plate's *The Dinosaur Hunters: Othniel C. March and Edward D. Cope* (New York: David McKay Co., Inc., 1964). Other good books dealing with the search for fossils include Colbert (1968), Moore (1963), and Wendt (1968) (references: see pp. T151–T152).

## INVESTIGATION 10.1

## PALEONTOLOGICAL COMPARISON
(pp. 360–362)

This investigation should give students an appreciation of how a paleontologist organizes and analyzes his data. It may, too, dispel the idea that a paleontologist's work only involves the digging up of fossils in some far-distant, romantic spot.

It would be ideal, of course, if students could work with actual fossil material, as a paleontologist does. Some horse fossils (teeth and feet) can be obtained from Ward's Natural Science Establishment (address: p. T144). The skull or jawbone of a modern horse makes the exercise more "real," and pictures of restorations of the extinct equids also help. Sample skeletal material proves quite useful for illustrating some characteristics—in addition to span of cheek teeth—that have been used in reconstructing the phylogeny of the Equidae.

Sketches of some equids, with forelegs and molar teeth, are included in Figure 18 · 15 (p. 696). *Hipparion* in this figure is a close relative of *Neohipparion*. Whether illustrative materials are available or not, with most students it is necessary to go over the "Background Information" and "Procedure" rather carefully. After this the actual construction of the chart can be done by students outside of class. Note: the name *Hyracotherium* has priority over the more familiar *Eohippus*. It is, however, perfectly permissible to use "eohippus" as a common name.

## Procedure

The following matters should be emphasized: (1) In Figure 10 · 26 the points are to be plotted just as they would be plotted on an ordinary line graph, but they should be placed midway *between* the lines dividing the time intervals rather than on the lines. And, of course, the line connecting the points will branch. (2) The directions in the last paragraph of page 361 and second paragraph of page 362 must be followed carefully; the aim is to show how data on a single characteristic—the span of cheek teeth—fit the scheme of phylogeny derived from the study of many characteristics. (3) *Miohippus*, like several other genera, is represented by two dots, which indicates existence of the genus at two time levels. It probably will not be obvious to the student that the genera *Anchitherium* and *Parahippus*

could not very well have evolved from species of *Miohippus* that existed contemporaneously with them (in the early Miocene). Explain that *Anchitherium* and *Parahippus* were more likely to have arisen from species of *Miohippus* living in the late Oligocene.

You can facilitate the work of the students by providing them with copies of a form similar to Figure 10 · 26. If a uniform horizontal scale of 4 cm per million years is used, this form may be conveniently duplicated (lengthwise) on 8 1/2" × 11" paper.

## Conclusions

- (5): 0.15 cm/million years.
- (6): 0.57 cm/million years. Some variation is to be expected in answers to this and the following two items. The difference between *Hyracotherium* and the first *Miohippus* is $8.4 - 4.3 = 4.1$ cm. The time difference from the beginning of the Eocene to the beginning of the late Oligocene is about twenty-seven million years: $4.1 \div 27 = 0.15$ cm/million years.
- (7): 0.35 cm/million years, using the earliest *Miohippus* and earliest *Equus*.
- (8): The principal generalization from these figures is that the rate of change in cheek-teeth span varied during the evolutionary history of the Equidae.
- (9): Although the general trend through the history of the Equidae was toward the lengthening of the cheek-teeth span, the change from *Merychippus* to *Calippus* was a shortening of the span, and in a few other instances (shown by the negative slope of the graph line) a similar reversal of the general trend occurred.

## THE WORK OF THE PALEONTOLOGIST (cont.) (pp. 362–371)

**p. 362, ¶ 6:** A restoration of an extinct Irish elk, based upon skeletal material, is illustrated in Figure 18 · 11.

**p. 363, Fig. 10 · 27:** The picture itself rather clearly suggests that the exact position of each bone in relation to the positions of all others must be carefully recorded. Less obvious is the need for recording the rock stratum in which the fossil occurs and the relation to other strata.

**p. 363, Fig. 10 · 28:** This is *Varanosaurus*, one of the earliest genera of reptiles. The caption question merely calls for an echo of the discussion in paragraphs 2 and 3 of this same page. However, in the case of this particular fossil, the reptilian giveaway is the hole — temporal opening — behind the eye socket (orbit). Although some early reptiles lacked temporal openings, any skull possessing one or more such openings behind each orbit is reptilian. Other reptilian characteristics that may be detected in this sketch are the somewhat arched skull (amphibians tend to have a flat-topped skull), the apparent single articulation (single occipital condyle) between the vertebral column and skull, and well-developed pectoral and pelvic girdles and appendages.

**p. 364, heading 2:** This contrast in ideas will recur in Chapter 18. Here it is principally a historical matter; there it becomes a part of the concept of evolution.

**p. 364, ¶ 5:** There is a new hypothesis that man, rather than climatic change or other natural force, may have caused the extinction of some of the large Pleistocene mammals (Martin, Paul S. "Pleistocene Overkill," *Natural History*, Dec., 1967. Pp. 32 – 38).

**p. 365, Fig. 10 · 29:** This figure is intended to emphasize the need for caution in accepting restorations. The evidence found in the rocks (top photograph) clearly requires a great deal of interpretation even before it undergoes transformation to the mounted skeleton (middle photograph). Still further interpretation is required before it arrives at a three-dimensional model — and interpretations may differ (bottom photographs). When only a few fragments are preserved, how much greater must be the distance between fossil and restoration!

**p. 367, Fig. 10 · 31:** The term "pterosaur" in this figure is equivalent to the more familiar "pterodactyl."

**p. 367, note 1:** The question may be a real puzzler at this point, but it may also pave the way for ideas developed in Chapter 18. The basic point is that evolution involves interactions between changes in environment and changes in inheritable characteristics of organisms. But do not try to state this now; accept any reasonable speculations.

**p. 368, Fig. 10 · 33:** Both students and teachers may have used "carnivores" in a popular ecological sense, usually as an equivalent to "predator." It may be well, therefore, to note that in this figure it is used in a taxonomic sense, as the English form of "Carnivora" (used in Chapter 4).

**p. 369, ¶ 1:** One of the best examples of adaptive radiation involves the mammalian order of marsupials, whose primitive members within the isolated continent of Australia have occupied almost every niche represented by all other orders of the class Mammalia elsewhere. A good presentation on marsupials is to be found in David Bergamini's book *The Land and Wildlife of Australia* (New York: Time, Inc., 1964). Two new books about Australian marsupials are Bernhard Grzimek, *Fourlegged Australians* (New York: Hill & Wang, 1967) and Axel Poignant, *Animals of Australia* (New York: Dodd, Mead & Company, 1967).

**p. 370, ¶ 3:** Refer to Figure 8 · 39 for illustrations of modern tapirs.

**p. 371, Fig. 10 · 37:** Determining the site of origin for taxonomic groups is an intriguing pursuit. The location of the oldest fossil representative of a genus provides some evidence. Since evolution proceeds most rapidly in areas of great variability, where many niches are available, such paleoecological situations are considered favorable centers of origin. Also, sites where there are many species of a genus might represent the origin center of that genus.

GUIDE QUESTIONS (pp. 372–373)

8. By the time this question is encountered, its answer may very well differ from an answer obtained by reading Chapter 10, written in 1968. Students should be encouraged to present information superseding that in the textbook.

15. It is possible to give nonscientific reasons for differences—for example, differences in the skill or technique of artists. These, of course, are valid reasons but contribute nothing to the point at hand.

PROBLEMS (pp. 373–374)

1. Geological maps for each state can be obtained through the U.S. Geological Survey (Washington, D.C. 20242). In addition, some states have geological surveys which have published maps and state geology guides. The American Association of Petroleum Geologists has prepared a series of geological highway maps for regions of the United States (available from the A.A.P.G., P.O. Box 979, Tulsa, Oklahoma 74101). The Geological Society of America (P.O. Box 1719, Boulder, Colorado 80302) has published a number of state and regional geology guides that include road logs most helpful for a biology teacher who wishes to incorporate some geology into his biology field trips. Three good references for those who would like to do some fossil hunting are: Casanova, Richard. *An Illustrated Guide to Fossil Collecting*. Healdsburg, Calif.: Naturegraph Co., 1957 (in paperback—includes list of fossil-collecting sites); Murray, Marian. *Hunting for Fossils*. New York: The Macmillan Co., 1967 (an excellent, comprehensive guide to fossil-collecting techniques and sites); and Ransom, Jay E. *Fossils in America*. New York: Harper & Row, 1964. Guides for identification of fossils are included in the reference list on pp. T151–T152.

2. There have been several explanations, but in very recent years the idea of continental drift has become more and more seriously considered by geologists, especially with respect to Antarctica. There are innumerable contemporary articles dealing with this topic. One of the best summaries of current thinking is Patrick M. Hurley's "The Confirmation of Continental Drift," *Scientific American*, April, 1968, pp. 52–64. The changing view with respect to continental drift and associated biological phenomena makes a good discussion topic, showing students why scientists change their minds and that scientific "eternal truths" (such as the permanence of the continents) may not be very "eternal" after all.

3. *Webster's New International Dictionary* (unabridged) is a good source of information on these names.

5. There is much written on these two famous fossil sites, but it may be difficult for students to locate or may prove too technical. Among good references about La Brea are Fenton, Carroll L., and Mildred A. Fenton, *The Fossil Book*, pp. 436–444. Garden City, N.Y.: Doubleday & Co., 1959; Humphrey, Blackmer, "Tar-trap Treasure," *Natural History*, March, 1950, pp. 120–127; Kemmerer, J. B., "Los Angeles 60,000 Years Ago; Tar Pits in Hancock Park," *Science Digest*, Sept., 1963, pp. 48–51; and Stock, Chester, "Rancho La Brea, a Record of Pleistocene Life in California," *Los Angeles Museum Publication No. 1*, 1930. Helpful references on Florissant include Gamer, Eleanor E., "The Fossil Beds of Florissant," *National Parks Magazine*, July, 1965, pp. 16–19; MacGinitie, H. D., "Fossil Plants of the Florissant Beds, Colorado," *Carnegie Institute of Washington Publication No. 599*, 1953; Scudder, S. H., "The Tertiary Insects of North America," *Hayden Survey Monograph No. 13*, 1890, pp. 127–217; and Teale, Edwin Way, *Journey into Summer*. New York: Dodd, Mead & Co., 1960, pp. 294–303. (Published separately as "The Valley of Fossil Insects," *Audubon Magazine*, Sept.-Oct., 1960, pp. 222–225, 239–242.) The

Florissant fossil beds, by the way, are being set aside as a national monument.

7. While students may jump to the conclusion that the large ichthyosaurs had eaten the smaller ones, some may remember that certain reptiles give birth to "live" young, which have developed within eggs inside the female (ovoviviparous). Kinds of evidence that might be sought: where the small skeletons are located within the large skeleton; whether they are disarticulated or otherwise damaged as a possible result of having been eaten; whether they have embryonic characteristics.

8. Students will discover many hypotheses but little agreement. There is a pertinent chapter in Colbert, Edwin H., *The Age of Reptiles*, pp. 191–207 (New York: W. W. Norton & Co., Inc., 1965) about "The Great Extinction," in which Colbert aptly notes that "It was an event that has defied all attempts at a satisfactory explanation, for which reason, among others, it has fascinated paleontologists for decades."

11. The situation in South America can be compared with that in Australia, which still is isolated from other major land masses and still contains an array of bizarre, primitive animals that have survived because of long isolation from more advanced animals. The primitive South American mammals did not fare so well because of the geologically recent reestablishment of the Panama land bridge and consequent contact with more "efficient" predators and competitors from the north.

## SUPPLEMENTARY MATERIALS

### Audiovisual Materials

**Phonograph record:** *The Scientists Speak: Biology.* Harcourt, Brace and Co., 1959. George Gaylord Simpson talks about his work as a paleontologist.

**Filmstrips:** *Reptiles Inherit the Earth.* ("The World We Live In," Part V). Color. New York: LIFE Filmstrips, 1955. A wonderful gallery of paintings, with all the familiar and many unfamiliar Permian and Mesozoic amphibians and reptiles represented. But there is no mention at all of the fossil evidence on which the magnificent imagery is based.

*The Age of Mammals.* ("The World We Live In," Part VI). Color. New York: LIFE Filmstrips, 1955. Another fine collection of paintings. Includes some introductory matter on stratigraphy, which links the pictures to the fossil evidence.

*Fossils.* Encyclopaedia Britannica Educational Corp., EB 6413 — five color filmstrips and five phono-discs. Contents: *How Fossils Are Formed; Collecting and Interpreting Fossils; Fossils and the Relative Ages of Rocks; Fossils and Prehistoric Environments; Fossils and Organic Change.* One of the best audiovisual treatments of this subject available.

*South American Fossils.* ("Darwin's World of Nature," Part IV). Color. New York: LIFE Filmstrips, 1960. Deals with the development of the South American vertebrate land fauna after its isolation in the Cretaceous and with the results of the rejoining of South and North America in the Pleistocene. The pictures are good, and the zoogeographical principles have been well presented.

**Motion-picture films:** *Australian Marsupials.* BSCS Inquiry Film Loop. (Rand McNally #11–2981, 1968.) An inquiry reflecting adaptive radiation and the past as explanation of the present.

*Story in the Rocks.* Shell Oil Co. 16 mm. Color. $17\frac{1}{2}$ min. Deals interestingly with the more glamorous activities of paleontologists, emphasizing their skill in interpreting bits and pieces of evidence.

*The Fossil Story.* Shell Oil Co. 16 mm. Color. 19 min. The practical importance of paleontology in exploring for oil is the theme. Adds an important facet to Chapter 10.

*How Did Life Begin?* National Aeronautics and Space Administration. 16 mm. Color. 20 min. Dr. Sidney Fox discusses the evolutionary relationships of various protein molecules and traces his synthesis of artificial protein.

*History Layer by Layer.* McGraw-Hill Book Co., Inc. 16 mm. Color. 23 min. An excellent presentation of the specialized paleontological field in which microfossils in cores taken from the ocean bottom are studied for evidence of past climatic changes.

## Teacher's References

AGER, D. V. *Principles of Paleoecology.* New York: McGraw-Hill Book Co., Inc., 1963. (An "introduction to the study of how and where animals and plants lived in the past." Provides an excellent background for the point of view that dominates Chapter 10 of the *Green Version.*)

ANDREWS, H. N. *Studies in Paleobotany.* New York: John Wiley & Sons, Inc., 1961. (Explores in depth some of the most important problems of plant evolution.)

BROUWER, A. *General Paleontology.* Chicago: University of Chicago Press, 1967. (This book emphasizes the principles of paleontological science, rather than the descriptions of fossils and the chronological story of evolution.)

COLBERT, E. H. *The Age of Reptiles.* New York: W. W. Norton & Co., 1965. (A popular account of the Mesozoic era, focusing especially on the rise and decline of the reptiles.)

———. *Men and Dinosaurs.* New York: E. P. Dutton & Co., Inc., 1968. (This book deals with the fascinating story of the search for dinosaurs and the men who discovered them.)

EASTON, W. H. *Invertebrate Paleontology.* New York: Harper & Brothers, 1960. (A systematic enumeration of fossil invertebrates, with numerous illustrations.)

FENTON, C. L., and M. A. FENTON. *The Fossil Book.* Garden City, N.Y.: Doubleday & Co., 1959. (A comprehensive and well-illustrated popular guide to fossils.)

GOLDRING, W. *Handbook of Paleontology for Beginners and Amateurs.* Part 1, "The Fossils." Ithaca, N.Y.: Paleontological Research Institution, 1960. (A paper-back guide to fossil groups, with tips on fossil collecting and preservation.)

KNIGHT, C. R. "Parade of Life through the Ages," *National Geographic Magazine*, Feb., 1942, pp. 141–184. (This old article is notable for its color paintings of past ecosystems and associated organisms.)

MOORE, R. *Man, Time and Fossils.* Rev. ed. New York: Alfred A. Knopf, Inc., 1963. (This story of evolution focuses especially on the search for remains of fossil man.)

MOORE, R. C. *Introduction to Historical Geology.* 2nd ed. New York: McGraw-Hill Book Co., Inc., 1958. (A general text on the history of the earth. The geologist views the fossil record as a key to earth history rather than as a key to evolutionary processes; both viewpoints should be in the teacher's background.)

———, C. G. LALICKER, and A. G. FISCHER. *Invertebrate Fossils.* New York: McGraw-Hill Book Co., Inc., 1952. (Books on invertebrate paleontology are rather specialized; this one furnishes a good beginning.)

OAKLEY, K. P., and H. M. MUIRWOOD. *The Succession of Life through Geological Time.* London: The British Museum (of Natural History), 1958. (An inexpensive and concise paleontological review by geological periods, well illustrated and with maps.)

OPARIN, A. I. *The Origin of Life.* 2nd ed. New York: Dover Publications, Inc., 1953. (The source of much current thinking on the origin of life; originally published several decades ago.)

RHODES, F., H. S. ZIM, and P. R. SHAFFER. *Fossils—a Guide to Prehistoric Life.* New York: Golden Press, 1962. (An inexpensive, well-illustrated, and easy pocket guide to fossils.)

ROMER, A. S. *Vertebrate Paleontology.* 3rd ed. Chicago: University of Chicago Press, 1966. (A systematic enumeration of fossil vertebrates. Emphasis is on remains rather than restorations.)

————. *The Vertebrate Story.* 4th ed. Chicago: University of Chicago Press, 1959. (A narrative account of the fossil history of vertebrate animals.)

SIMAK, C. D. *Trilobite, Dinosaur and Man: Earth's Story.* New York: St. Martin's Press, 1966. (An extensive paleonto-logical review by geological periods, with maps of past geography and illustrations of fossils.)

WENDT, H. *Before the Deluge.* Garden City, N.Y.: Doubleday & Co., 1968. (A popular consideration of the history of paleontology.)

# Section Four WITHIN THE INDIVIDUAL ORGANISM

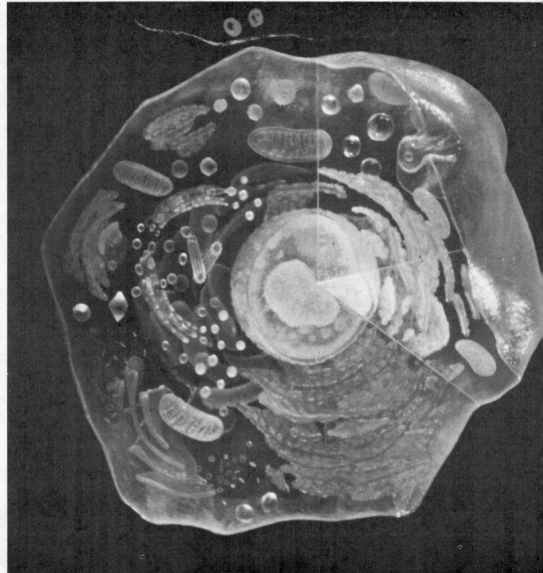

Section Four begins the second half of the six sections in the student's book, and Chapter 11 begins the second half of the twenty chapters in it. But the halfway point has not yet been reached with respect to the learning load in the course. The density of ideas now becomes much greater than it was in any of the first ten chapters; thus, increasing student effort is required. The heavier burden in the second half of the course may, in part, be balanced by the students' increasing familiarity with techniques of studying and of pondering biological science.

Through several generations of biological investigators, heavy emphasis was placed upon the morphology and gross internal physiology of organisms. This emphasis has persisted in high school biology-teaching long after its decline in biological research. In Section Four is concentrated much of this "traditional" high school biology, the biology familiar to the majority of today's biology teachers. In contrast, also encountered in Section Four is material from the burgeoning field of biochemistry—a branch of science changing with such rapidity that the factual knowledge of even last year's college graduate may be obsolete before he is established in his first year of teaching. The same can be said concerning the field of animal behavior, except that even recent graduates may have had little preparation in this field.

The blend of the familiar and the unfamiliar in this section may prove challenging to the teacher—or it may only be exasperating. A critic of the 1963 edition protested such "gross omissions" as the structure of the human eye and ear. But to achieve the purposes of the *Green Version*, the writers found it necessary to reduce what has frequently been the substance of an entire course to less than one section. In general, it was felt that much such material is now treated effectively in earlier grades. However, the trend in this direction during the past five years has not been sufficiently impressive to induce much further reduction.

Section Illustration

This large plastic model of a cell was constructed according to information obtained from the study of numerous electronmicrographs. Students should be able to recognize in it many of the structures shown in Figure 11 · 3.

# 11

# The
# Cell

## MAJOR IDEAS

1. Observation and reasoning by men of many nations contributed to the development of the cell theory. This theory, though imperfect in details, is an important guide in the investigation of biological structure and function.

2. Cell structure varies and therefore generalizations are inevitably misleading. This applies both to the chemical composition of the cell and to the organelles visible within it.

3. Biologists aim to explain the functioning of cells in terms of physical principles. This is illustrated by a discussion of the transport of substances into, out of, and within cells.

4. Among cells that have recognizable nuclei, the process of cell division is remarkably uniform, involving a definite sequence of nuclear events—mitosis.

5. In species that are unicellular, cell division results in the production of new individuals; in multicellular species, it results in the addition of cells, usually leading to the growth of the individual.

6. The process by which successive generations of cells within a multicellular organism come to differ from each other—the process of cell differentiation—remains one of the major puzzles of biology.

7. Unless they periodically divide, most cells appear to age. The causes of aging in cells, tissues, and whole organisms represent another major problem in biology.

## PLANNING AHEAD

If you have been keeping up with the planning advice given in previous chapters, you have now reached a temporary rest point. Check the following: (1) Are you completely ready for Chapter 11? (2) Have you obtained pea seeds, glass beads, Ascarite, volumeters, fresh hydrogen peroxide, vacuum bottles, acetone, and petroleum ether (as well as the more usual materials) for the investigations in Chapter 12? (Try out the operation of a volumeter if you are unfamiliar with it, and prepare fine-pointed pipettes for Investigation 12.4.) (3) Have you arranged for the plant materials required in Investigations 13.1 and 13.2?

The only long-term preparation that might be undertaken at this time is to start growth of *Zebrina* (Investigation 15.1) and coleus (Investigation 16.1) if you have facilities for producing the plants yourself.

## GUIDELINES

As a term, "cell" is not new to most tenth-grade students. But since experience with cells is likely to have been vicarious, even in school systems that have good junior high school science programs, putting some observational foundations under the word is of first importance. You may therefore start work with Investigation 11.1. First "seeing," then "explaining" can lead to lasting, accurate understandings. This principle can be applied throughout the chapter.

The cell-physiology portion of the chapter (pp. 386–393) depends heavily on (1) an understanding of cell structure, and (2) acquaintance with the rudiments of the molecular theory. An adequate understanding of cell structure may be gained from the preceding part of the chapter. Some acquaintance with the molecular theory must, however, be expected in the student's background. It seems a preposterous assignment for a tenth-grade biology course to fill in adequately—that is, not merely with words but with a rich observational experience—a totally blank background. But the several fine curriculum projects for physical science on the junior high school level have not yet penetrated very far into the American educational system, and teachers cannot complacently allow today's student to suffer for lack of a background they hope the future student will possess. Fortunately, the amount of understanding expected in the *Green Version* is not as great as many persons seem to believe. The student who works through pages 387–392 thoughtfully will have a sufficient (though certainly neither broad nor profound) view of diffusion.

The best presentation of mitosis is, of course, by means of a motion picture. Avoid films combining mitosis and meiosis (or stop the film before meiosis appears). Meiosis is not relevant to Chapter 11 and can only confuse. If mitosis is thoroughly understood now, meiosis will be relatively easy when it is encountered in Chapter 16. But viewing a film does not assure understanding. Need for Investigation 11.3 remains.

Chapter 11 is difficult. The writers have undertaken to make it as clear as possible and have ruthlessly pruned away what they considered unessential detail. They have used an unusually spare running vocabulary. But the material remains difficult. The difficulty must be surmounted, for some understanding of cellular structure and function is essential to the student's appreciation of modern biology. And many things in the remainder of the course depend upon that understanding.

Your first response to the difficulty of Chapter 11 should be to reduce the length of assignments; the second should be to increase the time allowed for discussion of each assignment. Five assignments are suggested: pp. 378–381 (guide questions 1–2), 381–384 (guide questions 3–4), 386–388 and 390–393 (guide questions 5–11), 393–397 (guide questions 12–14), and 400–404 (guide questions 15–18).

## TEACHING NOTES

### SOME HISTORY (pp. 378–381)

This history illuminates the development of a biological concept and emphasizes the international character of science.

**p. 380, ¶4:** The development of the cell theory illustrates how more accurate understandings frequently depend on further technological developments. Use of dyes and of phase-contrast and electron microscopes has revealed increasingly detailed information about cells.

**p. 381, note 1:** This is a theory, because it is not merely descriptive but explanatory of the structure of organisms. It goes beyond the summarization of observations; obviously not *all* parts of *all* organisms have been examined.

## CELL STRUCTURE (pp. 381–384)

**p. 381, Fig. 11·3:** Compare this diagram with the photograph of a cell model (page 376). After students have finished Investigation 11.1, ask them whether this diagram more closely resembles an animal or a plant cell.

**p. 383, ¶ 2:** The term "cytoplast" for the structural region of a cell does not have the objectional connotations of "cytoplasm," a term for a supposed substance. "Cytoplasm" and "protoplasm" are both avoided in the 1968 edition of the *Green Version.*

**p. 384, Figs. 11·6 and 11·7:** In the first printing the captions of these two illustrations are reversed. They should read: "Figure 11·6 Detail of endoplasmic reticulum," and "Figure 11·7 Part of the cell membrane of a mouse cell." Note the layered structure. A fine collection of electronmicrographs showing minute detail of cell structure is found in Porter, K. R., and M. A. Bonneville (reference: p. T168). It is primarily a book of illustrations, mostly from human-tissue electronmicrographs of moderate magnification.

## INVESTIGATION 11.1

### DIVERSITY IN CELL STRUCTURE (pp. 385–386)

This investigation is purely observational. The emphasis is on *living* cells that the students can directly associate with whole organisms. Of course, only a limited number of cell structures can be seen. If you want students to see other structures—mitochondria, for example—you may wish to use some commercial slides to supplement the investigation. A few microscopes equipped with oil-immersion lenses are desirable for such observations.

### Materials

Onions can be cut into pieces at the beginning of the day; keep the pieces under water in finger bowls.

If an onion is cut into orange-section-like pieces, a student can remove a piece of the fleshy leaf from a section. Bending this backward until it snaps usually leaves a ragged piece of epidermis.

See p. T30 (Investigation 1.4) for preparation of $I_2KI$.

Elodea (*Anacharis*) is easy to maintain in an aquarium from which direct sunlight is excluded. To increase the likelihood of observing cyclosis in cells, place some of the material under a bell jar and illuminate it for at least twelve hours before using.

Make up packets of 5 to 10 toothpicks in aluminum foil and sterilize in a pressure cooker or autoclave. Have each student break his toothpick after use to prevent its reuse.

The frog material should be as fresh as possible. One frog should be used to provide material for morning classes; another should be used for afternoon classes. Etherize and pith the frog (see p. T198). With a medicine dropper obtain blood from a large vessel, or flush an area of bleeding with Ringer's solution. Place the blood in a small beaker of Ringer's solution.

You may use skin that is shed in the water in which the frogs are kept. Or the skin of the freshly killed frog may be scraped with a sharp scalpel. The materials thus obtained may be kept in a small beaker of Ringer's solution. Whole skin, of course, is much too thick for use.

*Methylene-blue solution:* Add 1.48 g of the dye to 100 ml of 95% ethyl alcohol; let stand for about two days, stirring frequently; filter and store as stock solution. Before using, add 10 ml of stock solution to 90 ml of distilled water.

*Saline solutions:* Physiological saline for this work is 7 g of NaCl in 1000 ml of water. Or use amphibian Ringer's solution:

| | |
|---|---|
| KCl | 0.14 g |
| NaCl | 6.50 g |
| CaCl₂ | 0.12 g |
| NaHCO₃ | 0.20 g |
| H₂O (distilled) | 1000.00 ml |

KCl .................... 0.14 g
NaCl .................... 6.50 g
CaCl$_2$ .................... 0.12 g
NaHCO$_3$ ................ 0.20 g
H$_2$O (distilled) ........ 1000.00 ml

### Procedure

Two full periods are required for this investigation. The observations can be accomplished in one period; but sketching the cells, completing the chart, and answering the questions in the data book make two periods necessary.

If students work in pairs, each pair may be provided with slides, cover slips, and dissecting tools; but to save time and trouble, place stains and the materials to be observed in one or a few centrally located places where students can go to prepare their mounts. Or you can conveniently arrange this investigation by setting up five stations, one for each observation. The class may then be divided into five groups of students, each to begin at a different station.

Demonstrate the techniques of removing the onion epidermis and transferring cheek cells to a slide. Even at this point in the year, students need to be cautioned to use *small* pieces of material. Have students avoid using circles to frame their sketches. Such figures suggest the whole field of view and would require the drawing of everything seen in that field. Only a *small* section of the field of view should be drawn to show how cells are arranged. The cell drawings should be large enough to clearly indicate details of structure. An example drawn on the board helps to get this idea across — but use a kind of cell not to be observed by the students.

During this investigation a good demonstration to show ciliary action may be set up. Cut away the lower jaw of a pithed frog;

then cut out small pieces from the lining of the mouth cavity in the region between the eye bulges and the throat. Mount a piece in Ringer's solution.

- (1): Review Item 13 of Investigation 1.4.
- (2): Cyclosis (if seen) is usually considered by students as evidence of life.

### Summary

Use pictures of cells to help increase the student's ideas of cell variability. Invite students to identify the cells pictured as plant or animal before you identify them.

- (4): Remind students of the limitations in magnification and resolving power of their microscopes. Moreover, adjustment of light intensity as well as special staining procedures may be involved in revealing cell structures.
- (7): The rigid cellulose cell walls of most plant cells are usually associated with definite cell boundaries and angular shapes.

---

### SOME CELL PHYSIOLOGY (in part) (pp. 386 – 388)

**p. 387, ¶ 2:** If you have any students with chemical sophistication, they may be cautioned to differentiate between steady state of a cell's composition and chemical equilibrium, in which no material is entering or leaving the system.

**p. 387, note 4:** The behavior of gases and of substances undergoing change of state is the best evidence available to students.

**p. 387, ¶ 5:** For a simple demonstration of diffusion, drop a large crystal of potassium permanganate into a small beaker of water and allow the beaker to sit undisturbed. A white card behind the beaker will make observation easier.

A somewhat more elaborate method: Lightly rub very small amounts of dry crystal violet, eosin, and methylene blue into the surface of bond paper. (Use a second, small piece of paper to do this — it will keep stains off your fingers.) Shake lightly to get rid of large particles. Hold paper with dye side down over a plate of 1 1/2% agar. Tap hard with your finger to dislodge stain particles and to permit them to fall on the agar surface. Diffusion takes place very quickly, and different dyes diffuse at different rates.

To demonstrate quickly and effectively the diffusion of gas molecules, crumple a paper towel in a dish and saturate it either with a fragrant cologne or with ammonium hydroxide.

**p. 388, Fig. 11 · 8:** Note that this does not illustrate the text discussion since only a single kind of molecule is involved.

**p. 388, ¶ 4:** Cell activity results in energy loss as heat. Since the heat must be dispelled anyway, that which is used to move molecules is not really a drain on the cell's energy supply.

## INVESTIGATION 11.2

### DIFFUSION THROUGH A MEMBRANE (pp. 388–389)

The equipment is simple and inexpensive, and when the investigation is done by groups of four students, everyone is close enough to the material to see the results. Presenting this investigation as a demonstration, though possible, is inadvisable.

### Materials

Cellulose tubing with a diameter of 3/8″ is convenient, but larger tubing may be used. Though cellulose tubing is recommended, collodion sacks may also be used. For construction of these, see E. Morholt *et al.*, (complete reference: see p. T105).

Prepare soluble-starch solution by adding about 10 g of soluble starch to about 500 ml of water. Stir or shake, and then filter. If you cannot obtain soluble starch, try laundry starch. Filter it through cloth and then through filter paper. It is desirable, but not essential, that the starch solution be clear. Some brands of soluble starch are reported to diffuse through cellulose membranes, so the starch should be tested before being used by students.

The glucose solution should be strong – close to saturation – but the exact concentration is not critical.

Iodine – potassium-iodide solution may be used for the iodine reaction with starch (see p. T30).

Wide-mouth jars may be used in place of the beakers. "Junior" baby-food jars are suitable.

Tes-tape or Clinitest tablets, used by diabetics to test for sugar in urine, can usually be purchased at drugstores. They do not require heating.

Two setups are employed because iodine in the water sometimes interferes with the use of Tes-tape or Clinitest tablets. If burners are available, Benedict's solution or Fehling's solution may be used to test for glucose. In this case only one setup is necessary, and both starch and glucose solutions can be placed in one tube.

### Procedure

In order to draw any conclusions from this investigation, students must know the reactions between: (1) starch and iodine, (2) glucose and Tes-tape, (3) starch and Tes-tape, (4) water and Tes-tape, (5) glucose and iodine. Before students begin their work, perform a quick, silent demonstration of these combinations.

Have the cellulose tubing cut into pieces of the proper length and soaking in water, and have all solutions and other materials conveniently available when students arrive in the classroom at the beginning of the first period. The setup should be completed as quickly as possible. About twenty minutes later, the glucose test can be made. The reaction of iodine with starch should be visible by the end of the period, but it will be more striking on the following day.

### Discussion

It is important that the results of this investigation, which involves purely physical systems, be related to living things. Therefore the questions on page 389 must

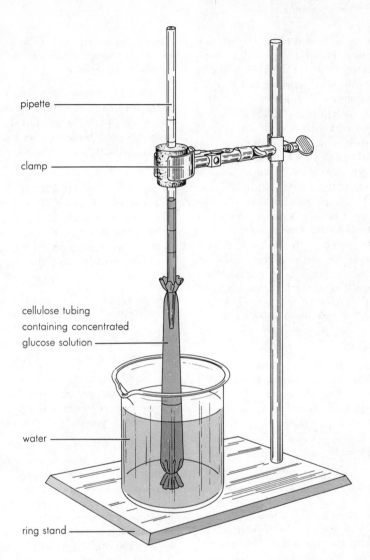

pipette

clamp

cellulose tubing
containing concentrated
glucose solution

water

ring stand

Figure T–13

be given special attention. Glucose and starch are both common materials in living things; the free diffusion of the former and the lack of diffusion of the latter can be linked to storage of starch in plant cells, the need to digest starch, the possibility of feeding glucose by direct injection, and many other biological matters.

• (3): The turgidity of the glucose tube after twenty-four hours not only indicates the diffusion of water but also

demonstrates diffusion pressure. For further demonstration, place a lettuce leaf or a piece of fresh carrot in a 10% salt solution for fifteen minutes. Then have students feel it for comparison with one soaked in plain water for an equal time. How is this related to the observation in the investigation? (Refer to results of Investigation 9.2.)

Turgor is perhaps the most important biological effect of diffusion pressure, but you may wish to demonstrate another effect by showing how diffusion pressure can support a column of liquid against the force of gravity. The apparatus shown in Figure T–13 can be used for this. A more difficult setup, but one that has a close connection with biology, can be provided as follows: Using the technique shown in Figure 11 · 15, suspend a raw carrot that has been hollowed out to about half its length, the hollow having been nearly filled with molasses. Shape the opening in the carrot with care, so that a single-hole stopper with glass tubing may be sealed into its top with paraffin or an adhesive compound. Compare the results in this setup with that in the purely physical setup.

- (4): If the starch passed through the membrane, then the water in beaker A should be blue. Actually, after twenty-four hours the water in beaker A is usually clear, because all the iodine has been bound to the starch molecules in the tube.

- (5) and • (6): The simplest hypothesis is that the tubing contains submicroscopic pores of such size that molecules of iodine, water, and glucose can pass through while molecules of starch cannot. This hypothesis merely assumes one of the points of the molecular theory: that even in solids there are molecular-size spaces between adjacent molecules.

---

## SOME CELL PHYSIOLOGY (cont.)
(pp. 390–393)

**p. 390, ¶ 2:** The term "differentially permeable" is preferred to "semi-permeable" (formerly much used); the latter is logically faulty, and the former is more descriptive.

The introduction of "differentially" here makes the later usage of "differentiation" (p. 400) less strange.

**p. 391, note 1:** Molecules of different substances cannot occupy the same space at the same time. The relationship is not exactly inverse, however, because of differential "packing" by molecules of different sizes.

**p. 391, Fig. 11 · 10:** In B, note there is the same number of molecules of the dissolved substance (blue dots) within the membrane in both sketches, although in the second the membrane has expanded. Have students explain why the membrane has expanded.

**p. 391, ¶ 3:** Have students locate the paramecium's "pumps," shown in Figure 11 · 2. Note the radial canals and discuss their function and that of the contractile vacuoles.

**p. 391, note 2:** With freshwater organisms, increasing the salt content of the environmental water sets up a water diffusion from organism to environment.

**p. 392, ¶ 3:** In discussing active transport, you may suggest the suspected role of enzymes in the membrane, or some other property of the membrane that forces materials to move against the diffusion gradient. These reactions may change a substance so that it can more readily enter a cell, and once inside, restore it to its original form. An informative reference on the role of certain fatty substances in transport of materials through cell membranes is an article by L. E. Hokin and M. R. Hokin, "The Chemistry of Cell Membranes," *Scientific American*, October, 1965, p. 78.

The importance of stressing the energy expenditure of active transport, pinocytosis, and cyclosis is evident when one looks ahead to the emphasis on bioenergetics in Chapter 12. You can strengthen the significance of that chapter by developing an understanding now of some of the cell's energy needs.

**p. 393, Fig. 11·11:** The term for taking in solid particles, if you wish to use it, is "phagocytosis." This photograph shows the granular nature of living matter well.

**p. 393, ¶ 3:** If students have not observed cyclosis in elodea, you may wish to demonstrate it in slime molds (pp. T165–T166).

## CELL DUPLICATION (pp. 393–397)

**p. 394, ¶ 1:** When contemplating why cells divide, students must remember that everything to maintain the volume of living matter in a given cell must pass through that cell's membrane. Refer to p. T179 for a discussion concerning Problem 3, page 440.

**p. 394, note 3:** *Rhizopus* may be considered an exception to the formal cell theory in that it exists with a multiplicity of nuclei and an absence of separating membranes, an arrangement referred to as a syncytium. However, this may be a derived condition.

**p. 395, Fig. 11·13:** Clearly distinguishable are cell membrane, cytoplast, centrosome, chromosomes, and spindle fibers.

**p. 396, note 2:** The writers prefer "kinetochore" to "centromere" because of possible centrosome–chromosome-centromere confusion.

**p. 396, ¶ 4:** The names of the phases of mitosis are omitted because their use tends to belie the uninterrupted continuity of the mitotic process. Though useful to the cytologist, they do nothing for a high school biology student but add terms to an already heavy vocabulary load.

## INVESTIGATION 11.3

### MITOSIS AND CELL DIVISION IN PLANT CELLS (pp. 397–400)

For many students, the observing of prepared slides is little more than a difficult way to look at pictures. This investigation allows students to associate a familiar macroscopic organism directly with the somewhat unconvincing story of mitosis told in the text.

### Materials

Onions obtained from a grocery store can usually be used. In some cases, however, you will find that onions have been treated to inhibit root formation. In this case, onion sets or garlic bulbs will provide good material.

Root tips (1 to 2 cm) should be cut between 11:30 A.M. and noon, or just before midnight. Tips collected at this time show a maximum number of mitotic figures. Very poor results may be obtained from roots harvested at other times.

*Fixative:* Fix the root tips for twenty-four hours in the following mixture:

  Absolute alcohol, 3 parts
  Glacial acetic acid, 1 part

If absolute ethanol is not available, denatured alcohol containing methanol and isopropyl alcohol as denaturants will work satisfactorily. We have used successfully alcohol, Baker, Reagent, consisting of:

  Specially denatured alcohol (3-A), 95
    parts by volume
  Isopropyl alcohol, 5 parts by volume

Fix for twenty-four hours, then store (indefinitely) in 70% alcohol.

*Carnoy's fluid:* absolute alcohol, 6 parts by volume; chloroform, 3 parts by volume; glacial acetic acid, 1 part by volume.

*Aceto-orcein stain:* orcein (synthetic), 1 g; glacial acetic acid, 45 ml; distilled water, 55 ml.

Dissolve orcein in hot glacial acetic acid. Use a large beaker, as foaming may result when dry stain is added to acid. Cool and then add distilled water. Filter just before use.

### Procedure

Students should observe the setup of the onion bulbs and the growth of the roots; this will allow them to clearly associate the small pieces of root (used later) with a real, living organism.

For the teacher who is unfamiliar with the "squash" technique, the BSCS Technique Film *Smear and Squash Techniques* may be useful (5 1/2 min. Thorne Films, 1229 University Ave., Boulder, Colo.).

Emphasize that drawings should be large enough to show all detail observed.

If you place pans containing water and detergent at strategic locations in the laboratory, students may conveniently wash their slides and leave them clean for the next group.

## Discussion

By comparing cell size in embryonic tissue with size of cells observed in older tissue farther away from the root tip, develop the idea that growth of roots depends upon both the increase of number of cells and their enlargement after cell division.

- (2): Further discussion, concerning changes in shape as well as in size, will lead effectively into the text's next consideration—differentiation.

  If a film on mitosis has been shown, discuss the dynamic activity within the cell during mitosis—activity which clearly evidences the need for energy to accomplish this work of the cell.

- (4): Emphasize similarities but note the formation of the new cell wall and the absence of centrosomes in plant cells. Ask students why plant cells do not "pinch in" during division, as do animal cells.

## DIFFERENTIATION (pp. 400–402)

**p. 400, ¶ 2:** Students have no difficulty recognizing the distinct differences of cells in various tissues and concluding that differentiation is a reality. They are less likely to see that the characteristics of a cell are to be expected in its daughter cells. Thus students often miss the point of the paradox. Questioning the obvious—the "natural"

—did not occur to any men until a few short millennia ago, and it is not a frequent practice among students today. Trying to increase its frequency is one of the reasons for this course.

**p. 402, note 1:** Specific techniques of tissue culture, as suggested in guidebooks on this topic, are not sought in answer to this question. Students may come up with: an energy source, provision against infection, prevention of drying.

## AGING (pp. 402–404)

It is difficult to interest high school students in this topic. Yet because it is a fundamental biological problem and one that is getting increasing attention from researchers, some consideration should be given it. Note that the discussion is primarily concerned with the aging of cells; the senescence of multicellular organisms—particularly animals—involves additional complications.

## PROBLEMS (p. 405)

1. Recently developed phase-contrast microscopy has made possible more effective examination of living, unstained cells.

3. Seen with a microscope, the presence or absence of cell structures such as chloroplast, cell wall, and centrosome would be evidence that the material is either plant or animal. Chemical tests for cellulose would confirm the identification.

4. The jellyfish would swell up if placed in fresh water, and the frog would dehydrate if placed in ocean water. Fish that live in both fresh and salt water maintain water balance in their tissues through various mechanisms. In salt water, they continuously drink, void very little urine, and excrete salts actively through their gills. In fresh water, they take in only a little water by drinking, absorb salts through their gills, and excrete much water as urine. See Prosser and Brown (reference: p. T212).

5. (*a*) In some "unicellular organisms" —such as paramecia—the macronucleus

merely pulls apart, but the micronucleus divides by mitosis. See Moment, *General Zoology* (reference: p. 213). (*b*) In division of a blue-green alga, presumably equal portions of chromatin material find their way to each of the two daughter cells.

6. In many ways cancer cells act as rejuvenated, undifferentiated cells. If it can be learned why and how cells differentiate, a way may be determined to control the reversal of the process in cancer cells.

7. In multicellular animals connective tissues in wide variety hold cells together. All these tissues have an extensive matrix of extracellular material containing fibers. Such extracellular material is manufactured by the connective tissue cells and serves to hold these cells together; and in turn, the connective tissue holds other tissues — such as muscle and nerve. Plant cells are held together primarily by the adhesive qualities of cellulose cell walls.

8. The term "protoplasm" suggests that there is a fundamental substance in living cells. This is anything but accurate. Not only does the matter within living things differ among different kinds of organisms, but within a particular organism it is of quite dissimilar characteristics and composition. Further, within a given cell, substances are constantly undergoing physical and chemical changes. The matter within a living being is a dynamic condition, not a single substance.

9. Electron microscopes have provided information on intracellular fine structure. Phase-contrast microscopes make possible the study of living, unstained material — thus eliminating the physiological effects of the usual histological fixing and staining procedures.

## SUPPLEMENTARY MATERIALS

### Slime-Mold Demonstration

Not only is a slime-mold culture useful for demonstrating cyclosis; it is also convenient for reviewing the problems associated with a two-kingdom system of classification and pointing up some difficulties in the cell theory.

Preparations for this demonstration must be started fourteen days before its use.

Cultures of *Physarum polycephalum* should be started from sclerotia, which may be purchased from most biological supply

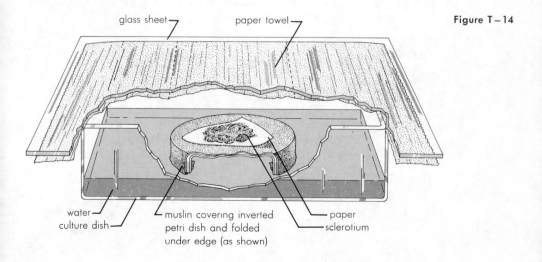

glass sheet — paper towel — Figure T–14

water — culture dish — muslin covering inverted petri dish and folded under edge (as shown) — paper sclerotium

houses. Directions in the following paragraph may be supplemented by BSCS Technique Film *Culturing Slime Mold Plasmodium* (6 1/2 min. Thorne Films, 1229 University Ave., Boulder, Colo.).

Sterilize a large culture dish (about 8″ diameter) with sodium hypochlorite and rinse thoroughly. Cut two circular pieces of muslin (old sheeting is fine); the diameter of each piece should be about 5 cm greater than the diameter of a petri dish. Boil them. Cover the outer surface of one half of a petri dish with the double thickness of muslin, and fold the edges tightly under the rim of the dish (see Figure T–14). Place this muslin "table" in the culture dish, and add water to a depth of about 5 mm. Place paper bearing the *Physarum* sclerotium in the middle of this "table," colored side (the sclerotium side) up. Cover the culture dish with a sheet of glass or a larger dish. A paper towel helps maintain a humidity gradient in the chamber and, in addition, prevents condensed moisture from dropping onto the slime mold.

Store the setup in *indirect* light at a temperature of about 20°C. When the slime mold has "crawled" onto the muslin, remove the paper. Then feed daily by sprinkling on the surface of the plasmodium a small quantity of oatmeal that has been pushed through a wire kitchen strainer. Avoid dropping oatmeal in the water. Change the water daily. If contaminating molds appear in the culture, they should be cut out with a sterile scalpel. Always cut outside the apparent margin of the mold.

When the slime mold has spread over the entire muslin "table," transfer small bits of the plasmodium to a petri dish containing a *thin* layer of nonnutrient agar. (Prepare by dissolving 1.5 g of agar in 100 ml of hot water.) It is not necessary to autoclave the dishes or the agar, since slime molds live on bacteria and mold spores. Maintain these cultures for *two days* under the same light and temperature conditions as above. If necessary, the petri dishes containing agar and bits of plasmodium may then be stored for a few days in the refrigerator. Several hours before use, they should be removed from the refrigerator and allowed to warm to room temperature.

The remainder of the plasmodium in the humidity chamber may be sclerotized and stored for later use, as follows: Spread a piece of moistened absorbent paper on the walls of the culture chamber. Move the muslin "table" to the edge of the culture chamber so that it is in contact with the vertical layer of paper. Discontinue feeding. In a short time the plasmodium will "crawl" onto the paper. Remove the paper, place it in a loosely covered container, and allow it to dry slowly. After several days the paper containing the sclerotium may be removed, cut into pieces of convenient size, and stored in an envelope for later use. The dormant organism will remain viable for one to two years.

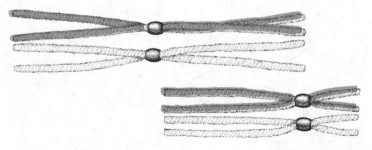

Figure T–15

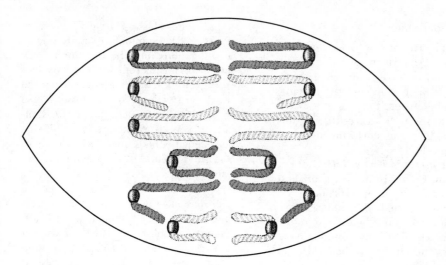

## A Mitosis Model

In Investigation 16.2 meiosis is illustrated by means of a model. A similar model illustrating mitosis may be used in Chapter 11 if time permits—especially if a good film showing mitosis in living cells is not available. In the meiosis model, strands of poppit beads represent chromatids; for mitosis, pipe cleaners will serve just as well, since it is not necessary to show crossing-over and, therefore, the "chromosomes" do not need to be broken. Students can make the "chromosomes" by threading two pipe cleaners through a small bead representing a kinetochore. If they use poppit beads, they can make a "chromosome" by fastening two strands together with a piece of pipe cleaner representing a kinetochore.

In the procedure given below, maternal and paternal "chromosomes" are differentiated by color. At this point the distinction is not necessary, and therefore a single color can be used. But there is something to be said for the pedagogical value of anticipating future developments (if such action does not obscure the present point), so you may wish to use two colors and briefly answer the inevitable questions. Be sure, however, to emphasize that the colors are symbolic rather than actual.

Make up 6 "chromosomes"—2 of them long, with the kinetochore in the middle; 2 medium-sized, with the kinetochore one-fourth of the way from the end; and 2 short, with the kinetochore in the middle. In each pair, make one "chromosome" of one color, one of another (see Figure T – 15).

Using a crayon, draw a spindle on a large piece of wrapping paper spread out on a table. The spindle should be large enough to accommodate the 6 "chromosomes" when they are arrayed on its equator.

Begin with the "chromosomes" lying at random on the spindle. Bring them from their position into line at the equator. To represent the splitting of the kinetochore, uncouple the "chromatids" and provide each pipe cleaner with a separate bead (or provide each strand of beads with a piece of pipe cleaner).

Now move one pipe cleaner of each pair toward one pole of the spindle and the other toward the other pole of the spindle. If six students are lined up on one side of the table and six on the other side, all the pipe cleaners can be moved simultaneously, just as the chromosomes move in mitosis. The pipe cleaners should be bent at the bead to represent the shape of chromosomes as they migrate to the poles of the spindle (Figure T – 16). Finally, compare the makeup of the set of "chromosomes" at each pole with that of the original set of "chromosomes."

## Audiovisual Materials

**Motion-picture films:** *The Life and Death of a Cell.* Department of Visual Communication, University of California. 16 mm. Color. 26 min. Significant content: The importance of the nucleus to the life of a cell, demonstrated through microsurgery; mitosis; effects of various environmental factors on living cells.

*The Cell, Structural Unit of Life.* Coronet Films. 16 mm. Color. 10 min. A short and simple film, useful as an introduction.

*Mitosis.* Encyclopaedia Britannica Films. 16 mm. Color. 24 min. Photomicrography shows the process of cell division in a living cell. Includes the effects of chemicals and radiation on mitosis.

*Cytoplasmic Streaming in Plant Cells.* Ealing Film-Loops (R. Allen and M. Allen, Princeton University). Color. 4 min., 5 sec. Film loop.

*An Inquiry: The Importance of the Nucleus.* BSCS Inquiry Film Loop. (Rand McNally #11–2971, 1968). What is the role of the nucleus? How would you test your ideas?

*Mitosis.* BSCS Inquiry Film Loop. (Rand McNally #11–2963, 1968). Attempts to lead the student to see the significance of mitotic events.

## Teacher's References

CHAMBERS, R., and E. L. CHAMBERS. *Explorations into the Nature of the Living Cell.* Cambridge, Mass.: Harvard University Press, 1961. (Summary of a lifetime of investigations into the functioning cell by means of microdissection. Excellent background to more recent biochemical work on fractionated cell constituents.)

GIESE, A. C. *Cell Physiology.* 2nd ed. Philadelphia: W. B. Saunders Co., 1962. (An excellent textbook that sticks closely to the fundamental physiology of the isolated cell.)

PORTER, K. R., and M. A. BONNEVILLE. *An Introduction to the Fine Structure of Cells and Tissues.* 2nd ed. Philadelphia: Lea & Febiger, Publishers, 1964. (Excellent illustrations, mostly from electronmicrographs of moderate magnification.)

ROBERTS, E. D., W. NOWINSKI, and F. A. SAEZ. *General Cytology.* 3rd ed. Philadelphia: W. B. Saunders Co., 1960. (A good standard textbook.)

SCHRADER, F. *Mitosis.* 2nd ed. New York: Columbia University Press, 1953.

STREHLER, B. L. *Time, Cells, and Aging.* New York: Academic Press, 1962. (Excellent summary of current knowledge by a leader in gerontological study.)

WHITE, P. R. *The Cultivation of Animal and Plant Cells.* 2nd ed. New York: The Ronald Press Co., 1963. (The techniques of *in vitro* cultivation of cells are not likely to be of everyday use to the high school teacher, but you should become familiar with their history.)

# 12

# Bioenergetics

---

## MAJOR IDEAS

1. Bioenergetics is the study of the chemistry of energy capture by organisms and energy transfer through the biosphere.

2. Chemical reactions in living cells are catalyzed by enzymes, which are proteins synthesized by the cells. Enzymes are highly specific in function.

3. Cellular respiration is a chemical process in which large multicarbon molecules release their energy as they are converted to smaller molecules. Oxygen is required in this process, and carbon dioxide and water are products.

4. Fermentation processes release energy from multicarbon molecules without the need for oxygen but result in products that still contain usable energy.

5. Energy released by respiration or fermentation is temporarily stored in adenosine triphosphate, from which it is released as needed for the activities of cells.

6. One such activity is the synthesis of the complex organic substances that account for almost all the dry weight of cells. For the most part, these cell substances turn out to be the familiar food substances: carbohydrates, fats, and proteins — plus nucleic acids.

7. Man's understanding of photosynthesis began with the chemical revolution that brought about the downfall of the phlogiston theory and reached a basic formulation in the first half of the nineteenth century. In the twentieth century new methods — especially chromatography and isotope techniques — have revealed the enormous physicochemical complexity behind the simple term "photosynthesis."

8. The present understanding of photosynthesis may be summarized in three sets of reactions. Two involve the transfer of light energy into chemical energy; the third, not requiring light, incorporates carbon dioxide into organic compounds. It appears that only "light capture" is unique to chlorophyll-bearing organisms.

## PLANNING AHEAD

If you have no experience with the apparatus to be used in Investigation 13.1, it would be wise to set it up and test its operation. If spring comes early in your locality, collect some dormant twigs and store in a refrigerator for use in illustrating stem structure.

Order frogs for Investigation 14.1 and *Daphnia* for Investigation 14.3. If you do not have facilities for maintaining these animals in your laboratory, you will have to estimate closely the time at which you will require them and specify a shipping date on your order. *Daphnia* are more difficult than frogs to maintain after arrival from the supplier.

Have you obtained the *Zebrina* that you will require for Investigation 15.1?

## GUIDELINES

You may feel that an understanding of biochemistry on the level treated in the *Green Version* is insufficient. The pertinent arguments in rebuttal are given on pp. T5 and T6. Nevertheless, although the writers see no reason for leading the bulk of tenth graders deep into the terminological jungles of biochemistry, they certainly believe that you, the teacher, should be well acquainted with the scheme of modern biochemistry and thus prepared to expand on the text with the occasional interested student or with superior, science-oriented classes. If you feel that your preparation is weak, fortify yourself with a careful reading of Lehninger's *Bioenergetics* (reference: p. 441).

Though energy flow is continuous, it must be reduced to sequential steps for study. You must do what you can to clarify the separate steps for your students, but convey the final impression that energy *flows* through the biosphere.

Work on bioenergetics can be conveniently begun by setting up Investigation 12.1. This should stimulate thinking about biochemical processes. While work on the investigation proceeds, a first study assignment might be pp. 407–408 (guide question 1) and 410–411 (guide question 3).

Following discussion of results from Investigations 12.1 and 12.2 is a rather long assignment (considering its complexity), pp. 413–419 (guide questions 4–9). Here considerable teacher explication may be required, but only as much as you think suitable for the particular students in each class. A rough understanding of Figure 12·10 may be all that can be achieved in many cases, and Investigation 12.3 may be assigned to a group of students for demonstration to the class.

Pp. 421–426 (guide questions 10–15) form another difficult assignment. Help will be required on structural formulas; they look quite formidable to beginners. You will find it useful to have molecular-model kits available; you may be able to borrow these from the chemistry teachers. Or quite serviceable "exploded" models can be constructed from Styrofoam balls and toothpicks. Avoid getting involved at this time in the genetic significance of nucleic acids.

Pp. 426–429 (guide questions 16–17) form a relatively simple prelude to Investigation 12.4. Finally, pp. 431–437 (guide questions 19–23) can be skimmed rather lightly if your classes show signs of restlessness with biochemistry, but some attention should be given to Investigation 12.5.

## TEACHING NOTES

### LIFE, ENERGY, AND CELLS
(pp. 407–408)

Stress that the bulk of living things are alike in the way they store and utilize chemical energy. Plants and animals (as well as most protists) utilize the same chemicals and processes to obtain energy from their stored fuel.

### INVESTIGATION 12.1

### BIOENERGETICS: AN INTRODUCTORY VIEW (pp. 408–410)

#### Materials

Any variety of pea will do. Beans may be substituted.

For information on the construction and use of volumeters, see p. 51 of *Innovations in Equipment and Techniques for the Biology Teaching Laboratory* (reference: see p. T91). The jar should be filled with tap water and allowed to stand overnight so that the water will come to room temperature. Some volumeters come equipped with syringes on the adjustment tube. If you do not have syringes, you may insert droppers in the tubing above the pinch clamps. The syringes or droppers will allow you to adjust the position of the indicator drops in the pipettes after the stopper has been placed in the test tube. Inexpensive plastic syringes are handy for placing the indicator drop in the pipette. Glass tubing drawn out to a fine point will also aid in doing this tricky job. The indicator solution should have a little detergent added to it so that the drop will hold together in the pipette. Food coloring can be used in place of eosin. Attach the pipettes so that the lower numbers are toward the volumeter. This gives negative numbers when zero readings are subtracted if the indicator drop moves toward the volumeter (as it should in the pipettes attached to respiring peas). Small-bore glass tubing may be attached to rulers if pipettes are not available.

Glass beads may be of any size, but the nearer to pea size the better.

When inserting glass tubing or thermometers into rubber stoppers, use a cork-boring set. (See p. T94.)

#### Procedure

A schedule is presented here to assist you in organizing this investigation:

**Day 1.** Special team assembles vacuum bottles and obtains two batches of peas, each equal to 200 ml in volume. One batch of peas is covered with water, the other left dry. Other teams assemble volumeters and count out peas. One set of peas is soaked overnight, the other left dry. Volumeter jars are to be filled with tap water.

**Day 2.** Special team places peas in vacuum bottles A and B as directed and takes initial temperature readings. Other teams place peas and beads in volumeter tubes and make readings of the positions of indicator drops.

**Day 3.** Special team disassembles apparatus after taking final readings. Ask this team to record any odor noted in the vacuum bottles. (The lack of alcohol will be useful in comparing this investigation with 12.3 later.) Special team reports results to class. Other teams disassemble apparatus and plot data.

Great care must be taken in placing the Ascarite on the cotton. The inside walls of the test tubes must be thoroughly dry. Moisture coming in contact with Ascarite liberates heat, causing an expansion of the air in the closed system. This upsets readings. If your students have developed a genuine "show-me" attitude, the ability of Ascarite to absorb $CO_2$ should be demonstrated.

Working with volumeters is sometimes discouraging. A number of factors have noticeable effects on confined gases (changes in temperature, changes in atmospheric pressure), and gravity can affect the indicator drop. But perhaps the greatest source of error is a system that is not airtight.

If possible, provide time for two or more sets of readings of the volumeter. You may want students to graph class averages rather than individual team results.

## Discussion

The discussion should be based on the graphs produced by the teams. The chemistry involved here is simple: germinating seeds require oxygen to release the energy of their stored food. As oxygen is used by the germinating peas (dry peas use so little that, at most, only a slight change in the volume of the air will be noted), atmospheric pressure exceeds the pressure of the confined air, and the indicator drop is forced farther into the pipette.

- (2): The third tube is an overall control.

- (3): The glass beads are used to equalize the volume of solid matter in the three tubes.

- (4) and • (5): If the pipettes are attached so that the zero is at the end next to the rubber tubing, the numbers recorded as the drop moves toward the volumeter are smaller than the initial rest-position number. Then subtracting the rest position from the readings produces negative numbers; these correspond to decreases in the volume of confined air. Positive numbers indicate that the confined air is expanding. Of course, if the zero on a pipette is distal to the volumeter (as seems to be the case in Figure 12 · 1), the reverse is true: a positive number indicates volume decrease and a negative number indicates volume increase.

- (7): The tube containing dry peas and glass beads should perform much like the tube containing only glass beads.

- (8): Soaked peas use up oxygen, thus decreasing the volume of air in that chamber. Dry peas do not use enough oxygen to produce a similar change.

- (9): There is, of course, no evidence in this investigation to rule out nitrogen. Be sure the cocksure student is deflated.

- (10): Use of Ascarite implies that something is likely to happen that would increase the volume of $CO_2$, thus masking volume change due to other air gases. Could it be that germinating seeds produce $CO_2$?

- (11): The amounts of substances are changing. Oxygen or nitrogen from the air is apparently being used by the germinating seeds, and it seems reasonable to suppose that $CO_2$ is produced.

- (12): If all goes well, the temperature of the germinating peas is higher than that of the dry peas. Thus, the germinating peas must liberate heat, a form of energy, while the dormant peas do not.

---

## ENERGY-RELEASING PROCESSES
(in part — pp. 410–411)

**p. 410, ¶ 4:** A little practice with the calculation of calories will help establish the concept. How many calories are absorbed by 20 g (20 ml) of water if the temperature of the water rises 3 degrees Celsius? A medium-sized apple contains about 100 Calories. How many calories is this? By how many degrees would this much energy raise the temperature of one liter (1000 g) of water?

**p. 411, note 1:** Kcal = kilogram calorie, that is, amount of heat required to raise 1000 g of water 1°C.

**p. 411, ¶ 4:** Students who have encountered enzymes in previous science study are likely to have the idea that enzymes act only in digestion. This is a difficult idea to eradicate; Investigation 12.2 should help.

---

## INVESTIGATION 12.2

---

## A STUDY OF BIOCHEMICAL REACTIONS (pp. 411–412)

### Materials

Three-percent hydrogen peroxide, or $H_2O_2$, is available at the drugstore or supermarket. It is better not to buy it until you are ready to use it — the fresher the better.

Use only fresh liver; it is important to be sure that it has not been frozen. Unfrozen liver is becoming difficult to obtain in markets. If necessary, sacrifice a frog.

Fine sand intended for grinding is available from supply houses, but washed builder's sand will do.

It is not necessary for each team to have its own boiling water. Have a couple of liters of hot water ready at two or three points in the lab, and as the work begins bring these to the boiling point.

## Procedure

Directions to the student are quite simple, and you should not need to do much more than provide the equipment and materials. If everything is ready, the procedure can easily be carried out in only one period.

## Discussion

No investigation in the course has tighter reasoning from observations to conclusion than this one. Be sure that you guide the discussion along lines of disciplined thought in order to take advantage of this construction.

- (1): Tube 1 establishes the lack of reactivity between $MnO_2$ and $H_2O$. This is necessary because the remaining tubes contain 97% $H_2O$ and only 3% $H_2O_2$.

- (2): The only evidence is that there appears to be as much $MnO_2$ following the reaction as there was before.

- (3): If the student weighed the amount of $MnO_2$ added and after the reaction reclaimed an equal amount of $MnO_2$, he might conclude that the $MnO_2$ was a catalyst rather than a reactant.

- (4): Both $H_2O_2 \rightarrow H_2 + O_2$, and $2\,H_2O_2 \rightarrow 2\,H_2O + O_2$ are logical possibilities for production of the gas evident in the reaction.

- (5): A glowing splint bursts into flame when placed in the mouth of a test tube where oxygen is being produced, but if a mixture of $H_2$ and $O_2$ is produced, a small explosion occurs on ignition. You may have to supply some background at this point and repeat the operation of Tube 2 during the discussion so that the splint test may be applied.

- (6): If liver contains a substance that catalyzes decomposition of $H_2O_2$, grinding might liberate more of the substance.

- (7): To demonstrate that sand has no effect upon $H_2O_2$.

- (8): The substance in liver that catalyzes decomposition of $H_2O_2$ is destroyed by heat.

- (9): The catalyst in liver is made inactive by heating, but $MnO_2$ continues to act as a catalyst after being heated. In addition, of course, no black powder is visible in liver, but most students recognize this as weak evidence.

- (11): The $H_2O_2$-decomposing substance is found in plants as well as animals.

By this time most students will recognize that the substance decomposing $H_2O_2$ is probably an enzyme. The teacher may supply the information that enzymes are proteins and proteins are sensitive to high temperatures.

---

## ENERGY-RELEASING PROCESSES
(cont. — pp. 413–419)

**p. 413, ¶ 1:** A distinction between breathing and respiration can be made. Breathing is the process that moves respiratory gases to and from respiratory organs such as lungs or gills; respiration is the exchange of $O_2$ and $CO_2$ and, by extension, the chemical process that involves this exchange in cells.

**p. 413, note 2:** The "lost" heat of metabolism provides the cells of a "warm-blooded" animal with an internal environment that is warmer (usually) than the external environment, and this in general allows the cells to carry on metabolic reactions at a greater rate. To some extent this is true of any organism, but "warm-blooded" animals have means to conserve metabolic heat.

**p. 413, Fig. 12·2:** You will find molecular-model kits effective teaching aids in introducing students to structural formulas. Point out that the three-dimensional character of molecules such as glucose allows points of attachment for enzymes. The structural formulas given here and on following pages are, of course, not to be memorized. They are intended to show the complexity of even relatively simple organic compounds and to provide a mental image for differentiating large classes of such compounds.

**p. 414, Fig. 12·3:** The type used in the diagram does not show that the calories referred to are Kcal.

**p. 414, ¶ 3:** ATP is a large molecule. When a phosphate group is hydrolyzed from the parent molecule by enzymes, electrons throughout the molecule are allowed to assume lower energy states. Thus the electrons in ATP as a whole—not alone at the position indicated by the wavy line—are of higher energy than are the electrons in ADP and the released phosphate group. It is the stabilizing of the entire ADP molecule by lowering the energy states of the electrons that is believed to account for the release of energy in the reaction:

$$ATP \rightarrow ADP + \textcircled{P} + energy$$

The energy state of ATP is lowered by at least 7000 calories per mole when ADP is produced from it. It has been calculated that a minimum of 2,500,000 molecules of ATP are broken down to ADP and phosphate per second during synthesis in a bacterial cell.

**p. 415, Fig. 12·4:** If your students are encountering chemical formulas for the first time, they may easily confuse the biochemist's abbreviations, such as ATP and ADP, for formulas. Even if students have some familiarity with formulas, it is well to emphasize the distinction.

**p. 415, Fig. 12·5:** The diagram will have to be discussed in class. Help the student to trace the reactions, but do not dwell on specific steps. The point to make is that during chemical breakdown of a fairly large molecule, such as glucose, to small molecules of $H_2O$ and $CO_2$, the energy of the larger molecule is transferred (as high-energy electrons) to ADP + $\textcircled{P}$ → ATP. The colored lines represent principal energy transfers within the system of reactions.

**pp. 415–417:** These pages explain Figure 12·5. Electron carriers are the large organic molecules flavin adenine dinucleotide, FAD, and nicotinamide adenine dinucleotide, NAD. (In older works NAD is referred to as diphosphopyridine nucleotide, DPN.) Both FAD and NAD are derived from vitamins of the B group. Electrons are transferred from NAD and FAD to cytochromes on their way to the $H^+$ and $O_2$. Cytochrome action can be blocked by minute amounts of cyanide, explaining the toxicity of that compound.

**p. 418, Fig. 12·10:** In reviewing this diagram, stress the one-way flow of energy in the biosphere. Refer students to Figures 1·12 and 1·20. Students do not automatically link their understanding of biochemistry to their understanding of ecology.

**p. 419, Fig. 12·11:** Fermentation begins with glycolysis, as does cellular respiration (upper left of Figure 12·5). But in mammals lactic acid resulting from intensive work by skeletal muscle may be carried from muscle to liver and there oxidized aerobically or even regenerated into glucose.

**p. 419, note 1:** *Clostridium tetani* cells, like those of other strictly anaerobic organisms, do not possess the enzymes of the electron carrier system, so we might expect them to lack mitochondria (p. 418, ¶ 3). And this is, indeed, the case.

## INVESTIGATION 12.3

### FERMENTATION (pp. 420–421)

The objective in this investigation is to provide the student with an opportunity to obtain some qualitative data on the most familiar kind of fermentation.

#### Materials

The most convenient size for the vacuum bottle is 1 pint. You will need to make the limewater a day or two before use. Mix 10 g of calcium hydroxide, $Ca(OH)_2$, in a liter of water at room temperature. Decant and use the saturated solution formed, but do not disturb the $Ca(OH)_2$ that settles out.

Use unsulfured molasses only. Undiluted grape juice to which about 5 g of sugar per 100 ml has been added may be used in place of molasses.

#### Procedure

This investigation takes one period to set up and portions of two other days for observations.

See Investigation 6.4, p. T94, for a method of inserting the thermometer into the rubber stopper.

#### Discussion

- (1) and (2): In addition to the temperature change, the odor of alcohol, if detected, is evidence of a chemical reaction, as is any change noted in the limewater. An abundance of foam is evidence of the formation of a gas. If yeast or bacteria are accidentally introduced into Bottle B, some reactions may be noted in it, but they are not likely to be as great as in Bottle A. Compare odor with that detected in the vacuum bottle containing germinating peas in Investigation 12.1.
- (3): Conditions are not strictly anaerobic, since air is trapped above the solution. Yeasts are facultative anaerobes, using oxygen if it is available and reverting to fermentation when necessary.

- (8): The variable is the yeast introduced into Bottle A.
- (9): Heat is produced as in Bottle A of Investigation 12.1.
- (10): There was no alcohol produced by the peas.

### SYNTHESES (pp. 421–426)

Molecular models are useful throughout the teaching of this section.

**p. 422, ¶ 2:** If students use models of glucose and fructose molecules and attempt to combine them into a model of sucrose, they will eventually note that the equivalent of water—two H's and an O—has to be removed. This illustrates dehydration synthesis. But emphasize that enzyme mediation is necessary for the process to occur in cells.

**p. 422, note 6:** Weight is an impediment to locomotion, and so a low-weight fuel is an advantage to a locomoting organism. Compare use of gasoline in airplanes with use of coal in many stationary engines.

**p. 422, ¶ 5:** Glycerol is an alcohol sold under the commercial name glycerin.

**p. 422, note 8:** It was used as a lubricant in Investigation 12.3.

**p. 423, ¶ 2:** Working with models again demonstrates dehydration synthesis. If you call attention to the energy your students expend in making fat-molecule models, you may clinch the idea that all syntheses require energy available from ATP. Keep the thought of the expenditure of energy in biosynthesis before the students all the time. This is the real point of taking up synthesis in a chapter dealing with bioenergetics.

**p. 425, ¶ 2:** Deoxyribose differs from ribose merely in having one less oxygen atom. Unfortunately the term "base" appears here in association with nucleic *acids*. Students must be cautioned that in this context "base" does not mean "alkali." It simply means "that to which something else is attached."

**p. 425, ¶ 4:** This is not the time to enlarge on DNA and its structure; that is done later when it has meaningful application. Here nucleic acids are merely a class of organic constituents of living matter. At this point the most meaningful relationship is that between nucleic acids and ATP and ADP.

## PHOTOSYNTHESIS (in part)
(pp. 426–429)

From here on, the discussion deals with the cellular capture of external energy instead of the release and transformation of energy within organisms.

**pp. 426–427:** This is another opportunity to emphasize the international character of science.

**p. 428, note 2:** Enzymes *are* proteins (though, of course, not all proteins are enzymes).

**p. 428, Fig. 12·19:** Students may be struck by the similarity in structure between chloroplasts and mitochondria. Though the physiology is different, the stepwise changing of one compound into another requires an extensive and intimate interaction of enzymes. A layered construction appears to suit this purpose.

A single granum is made up of alternating protein and lipid layers. In one protein layer are the enzymes needed for the "light reaction" in photosynthesis. Below this, like the filling in a sandwich, is a lipid layer containing chlorophylls, carotenoids, and phospholipid molecules. The lower protein layer contains the enzymes of the "dark reactions."

## INVESTIGATION 12.4

### SEPARATION OF LEAF PIGMENTS
(pp. 429–431)

Though more sophisticated separation methods are now widely employed by biochemists, paper chromatography remains

useful. And as a demonstration of the basic principle of chromatography, the separation of leaf pigments is highly effective and meaningful to high school students. The materials and equipment required for this investigation are easily obtained in quantity, the manipulations are simple, and the students' satisfaction with their results is great; therefore it is desirable to have very small teams—preferably pairs. Some very useful background on plant pigments for both teacher and student may be found in Stegner (reference: p. 442).

### Materials

Use strips cut from a roll or large sheet of Whatman #1 filter paper. Care should be exercised in handling the paper so that fingerprints are kept to a minimum. The disks of filter paper ordinarily used in chemistry classes are too small to yield a strip the required length.

Ordinary ether (diethyl ether) *cannot be used*.

Theoretically, any leaves containing chlorophyll are usable, but some kinds are better than others. *Pelargonium* (household geranium) is good; but the pigments in spinach leaves are especially rich and easy to extract—and spinach is easily obtained at all seasons.

Pipettes with suitably fine tips may be made by heating a piece of tubing, pulling it out to a small diameter, allowing it to cool, and cutting it in two at the middle of the constriction. The large end of each piece can be made to fit the rubber bulb from an ordinary medicine dropper by heating to softness and enlarging with the shank of a triangular file.

### Procedure

One period is required to set up the chromatographic chamber and to prepare the leaf extract. An additional period is needed for developing the chromatogram, making observations, and discussing the results. If you do not have a double period, the assembly of the apparatus and extraction of the pigments may be done one day and the development of the chromatogram the next. Store the pigment extract in a refrigerator. Cutting the spinach leaves into pieces with scissors will make the grinding easier. Keep the amount of acetone very small (only a few milliliters are needed) to secure as concentrated a solution as possible.

Discussion

- (2): During discussion some students may attempt to report what they subsequently discovered instead of what they observed in the extracted pigment.

- (3): If good separation has been obtained, several bands of pigment can be seen. A band of yellow pigment is found close to the leading edge of the solvent. It is likely to be the palest of the bands. It contains carotenes and has an $R_f$ of almost 1.00. ($R_f$ = distance of band from origin divided by distance of leading edge of solvent from origin.) Much lower on the paper, starting at about $R_f$ 0.4, are, first, another yellow band (sometimes distinguishable as two separate bands) that contain xanthophylls; second, a band of bluish-green chlorophyll $a;$ and a third, a band of yellowish-green chlorophyll $b$. (If the pigment extract has been allowed to stand for some time, a gray band may be seen above the xanthophylls; this is pheophytin, a decomposition product of chlorophylls.)

- (6): Usually the chlorophylls are so abundant that other pigments are masked. But in some leaves, especially those of ornamental varieties developed by horticulturists (e.g., varieties of Japanese and Norway maples and of barberry), red anthocyanins may mask the chlorophylls. Anthocyanins are soluble in hot water and insoluble in acetone, so they may be separated by differential solution.

- (7): Spinach leaves do not normally contain anthocyanins. However, since

the mass of ground leaves is not likely to be left white by the process used in this investigation, students have little basis for answering this question except for a healthy skepticism.

- (8): Chlorophylls are rather unstable pigments. As they decompose, the other, more stable pigments in the leaf are unmasked. In addition, glucose in the leaf may be converted to anthocyanins.

- (9): They all started from the same point.

- (10): They all started at the same time (when the developer reached the pigment spot), and they all stopped at the same time (when the paper was removed from the tube and the developer dried).

- (11): Since they all moved for the same time but traveled different distances, they must have moved at different speeds. These differing speeds depend upon differences in adsorption to the molecules of the paper.

For well-known mixtures, such as leaf extract, identification of the major groups of substances (carotenes and xanthophylls are still mixtures) is sufficient on the basis of color and $R_f$. Positive identification is made by cutting the bands apart, separately redissolving the substances, running absorption spectra in a spectrophotometer, and then comparing the curves with curves obtained from the pure substances.

PHOTOSYNTHESIS (cont.)
(pp. 431–437)

Play down the terminology and emphasize the flow of energy—the bioenergetics. It is *not* intended that the student memorize the details of biochemistry involved in the description of photosynthesis. At the least, however, presentation of the letterpress and the diagrams (Figures 12·22, 12·23, and 12·24) should add up to some appreciation for the complexity of an apparently (p. 431) simple process and for the work of biochemists who have used great ingenuity in unraveling the tangled threads of evidence. In addition, most students should carry away the knowledge: that photosynthesis—as usually defined—consists of an initial light-trapping stage and a subsequent light-independent synthesis; that research in photosynthesis uses chromatography and analytical methods involving isotopes; and that knowledge has not yet reached the point where man is independent of plants. Even to accomplish these minimum aims, however, some details must be given; it is not enough merely to *state* that photosynthesis is complex.

**p. 431, ¶ 1:** You may find students saying that animals use respiration to obtain energy, but green plants use photosynthesis. This is true, but a misunderstanding often exists. Photosynthesis *is not* a green plant's way of obtaining energy from its stored food. Point out the difference in the source of energy in photosynthesis and respiration.

**p. 432, Fig. 12·21:** Point out that the horizontal axis of this graph represents a segment of Figure 1·10. Figure 12·21 gives a partial answer to the question, Why are plants green? Since chlorophylls absorb most light in the blue and the red ends of the spectrum, the green (mixed with some yellow), which chlorophylls absorb least, is reflected to our eyes. The figure does not, of course, give any clue to the reason chlorophyll fails to utilize energy in the green portion of the spectrum.

**p. 433, ¶ 3:** Remind students that ATP, ADP, PGAL, NADP, and RuDP, encountered here and later, are abbreviations rather than chemical formulas. Unfortunately, the situation is somewhat complicated by $NADPH_2$, where the $H_2$ does indicate two hydrogen atoms.

**p. 433, Fig. 12·22:** The electron carriers in photosynthesis are cytochromes (one is the same as used in respiration) and ferredoxin. Note that this diagram shows only one of the ways in which energy of sunlight is transferred to ATP in the "light reactions" of photosynthesis.

**p. 435, Fig. 12·24:** This sequence transfers the energy stored in ATP and $NADPH_2$ to phosphoglyceraldehyde, a three-carbon compound from which glucose (by now a familiar molecule to your students) can be made.

**p. 436, ¶ 3:** Literally speaking, the "dark reactions" are not a part of *photo*synthesis. They might occur in organisms that do not contain chlorophyll, and some biochemists think they do. The end point of photosynthesis is a matter of convention. We end with PGAL; often the production of glucose is considered the end, and for some purposes, the production of starch is considered a test for photosynthesis (Investigation 13.2).

## INVESTIGATION 12.5

### PHOTOSYNTHETIC RATE
(pp. 438–439)

### Materials

Large, healthy stalks of elodea are necessary for this investigation.

The reflectors on many gooseneck lamps do not accommodate 150-watt bulbs. You may need to experiment with improvised reflectors. Heavy aluminum foil is a good material for this.

### Procedure

If the water bath is set up a day ahead, most of the air and chlorine will escape. Otherwise, gases escaping from the water may obscure $O_2$ bubbles.

### Discussion

There are only three points to be graphed. Students have a tendency to bunch these points. Be sure the entire available width of the grid is used for the horizontal scale.

- (1): By this time your students have gained some facility in stating hypotheses. They may come up with a statement concerning decrease of photosynthetic rate with increase of distance but are not likely to be acquainted with the inverse-square law.
- (2)–• (4): Whatever results you obtain, they should be related to the hypothesis.
- (5): The age and condition of the plant are important considerations. Though the students have not yet studied leaf structure, some may know that pollutants in water and air can clog the stomata through which gases are exchanged. $CO_2$ must be present. The temperature of the environment is also important.
- (6): $CO_2$ is supplied by the $NaHCO_3$ in a sequence of reactions that may be summarized:

$$H^+ + HCO_3^- \leftrightarrow H_2CO_3 \leftrightarrow H_2O + CO_2$$

  Temperature is controlled and healthy elodea is used.
- (7): Organisms in the water capable of producing $O_2$ by photosynthesis, and organisms capable of using the $O_2$ produced, are uncontrolled factors. Filtering the aquarium or pond water would reduce this variable.

## GUIDE QUESTIONS (p. 440)

4. You may want a student to report on bomb calorimeters, in which total combustion of a substance occurs, permitting accurate measurement of calories of heat produced.

15. Ribose, phosphate groups, and a base (adenine in the case of ATP) are common to both.

## PROBLEMS (pp. 440–441)

2. If nitrate reductase can provide a ready source of nitrogen for the amine group of amino acids, then conceivably artificially produced proteins could be made to augment the diet of man and his domestic animals. This source of food would circumvent the slow nitrogen cycle.

3. See C. P. Swanson, *The Cell* (reference: p. 406). The point here is that volume increases much faster than surface area. All the materials utilized and discarded by the volume of a cell must enter via the surface; as a result, the surface/volume ratio sets a practical limit to the size of a physiologically active cell. A sphere is the extreme demonstration of surface/volume ratio; flattening and elongation reduce the disparity.

4. The oxygen debt arises when ATP is used faster than it can be restored through aerobic respiration. The limiting factor is the rate at which oxygen can be delivered to the cell to act as electron acceptor in the last part of respiration. When oxygen is not available, anaerobic energy release occurs, leaving lactic acid. Following exertion, heavy breathing is required to supply oxygen needed for final oxidation of lactic acid.

5. Enzymes put amino-acid building blocks in sequences characteristic of wheat physiology. Through digestion, wheat proteins are reduced to amino acids and these are then synthesized into new proteins characteristic of human physiology. Unfortunately, wheat proteins do not contain the various amino acids in proper quantities to synthesize human proteins adequately, and human physiology is deficient in ability to synthesize amino acids; therefore wheat is not a sufficient source of protein in human diet. (See p. 747, ¶ 3.)

6. By rapid photosynthesis the by-product oxygen can be supplied in quantities sufficient to meet a plant's needs. The increased photosynthesis is a homeostatic mechanism that would tend to maintain the equilibrium that normally exists between $CO_2$ and $O_2$ in our atmosphere. This tends to confirm Oparin's assumption that the primitive atmosphere was deficient in $O_2$ and the consequent idea

that photosynthetic organisms changed the composition of the atmosphere as they became numerous.

7. $CO_2$ in the atmosphere produces a so-called "greenhouse" effect: radiant energy from the sun penetrates the atmosphere to reach the hydrosphere and lithosphere, but the radiation of heat from the earth is hindered. If there were higher concentrations of $CO_2$ during the Carboniferous, this might explain the tropic-like conditions then prevailing in vast areas of middle and even high latitudes. An abundance of $CO_2$ would also have promoted the rapid photosynthesis that evidently prevailed in coal-age forests. The Industrial Revolution, dating from the late eighteenth century, has returned much of the carbon in coal beds to the atmosphere in the form of $CO_2$. Thus there has been a steady increase in the $CO_2$ concentration in our atmosphere. (See p. 765, ¶ 2.)

8. See note to p. 436, ¶ 3 (p. T178).

9. Once amino acids were available, enzymes could be produced by dehydration synthesis. Any such enzyme that could catalyze reactions using radiant energy would have given proto-organisms that possessed it a distinct advantage since radiant energy was much more abundant than the declining heat and electrical energy resources of the aging earth.


## SUPPLEMENTARY MATERIALS

### Additional Problems

1. Although they are built of the same amino acids, the proteins in the cells of a bean plant are different from those in the cells of a dog. How can you explain this? [*This involves the same reasoning as Problem #5, p. 441.*]

2. Why does an enzyme catalyze only a specific reaction rather than many different reactions? [*This involves current theory of enzyme action. See Simpson and Beck (reference: p. 442), pp. 59–61.*]

3. Most consumers—including man—are unable to synthesize many of the substances needed for their metabolism. For example, man cannot synthesize many of the amino acids and some of the essential parts of the enzymes involved in respiration. How does this situation complicate the nutrition of such organisms? How can you explain an inability to synthesize a substance? [*Such organisms require more than an energy source and inorganic materials. They must also take in with their food the molecules they cannot synthesize. Some of these, precursors of enzymes, are called vitamins. Synthetic inabilities are due to lack of the necessary enzymes.*]

4. When isolated chloroplasts are used in research on photosynthesis, what assumption must be made? [*It must be assumed that all of the enzymes required are located in the chloroplasts.*]

5. ATP from the cells of plants has been used to energize the life activities of animal cells. What further question does this suggest to you? [*Perhaps the most obvious is, Can ATP derived from animal cells be used to energize the dark reactions of photosynthesis in plant cells?*]

### Invitations to Enquiry

Invitation 19, *Biology Teacher's Handbook* (reference: p. T35), pp. 113–115, deals with photosynthesis and the concept of serial causation in natural processes.

Invitation 27, p. 148 of the *Handbook*, deals with photosynthesis and the concept of limiting factors. Be sure to relate this to the idea of limiting factors in population dynamics.

### Audiovisual Materials

**Motion-picture films:** *Biochemistry and Molecular Structure* (A Chem Study Film). Color. 13 min. University of California. An excellent background film.

*Pattern of Energy Transfer.* Color. 28 min. McGraw-Hill Book Co., Inc. Considers energy transfer from sunlight to utilization in cell metabolism.

*Cell Biology: Life Functions.* Color. 19 min. Coronet Films. Considers both physical and chemical functions. Animation helps to explain some organic chemistry.

*Photosynthesis.* Color. 21 min. Encyclopaedia Britannica Films, Inc. Laboratory demonstrations are used to show how the process of photosynthesis is studied.

*Measuring Rate of Photosynthesis,* by J. W. Kimball, Phillips Academy, Andover, Mass. Color. 4 min. Disks of bean leaf are floated on $NaHCO_3$ solution. When oxygen is removed from the leaf, it sinks. As irradiated disks produce oxygen through photosynthesis, they float to the top. Available from Ealing.

*Photosynthetic Fixation of Carbon Dioxide, Parts I and II.* Color. 7 min. Iowa State University. Carbon-14 is used as a tracer in coleus-leaf photosynthesis. Available from Ealing.

## Teacher's References

See also the references for Chapter 11 (p. T168).

CAMPBELL, P. N., and G. D. GRENVILLE (eds.). *Essays in Biochemistry.* 2 vols. New York: Academic Press, Inc., 1965 and 1966. (Reviews of five fields in biochemistry for those who have some background in the physical sciences.)

CHANGEUX, J. P. "The Control of Biochemical Reactions," *Scientific American,* April, 1965. P. 36.

CHELDELIN, V. H., and R. W. NEWBURGH. *The Chemistry of Some Life Processes.* New York: Reinhold Publishing Corp., 1962. (A summary of research and some leading theories.)

CLARK, B. F. C., and KJELD A. MARCKER. "How Proteins Start," *Scientific American,* Jan., 1968. P. 36.

DAWKINS, M. J. R., and DAVID HULL. "The Production of Heat by Fat," *Scientific American,* Aug., 1965. P. 62.

GREEN, D. E. "The Mitochondrion," *Scientific American,* Jan., 1964. P. 63.

LWOFF, A. *Biological Order.* Cambridge, Mass.: The M.I.T. Press, 1962. (A theoretical consideration of the nature of biological organization by a leader in molecular biology.)

# 13

## The Functioning Plant

---

## MAJOR IDEAS

1. The growth and development of plants depend upon use of nutrients, transformation of energy, internal circulation of materials, synthesis of new molecules, and chemical controls, much as do the growth and development of animals.

2. A high degree of differentiation of tissues and organs is characteristic of the most abundant and conspicuous land plants.

3. As specialized organs of photosynthesis, leaves exhibit (both externally and internally) close correlation between form and function.

4. Complementarity of form and function is as conspicuous in roots as in leaves and is only a little less so in stems.

5. In the majority of land plants, water is constantly being lost (principally through leaves) and is constantly being absorbed from soil (through roots). In addition to performing the function of absorption, roots usually furnish plants with anchorage and with a site for the storage of food.

6. The complex microscopic structure of stems is primarily associated with conduction of liquids in the plant body. As yet, biophysical explanations of conduction do not completely account for all observations.

7. In contrast to animal growth, the growth of multicellular plants is a result of mitotic activity in persistently undifferentiated tissues — meristems.

8. After plant cells have been formed by mitosis, their increase in size is, in many cases, under the control of auxins. Auxin distribution is influenced by gravity and light; differential

distribution of auxin results in changes in the direction of stem elongation.

9. Because they are the most conspicuous plants and the most important ones to man, tracheophytes receive the major emphasis in studies of plant structure and function. But all plants have varying synthetic powers—even the fungi, which lack photosynthesis—and they all exchange substances with their environment.

## PLANNING AHEAD

If you have delayed ordering frogs for Investigation 14.1 and *Daphnia* for Investigation 14.3, this is the last possible moment to do so. To avoid a last-minute rush, prepare the hydrochloric acid dilutions and the sucrose, acetic acid, quinine sulfate, and sodium chloride solutions required for Investigations 14.2 and 14.4. However, the solutions for Procedure C of Investigation 14.4 must be prepared just before use. Quinine sulfate may be difficult to obtain.

If you have a greenhouse, you should be propagating quantities of *Zebrina* for Investigation 15.1 and coleus for Investigation 16.1. If you do not, you should have made arrangements for obtaining these materials at the time when they will be needed.

In many localities fertile chicken eggs are not easy to obtain. You might, therefore, begin to look for egg sources for Investigation 16.3.

## GUIDELINES

By and large, high school students are not greatly enamored of plants. This makes desirable for Chapter 13 a start that will capture attention if not engender enthusiasm. You undoubtedly know best how to do this with your students, but here are a few possibilities:

1. Begin by setting up Investigation 13.3. Many students develop special interest in plants they have themselves nurtured and thus become involved in plant study. Further, this approach allows you to finish this long investigation before you must shift attention to the more fascinating animals. And nothing in the earlier parts of the procedure requires previous study of the text materials.

2. Begin by displaying a variety of plants, including among usual kinds—such as geranium and coleus—some that exhibit special adaptations. Some suggestions for the latter: *Aloe* or *Agave* (with thick fleshy leaves that resist desiccation), *Kalanchoe* (plantlets on leaf margins), *Monstera* (perforated leaves), *Maranta* (leaf enfolding at night), and, of course, various cacti. A *Sanseveria* placed in the dark for several weeks makes a good contrast with one kept in the light and is interesting to watch as the work on Chapter 13 proceeds.

3. For students who tend toward an intellectual approach, the talk by Rabinowitch on the record *The Scientists Speak* (cited: p. T34) makes an excellent beginning by linking the study of photosynthesis at the end of Chapter 12 to the study of general anatomy and physiology of plants in Chapter 13.

Parts of this chapter may be quite familiar to students and teachers. Insofar as material is familiar, no learning occurs, of course; you must not allow nostalgia to induce unprofitable lingering. If students are already well acquainted with macroscopic anatomy of vascular plants, attention should be focused on microscopic anatomy and, even more, on physiology. Although morphology and physiology are complementary, it is possible to approach the systems level of biology either by way of structure, which is then elucidated in terms of function, or by way of function, which is then explored in the light of observable structure. On the high school level the second approach seems preferable wherever a happy compromise between the two extremes cannot be arranged.

Depending upon the background of students and the extent of their need for concrete referents for their thinking, the teacher may introduce some purely illustrative laboratory work. A session or two devoted to observing the microstructure of plant organs may be desirable—preferably beginning with hand-sectioned materials (see filmstrip reference: p. T193).

A reasonable plan of study assignments for the chapter is: first, pp. 443–448 (guide questions 1–4), to which Investigations 13.1 and 13.2, concerning leaf functions, properly belong; second, pp. 451–465 (guide questions 5–13), with which some laboratory investigation of microscopic anatomy may be included; third, pp. 465–470 and 472–474 (guide questions 14–19) taken together while work on Investigation 13.3 is being concluded.

## TEACHING NOTES

### VASCULAR PLANTS: LEAVES
(pp. 443–448)

**p. 443, ¶ 2:** Reviewing Chapter 9, pp. 308–310 and pp. 325–326, may help students recall the importance of phytoplankton to productivity in the biosphere. Reference to these pages is especially important if you have skipped Chapter 9.

**p. 444, note 1:** Most cacti are essentially leafless except when young (some cactus spines may be modified leaves); so also many succulent euphorbias (Figure 10 · 35). In pinesap and beechdrop (*Epifagus*) and dodder (*Cuscuta*), which are nonphotosynthetic tracheophytes, leaves are represented by small, scalelike structures.

**p. 445, Fig. 13 · 2:** This is a wide open question. Examples: many ferns, clovers, vetches, ash, hickory, etc.

**p. 446, Fig. 13 · 3:** Examples of differences in *B* compared to *A:* thinner, one layer of palisade cells, palisade cells shorter. The term "palisade" need not be used.

**p. 446, Fig. 13 · 4:** Have students compare the epidermis of the leaves shown here with the sketch of elodea leaf epidermis drawn for Investigation 11.1. What explanation can be given for any difference noted?

**p. 447, note 1:** Respiration and photosynthesis both play an important role in the $CO_2$ supply. When $CO_2$ accumulates, pH shows a tendency to fall. This favors formation of starch from soluble sugar, reducing turgor and resulting in narrowing of the aperture. When a leaf is illuminated, photosynthesis uses up $CO_2$, the pH rises, and hydrolysis of starch is favored. Water then enters the guard cell, increasing turgor, and the stomatal apertures widen.

**p. 448, note 1:** Chiefly humidity and wind; to some extent, cloud cover. Soil-water supply has little effect except when extremely deficient.

## INVESTIGATION 13.1

### TRANSPIRATION (pp. 448–449)

This study quantitatively investigates the validity of a student-formulated hypothesis. It *can* be done as a demonstration set up by a single team. But if the rather simple apparatus is obtainable in sufficient quantity, work by a number of teams is much to be preferred. You then have another opportunity to point out the effect of pooling results from replication. Teams of four students should be able to work efficiently. Some students are disappointed by negative data; try not to assign them to the team for the control setup.

### Materials

If a number of teams are to work, all materials and equipment must be conveniently arranged when students enter the classroom, so they can pick them up easily as needed. Ideally, the leafy stems should be woody so that they can be forced through the stopper holes without damage. If leafy woody plants are not available at the time this work is to be done, tomato or sunflower plants grown indoors can be used. Be sure the potted plants have been well watered and are not wilted. The stems must be selected to fit the holes in the rubber stoppers and inserted with care.

If shoots are to be taken from different kinds of plants, some comparisons can be made among species, but the value of replication is lost. The bore of both glass and rubber tubing should be small.

The water in the flasks must be at room temperature; otherwise, expansion caused by warming will make the water column move upward. The flasks may be filled before class time and allowed to come to room temperature, or containers of water at room temperature may be provided. Sinks filled with water that has come to room temperature will eliminate the need for large battery jars or bowls. When students are cutting the stems and placing them in the stoppers, they keep the stems below water level all the while. When a flask is filled, the water level must come up to the top of the neck so that the insertion of the stopper will force the water out, leaving no airspace.

If paraffin is to be used to seal connections, have it melted. Small brushes are handy to use as applicators. Vacuum-pump compound has been found to be a good sealer. Vaseline is unsatisfactory.

If pipettes are not available, lengths of small-bore glass tubing may be used. With a rubber band, fasten a metric rule behind each piece of tubing. You may determine the volume of the tubing per centimeter of length by filling a piece with water and emptying this water into a small graduated cylinder. (The last of the water may need to be blown out.) Then divide the volume of the water (in milliliters) by the length of the tube (in centimeters) to find the milliliters per centimeter.

## Procedure

If students did not use pipettes in Investigation 12.1, practice in reading them should be given. Students may also have to be shown how to fill pipettes. Some teachers have found 5-ml pipettes more satisfactory than the 1-ml size, but 5-ml pipettes require a longer time between successive readings.

Be sure students keep the cut end of the plant under water at all times. Also, the rubber hose must be filled completely when the pipette (also filled with water) is inserted into it.

Before connections are sealed, each of the areas of connection should be dried with a bit of cotton or toweling.

Uniformity among teams can be enhanced if—when all setups are ready—an interval timer, set for two-minute intervals, is used as a signal for all teams to record their readings.

## Discussion

Teams may record their data in a large chart on the chalkboard. This will show distinctly the readings from the control group. Then the average for all the experimental teams can be used for plotting the graph, reducing experimental error.

If the leafy shoots are taken from a shrub near the school or from a greenhouse, an estimate of water loss from the whole plant may be made. Estimate the number of leaves on the shrub, divide by the number of leaves on the experimental shoot, and multiply by the volume of water lost in the pipette during the first ten minutes. You can multiply this figure by 6 to obtain the water loss per hour. Using the data for the second ten minutes gives an estimate of water loss from the plant on a windy day. This procedure provides an experience that helps to explain how data such as those given on p. 448 are obtained.

In all discussions of transpiration, make certain that students speak only of movement of water through the plant system, not movement of solute molecules. Water and solutes move independently of each other; they may even move in opposite directions.

- (2): *If* all connections are tight, water can be lost from the open end of the pipette (a very small free surface and therefore a negligible source of loss) and from the plant. Previous study of leaf structure suggests that the major loss from the plant might be through the leaves. Again, *if* all connections are tight, the control setup shows little loss of water. Therefore, greater loss in the experimental setups is linked to the factor by which these setups differed from the control—the plant.

- (3): The water "disappeared into thin air"—that is, it evaporated.

- (4): It is possible that vapor may condense on the inside of the plastic bags.

- (5): The amount of water loss can be read directly from the pipettes. If plain glass tubing has been used, see p. T185, ¶ 5. Note that the question concerns loss from the *apparatus;* this is loss from the plant only if all connections are tight.

- (6): The variable is the movement of air around this plant.

Some additional questions that may be used in discussion:

1. What other environmental factors might influence the rate of transpiration? [*See comment concerning p. 448, note 1 (p. T184).*]

2. What variations in plant structure might influence the rate of transpiration? [*Size of leaves, thickness of cuticle, number of stomates—among others.*]

3. When a plant is transplanted, its ability to obtain water may be impaired by the destruction of roots. On the basis of the results from this investigation, what suggestions might be made for treating a transplant to reduce dangers of wilting through excessive loss of water? [*Reduce number of leaves by pruning; protect from wind; increase humidity. All are used by horticulturists.*]

## INVESTIGATION 13.2

### STOMATA AND PHOTOSYNTHESIS
(pp. 450–451)

The procedures in this investigation, especially Part B, are frequently presented by teacher demonstration. This requires fewer materials and less equipment, but it robs the students of involvement in the study. Give them the chance to do the work, and it will be that much more meaningful to them.

The work on this investigation must extend over several days. Procedure A and the original setting up of the plants for Procedure B may be done on a Friday. The first part of Procedure B can then be done on the following Monday. Then on Thursday the final part of Procedure B can be done. Of course on Tuesday and Wednesday work on other matters in Chapter 13 can be continued.

### Materials

Be sure leaves are kept from wilting.

You need small potted plants, with abundant but not large leaves. Coleus or geranium is fine, but well-grown bean plants may be used.

For the iodine solution, see instructions for Investigation 1.4, p. T30.

### Procedure

You may need to assist some students in reviewing the computation of field-of-view area (Investigation 1.3, p. 14). Be sure students do not forget to check for watering the plants kept in the dark.

Two or three beakers of boiling water at strategic places in the laboratory may suffice for all teams. Note well the caution on heating of alcohol.

### Discussion

- (2): Many counts must be made and the counts averaged. Care should also be taken that counts are made on comparable leaves of the two plants: age of plant and leaf, position of leaves with respect to sun and shade, etc.

- (3): Explanations may be based on the discussion on p. 447, ¶ 2, but all must be inconclusive.

- (4): It blocks both entry and exit of gases: $CO_2$, $O_2$, $H_2$, $H_2O$ vapor, etc.

- (5): The first set of tests establishes a condition in plants exposed to light — photosynthesizing plants.

- (6): You assume that the presence of starch is an indication of photosynthesis. This is not necessarily true. Starch might be synthesized from glucose transported into a leaf from elsewhere in the plant. On the other hand, the synthesis of multicarbon compounds need not necessarily be carried as far as starch; it *might* stop with glucose or even phosphoglyceraldehyde. Nevertheless, starch in leaves is commonly regarded as an indication of photosynthesis and lack of starch as an indication of lack of photosynthesis.

- (11): See • (2) above.

---

## VASCULAR PLANTS: ROOTS
(pp. 451–456)

**p. 452, note 1:** The question asks for students' thinking, which must be judged on the basis of reason rather than correspondence to facts that may be unknown to the students. In general, tap roots provide better access to water when surface layers of the soil dry out in temporary droughts (cf. the mesquite in Investigation 8.3). However, some desert plants, such as cacti, have wide-spreading, shallow, fibrous root systems; these quickly absorb water from erratic rains, which often fail to penetrate the soil, and the water is then stored in the plant.

**p. 452, ¶ 2:** In addition to the primary root systems, there are roots that arise in many plants from aerial portions of the stem and from rhizomes, corms, and cuttings. These are adventitious roots.

**p. 452, Fig. 13 · 8:** In the photograph the shoot has still not emerged from the seed coat. First emergence of the root is the rule; students may have observed this for themselves in Investigation 1.2, and they will see it again in Investigation 17.1.

**p. 453, Fig. 13 · 9:** Have students suggest how the structure of the root hairs and the structure of other cells shown here (compare with root diagram in Figure 13 · 10) fit the functions each performs.

**p. 454, Fig. 13 · 10:** Some of the labeled structures are mentioned briefly or not at all in the text. These may raise student questions that can be the basis for reference to more advanced books. You may want to employ "pericycle" and "endodermis" if you undertake to explain the origin of secondary roots.

**p. 455, note 2:** Active transport requires expenditure of energy by a cell; respiration is the source of cellular energy. Hence, if other energy-requiring cell activities are kept constant, the speeding up of respiration indicates an increase in active transport.

**p. 455, Fig. 13 · 11:** Compare with Figure 13 · 7.

**p. 456, note 1:** Sugar beets are well known in some parts of the country but may be unknown elsewhere.

## VASCULAR PLANTS: STEMS
(pp. 456–465)

**p. 457, ¶ 3:** A variety of dormant woody stems are effective for comparison with the printed illustration when the students are studying macroscopic structure. If your season is early, collect the twigs before they begin developing and store them in a refrigerator. Bud packing can be examined without the aid of a lens if the end bud of horse chestnut is opened with a dissecting needle or teasing probe.

**p. 458, note 1:** Lack of rings in wood does not simply indicate a tropical climate, for rings indicate merely an alternation of weathers favorable and unfavorable for growth, and many tropical climates have such weathers. Rather, lack of rings indicates essentially no change in weather throughout the year, a characteristic of tropical rain forest.

**p. 458, Fig. 13 · 15:** Note the asymmetrical growth; the tree may have had competitors on the right side. The age was seven years. Sample slices of small tree trunks are not difficult to collect. They make a good interest-retaining device; pass out a variety of them and ask students to report what they can "read" from them.

**p. 459, note 4:** The principal one is flax; less well known are hemp, ramie, and jute.

**pp. 458–460:** Watch for flagging student interest. Some microscope work with prepared slides may help. The only terminology essential for the upcoming physiology is "cambium," "xylem," and "phloem."

**p. 461, note 1:** In our 1963 edition the involvement of air pressure in this situation was explained. Upgrading of pre-tenth-grade science courses renders this less necessary today. However, if none of your students can explain the situation, you will have to provide the background yourself.

**p. 463, note 1:** Xylem contains large amounts of dissolved food when material stored in roots or underground stems is being transported to the upper portions of the plant body; this is especially true after a period in which photosynthetic activity of the plant has been reduced or stopped completely—for example, during early spring. Sugar-rich maple sap comes from xylem.

**p. 464, Fig. 13 · 19:** Food storage, reproduction, and protection are stem functions represented here. The gladiolus corm is shown in section.

**p. 464, Fig. 13 · 20:** This is another example of adaptive convergence (pp. 369–370): the stems store water, as do those of many cacti.

**p. 465, note 1:** Jerusalem artichoke and groundnut (*Apios*) have tubers; plants other than gladiolus (Figure 13 · 19) having

corms are crocus, Jack-in-the-pulpit (*Ari-saema*), and *Caladium*.

## VASCULAR PLANTS: GROWTH
(pp. 465–470)

**p. 466, Fig. 13 · 23:** The base below the girdle and the tree roots contained enough food to survive up to the present time. The girdle has not cut off the supply of water and minerals, which move through the xylem, and so the crown of the tree has continued growth. However, food can no longer reach the roots and base because the phloem has been destroyed by the girdle, and so they will ultimately die; this of course will be followed by death of the plant.

**pp. 466–470:** This is another example of a historical approach to a field of biological study. It is also an excellent opportunity for a selected group of students to demonstrate the effect of auxins and gibberellins on plant growth. See Addison E. Lee, *Plant Growth and Development* (reference: p. T194), pp. 59–63 and 67–70.

**p. 466, Fig. 13 · 24:** Greater diameter, additional growth ring, relatively smaller size of pith, more cracking of bark.

**p. 468, ¶ 3:** A marginal note was omitted—Frits Went: 1903——. American (Dutch-born and -trained) botanist.

**p. 469, Fig. 13 · 28:** The picture really illustrates the question. Holly cuttings were once extremely difficult to root, and so varieties that would not come true from seed were difficult to propagate. Growth hormones have changed this, and greatly increased supplies of marketable hollies have resulted.

## INVESTIGATION 13.3

## RATE OF GROWTH: LEAVES
(pp. 470–472)

### Materials

Kentucky Wonder beans have proved useful; they are fairly large and usually have a rather high percentage of germination.

Lima beans have large embryos but often have a poor germination rate.

Bean seeds are especially susceptible to mold, so it is necessary to soak them in fungicide solution. See p. T27 for information on fungicides.

Used flats can be obtained cheaply from nurseries. Almost any kind of wooden box 8 to 15 cm deep may be substituted. Germination trays can also be made from cardboard shirt, shoe, or sweater boxes. To make these waterproof, line them with polyethylene film. This film, 2 to 4 mils thick, should be shaped to fit the bottom and continue up and over the sides. After folding the edges as in wrapping a package, staple near the top edge of the sides so that the film is not punctured in the parts where moisture is to be retained.

### Procedure

If this work is started on a Monday (with planting to be done on Tuesday), the days scheduled for measuring will be school days. Of course, adjustments can be made in the schedule, but the intervals between measurements should be about equal.

### Discussion

Making the comparisons suggested ought to result in recognition of a certain similarity in these curves—the sigmoid shape characteristic of the generalized growth curve. Many factors may alter or obscure this curve. In Investigation 2.1 the curve does not flatten out; in Investigation 2.2 the curve usually declines; in Investigation 2.3 (ring-necked pheasant) the curve approaches a fluctuating equilibrium. None of these patterns is likely to occur in the growth curve of an individual or in a part of an individual. However, each has the general characteristic of beginning with a gentle slope that steadily steepens.

### NONVASCULAR PLANTS
(pp. 472–474)

Of chief significance here are the physiological differences necessitated by the absence of xylem and phloem tissues in nonvascular plants. This section obviously dangles—almost appearing to be an afterthought. But under some circumstances—such as in a school situated near a coast studded with tide pools—you might want to make much more of it. At the least, you should provide plentiful examples: a variety of living mosses, some freshwater algae in aquariums, good herbarium sheets of larger marine algae, and some prepared microscope slides of planktonic algae. And refer students to Appendix II again.

**p. 472, ¶ 4:** Have students avoid the use of the terms "root," "stem," and "leaf" when referring to nonvascular plants. Botanists do not always do so, but terminological looseness that is permitted the initiated only confuses the learner.

### PROBLEMS (p. 475)

1. Leaves of water lilies float because of their highly developed spongy tissue. Their stems and long leaf petioles are fragile and soft, lacking the abundance of fibrous tissue characteristic of terrestrial tracheophytes; this correlates with the fact that the weight of the plant is largely supported by water. Water being directly available to all plant parts, the roots are not as extended or possessed of as many root hairs as are the roots of land plants.

2. Most parasitic or saprophytic tracheophytes have no leaves or very small ones. Tall stems from which leaves spread upward and outward to receive sunlight being of no advantage, these plants are in most cases small, though some are twiners. Roots function principally as organs that penetrate host organisms and absorb food from their tissues or (in saprophytes) from dead organic materials. Sometimes special absorptive organs are produced on twining stems.

3. The point of this question is that root cells are alive and carry on respiration at all times. Therefore, gas exchange between roots and soil air (or air dissolved in soil water) is primarily an intake of $O_2$

and an output of $CO_2$, just as in aerobic consumers—or in leaves during hours of darkness.

4. Cultivation breaks soil particles apart, increasing the size of the airspaces and thus reducing the movement of water upward by capillarity. At the same time, it allows air to penetrate into the soil.

 Dry farming is practiced in areas where annual precipitation is less than 20 inches and irrigation is impracticable. In a given strip of land, a crop is planted only every second or third year. Between crop years the soil is kept tilled to achieve maximum penetration of precipitation and minimum loss through capillarity and transpiration. Often contouring is used to reduce runoff of precipitation.

5. The attached end of the fence is the same height above the ground as it was ten years ago. The tree grew in height, but only the apical meristems moved upward; all tissues to which the fence was attached remained where they were when formed.

6. (a) An annual ring consists of an inner layer of large cells formed by the cambium during rapid growth in the spring of the year and an outer (not necessarily distinct) layer of smaller cells formed during slower growth in the summer. The thickness of the cell walls differs in these two layers also. The result is a light-dark pattern (see Figure 13 · 15), the combination being the ring. (b) A wet year causes an annual ring to be wide; a dry year results in a much narrower ring. (c) Drought or defoliation by insects may temporarily slow the growth, producing a band of small, thick-walled cells, followed by a band of large, thin-walled cells produced during late summer rains or after appearance of a new crop of leaves. This pattern produces "false" growth rings, suggesting two growing seasons. (d) Especially in arid and semiarid climates past climatic patterns are reflected in the patterns of growth rings in trees. This makes possible the determination of dates of events in former periods by comparative study of the sequence of growth rings in trees and aged wood. (e) Phloem tissue cells are short-lived; the functional life of the sieve tubes is usually a single growing season. The cells are soon crushed and broken by the outward growth of other stem tissues and are eventually sloughed off as part of the old outer bark. (f) Indistinct rings are produced in the bark by cork cambium and by growth of phloem from the principal cambium. But these rings are compressed by the outward growth of the wood. Eventually outermost layers of dead cells, unable to increase in circumference, break, forming a scaly, ridged, or roughened bark.

7. The plant might be non-photosynthetic. If it is a green plant, light energy or proper wavelengths may not be present. Or amounts of water or mineral nutri-

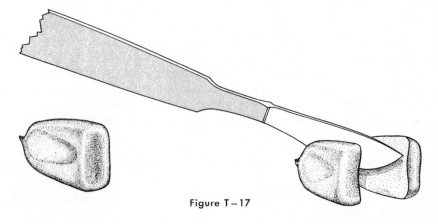

Figure T–17

ents may be insufficient. Or temperatures may be too low.

8. Comparatively large amounts of water are lost through the apple leaves, but this occurs only during the season when living leaves are on the trees. Comparatively small amounts of water are lost through the pine needles, but to some extent this occurs throughout the year.

## SUPPLEMENTARY MATERIALS

### Additional Investigation

### CHEMICAL ACTION IN A PLANT

#### Purpose

This is an investigation of chemical action produced by living plant tissues.

#### Materials and Equipment
(for each team)

Corn grains, 6
Paper towels, 2
Beakers, 2
Formalin-acetic alcohol (FAA)
Glass-marking crayon
Petri dishes containing sterile
    starch agar, 3
Petri dishes containing sterile
    plain agar
Scalpel
Forceps
Iodine solution
Medicine dropper
Tes-tape

#### Procedure

*Day 1.* Soak a paper towel in water. Wrap three corn grains in the towel. Place an inverted beaker over the towel.

*Day 3.* Remove the grains from the towel and place them in a beaker containing formalin-acetic alcohol, a fluid that kills and preserves the grains. Soak another paper towel in water. Wrap three more corn grains in the towel. Place an inverted beaker over the towel.

*Day 5.* Number three petri dishes containing sterile starch agar *1, 2,* and *3.* Number a dish containing sterile plain agar *4.*

Take two corn grains from the paper towel. Using a scalpel, cut the grains longitudinally and parallel to the flat surfaces (Figure T–17). Using the forceps, carefully place each half grain (cut surface downward) on the starch agar in Dish 1. (See Figures 6·9 and 6·10 for technique of preserving sterile conditions in dish.) Avoid pressure that might break the surface of the agar. Using the same techniques, cut two of the corn grains that were killed and preserved on Day 3, and place the four halves of these grains on the agar in Dish 2. Nothing is to be added to Dishes 3 and 4. Put all the dishes in a place designated by your teacher.

Cut the two remaining corn grains and test the cut surfaces with iodine solution. Note the result in your data book.

*Day 7 or 8.* Remove the lids from all the dishes. Using forceps, carefully remove the half grains from the surface of the agar. Place small strips of Tes-tape over the places where the grains lay in Dishes 1 and 2. Test the surfaces of the other dishes with Tes-tape. Record the results in your data book.

#### Studying the Data

First, compare the results of the Tes-tape test in Dish 1 with the results in Dish 3. • What do these results indicate?(1) Compare the appearance of Dish 1, after you flood it with iodine, with the appearance of Dish 3. • Is there any difference? If so, explain.(2) • What chemical change (if any) has occurred?(3) • What kind of substance may have been involved in any reaction that may have occurred?(4) • What name can be given to it?(5) Compare the results of both Tes-tape and iodine tests in Dish 1 with the results in Dish 2. • Explain the differences, if any.(6) • What is the purpose of Dish 4?(7)

#### Conclusion

• What do the results of this experiment reveal about the physiology of a germinating seed?(8)

## For the Teacher

To prepare FAA, mix 500 ml of 95% ethyl alcohol, 20 ml of glacial acetic acid, 100 ml of 40% formaldehyde solution, and 400 ml of water.

To prepare starch agar, mix 10 g of powdered starch and 10 g of agar in 980 ml of water and heat until agar is dissolved.

To prepare plain agar, mix 20 g of agar in 980 ml of water and heat until agar is dissolved. Approximately 15 ml of agar will make a thin layer in a 100-mm petri dish. Avoid making the layer of agar too thick.

If Tes-tape is not available, cut small pieces of agar from the plates and heat in a test tube with Benedict's or Fehling's solution.

The scalpels must be quite sharp. To conserve corn—and fingers—it would be well to demonstrate the proper technique for cutting the corn grains. Those cut at odd angles will still serve for the iodine test.

Molds are sometimes troublesome. Careful attention to proper technique in handling petri dishes will help.

• (1): If all goes well, places where corn grains lay in Dish 1 give a positive test for sugar and Dish 3 gives a negative test, indicating the change of starch to sugar by something in the corn.

• (2): Where the corn grain lay in Dish 1, light spots occur in the dark background of starch-iodine complex, indicating some diminution in the amount of starch at these places. No such spots should occur in Dish 3. Evidently something in the corn grain reduced the amount of starch.

• (3): Putting • (1) and • (2) together leads to the conclusion that some starch has been changed to sugar.

• (4) and • (5): Both these questions lead to the recall of enzymes.

• (6): Usually Dish 2 gives results similar to those given by Dish 3. Although enzyme production may have begun

in the grains in Dish 2 before the grains were killed, little or none of the enzyme usually remains by the time the test is made.

• (7): Dish 4 is an overall control, indicating that the changes involve starch and not just something in the agar.

Some additional questions that may be used in discussion:

1. What advantage lies in the storage of food in the form of substances insoluble in water? [*The food "stays put" and does not diffuse away.*]

2. Why must such substances be changed to soluble forms before they can be transported? [*Most plant transport involves passage through cell membranes; in general, solids do not diffuse through the membranes.*]

3. As it ripens, a banana becomes increasingly sweet. How might this be explained in the light of the investigation? Can you show that an unripe banana contains starch? [*During ripening, starch is changed to sugar. Use iodine.*]

4. Can the chemical change in the investigation proceed in the opposite direction? Why is young corn sweet? [*In both sweet corn and garden peas sugars are rapidly changed to starch after picking; the sooner they are cooked and eaten the sweeter they are. Even in sweet-corn varieties some conversion of sugar to starch occurs as the grain matures.*]

## Invitations to Enquiry

*Invitation 14*, pp. 93–96 of *The Biology Teacher's Handbook.* (Reference: p. T35). The role of hypothesis in experimentation is considered, with some attention to teleological thinking. This invitation on phototropism makes a good introduction to pp. 466–470.

*Invitation 29*, pp. 161–164 of the *Handbook.* Dealing with growth regulation in leaves through application of 2,4-D, this invitation provides a good review of the logarithmic growth curve, which the students encountered in Investigation 2.1 and, more recently, in Investigation 13.3.

*Invitation 30*, **pp. 165–167 of the *Handbook*.** The relationship between light and auxin formation is used to develop one kind of nonlinear curve.

## Audiovisual Materials

**Models:** Large-scale models are excellent devices for showing microscopic structure quickly. Perhaps the most useful for this course are those showing the microscopic structure of leaves, stems, and roots. Models give a three-dimensional impression that cannot be obtained from Figure 13 · 10. On the other hand, models are misleading in some respects—especially as to relative size of microscopic and macroscopic structures—and they must emphasize the "typical." Therefore, students should have an opportunity to see a good variety of real plant materials both macroscopically and microscopically.

**Phonograph record:** *The Scientists Speak: Biology.* Harcourt, Brace and Co., 1959. Dr. Eugene Rabinowitch emphasizes the physicochemical basis of research on photosynthesis. The textbook account is more detailed and more up-to-date, but this record carries the thread of thought directly from Chapter 12 into Chapter 13. You will find that it is inspirational rather than informational.

**Filmstrip:** *Introduction to Stem Sectioning and Staining.* Society for Visual Education. Color. Useful for showing techniques.

**Motion-picture films:** *Colour of Life.* National Film Board of Canada. 16 mm. Color. 24 min. Illustrates the development of the maple seedling (by time-lapse photography); also shows seasonal changes and the process of photosynthesis in leaves.

*Rhythmic Motions in Growing Plants.* William Harlow, Syracuse 10, N.Y. 16 mm. Color. 11 min. Excellent on plant movements—both those that represent responses to external stimuli and those that are intrinsic.

*Pathways of Water in Woody Plants.* Iowa State University (Ealing). Movement of dye solution through a living woody plant provides a good basis for class discussion.

*Phototropic Response in Coleoptiles.* Iowa State University (Ealing). Time-lapse photography shows reactions of corn coleoptiles to various treatments.

*Plant Growth and Development.* Ealing. Series of eleven film loops, using time-lapse photography to telescope plant processes. This set includes film loops produced by Educational Services, Inc.; Iowa State University; Heidenkamp Nature Pictures; and Walt Disney Nature Library.

*Phototropism.* BSCS Inquiry Film Loop. (Rand McNally #11-2975, 1968). Why is it unsatisfactory to say, "Plants bend toward light because they need it?"

*Water and Desert Plants.* BSCS Inquiry Film Loop. (Rand McNally #11-2979, 1968). Good if not already used with Chapter 8.

## Teacher's References

CORNER, E. J. H. *The Life of Plants.* Cleveland, Ohio: The World Publishing Co., 1964. (A small book, well written and beautifully illustrated, about plants as whole organisms.)

CRONQUIST, A. *Introductory Botany.* New York: Harper and Row, Publishers, 1961. (A college textbook of a somewhat encyclopedic nature.)

FOSTER, A. F., and E. M. GIFFORD, JR. *Comparative Morphology of Vascular Plants.* San Francisco: W. H. Freeman Co., Publishers, 1959. (A somewhat advanced textbook on the structure of vascular plants; good background for the first section of Chapter 13.)

JAMES, W. O. *An Introduction to Plant Physiology.* 6th ed. New York: Oxford University Press, 1963. (A good, brief treatment of general plant physiology.)

JENSEN, W. A., and L. G. KAVALJIAN (eds.). *Plant Biology Today; Advances and Challenges.* Belmont, Calif.: Wadsworth Publishing Co., Inc., 1963. (Devoted to papers presented at a symposium sponsored by the AAAS and the Botanical Society of America; a good survey of the growing points in modern botany.)

LEE, A. E. *A BSCS Laboratory Block: Plant Growth and Development*. Boston: D. C. Heath & Co., 1963. (Techniques for plant experiments.)

————, and C. HEIMSCH. *Development and Structure of Plants*. New York: Holt, Rinehart & Winston, Inc., 1962. (A booklet of 64 large-size pages devoted entirely to photographs of the macro- and microstructure of tracheophytes.)

SALISBURY, F. B., and R. V. PARKE. *Vascular Plants: Form and Function*. Belmont, Calif.: Wadsworth Publishing Co., Inc., 1965. (Simply written and short; useful both for you and for your students.)

THOMAS, M., S. L. RANSON, and J. A. RICHARDSON. *Plant Physiology*. 4th ed. New York: Philosophical Library, 1958. (A detailed analysis of the particularly fine work in plant physiology for which the British are noted.)

WEISZ, P. B., and M. S. FULLER. *The Science of Botany*. New York: McGraw-Hill Book Co., Inc., 1962. (A college textbook that stresses biochemical aspects of botany.)

WHITTINGHAM, C. P. *The Chemistry of Plant Processes*. New York: Philosophical Library, 1965. (Not for your students, but good for you if you already have some background to build on.)

CHAPTER

# 14

# The Functioning
# Animal

## MAJOR IDEAS

1. Ecologically all animals are consumers. To obtain their energy, they capture or otherwise secure food and ingest it.

2. In animals digestion always occurs in a cavity of the body. From the cavity the digested foods — that is, foods changed to a diffusible form — pass through cell membranes into the cells of the body.

3. Since energy-release is basically aerobic in animals, oxygen is eventually required, and therefore all animals have means by which oxygen may be obtained from the environment.

4. Most animals have a transport system by which substances are carried through the body. Auxiliary to transport through cell membranes and within cells there is, in larger animals, a vascular system, containing a fluid that is pumped by muscular movements of a heart.

5. Metabolic activities result in the accumulation of substances that are either useless or poisonous. These substances are excreted into the environment — in many animals by means of special organs or organ systems.

6. By means of homeostatic mechanisms involving chemical and nervous coordination, an animal maintains an internal steady state and copes with the vagaries of the external environment.

7. Nervous systems range from a very simple network of nerve cells to a complex system of highly specialized neurons coordinated by a brain.

8. Animals move by means of muscles. In most cases these are attached to the inside of an external skeleton or to the outside of an internal skeleton.

## PLANNING AHEAD

Make a final check of materials for Chapter 15. If you have not been growing *Zebrina*, arrange for a supply (Investigation 15.1). If sow bugs cannot be collected locally, they should be ordered for Investigation 15.2. Have you decided what animals to make available to students for Investigation 15.4?

Looking farther ahead, check on coleus for Investigation 16.1 and fertilized chicken eggs for Investigation 16.3. For the latter you will need an egg incubator. If you have not already done so, calculate the number of eggs you will need, based on the number of teams. This will give you an indication of the incubator capacity you will require.

Have you had experience in rearing and handling fruit flies? If not, after reading over Investigation 17.2 (pp. 636–641) and the commentary on it (pp. T261–T266), order some cultures and gain some experience before your students approach this work.

## GUIDELINES

Many teachers feel a frustrating sense of incompleteness throughout this chapter. Here one might expect the venerable crayfish, with his exopodites and endopodites — and *the* clam, *the* starfish, *the* dogfish, *the* perch. Or one might expect human anatomy and physiology in a setting of hygienic and wholesome living. All these are important. But if the many aspects of biology that occupy so much space in the *Green Version* are conceded to have value for the tenth-grade student, then much that has been part of biology courses in the past must be omitted. For the omission of "type animals" the authors submit no apology: depth studies of selected forms are important in the training of zoologists, but this is not our purpose. As for the omission of much human anatomy

and physiology, the authors believe that a great deal of such material is repetitious at the tenth-grade level: excellent heart models recur in science fairs from the fourth grade upward.

Essentially, the chapter is a survey of the ways in which animal structure is correlated with the requirements of "the animal way of life": the intake of materials, the release of energy from foods, the disposal of excess and poisonous substances, the internal coordination of all metabolic activities, and the means of coping with the environment. Two major viewpoints pervade the chapter: the diversity of ways in which physiological requirements have been met among diverse animal groups and the relationship between ecological conditions and physiological adaptations.

Such a view of animal structure and function is consistent with the ecological orientation of the *Green Version*. While somewhat abstract, this view has been successfully grasped by both ninth- and tenth-grade students. You must, however, do whatever you can to reduce the abstractness by constantly providing examples of live animals, preserved specimens, and pictures. The textbook aids in this effort by using the physiology of man as the terminal and most completely developed example of each major life function. Use your students as laboratory subjects wherever possible.

Chapter 14 does not include discussion of health and disease, but it will stimulate questions about diets, heart attacks, high blood pressure, cancer, nervous disorders, organ transplants, and so forth. Take advantage of the cases your students bring up in class and those that you find currently discussed in news media to demonstrate the relationship between the general problems of animal physiology and whatever subject has current interest.

Work on the chapter appropriately begins with an investigation of the structure and function of a living animal. This experience should be a base point to which a return should frequently be made throughout the study of the remaining parts of the chapter.

Once Investigation 14.1 is well under way, begin making study assignments. But before proceeding very far, you would do well to review Chapter 4 and appropriate portions of Appendix II, where animals used as examples in Chapter 14 may be placed in their taxonomic relationships.

Because discussion of this chapter is not difficult to stimulate, some teachers prefer a large number of short assignments such as: pp. 482–486 (guide questions 1–4), 486–489 (guide questions 5 and 6), 492–494 (guide questions 7–9), 494–498 (guide questions 13–17), 504–511 (guide questions 18–21), 511–515 (guide questions 22–24), 516–520 (guide questions 25–28), 520–527 (guide questions 29–32). However, by this time in the course, most students can handle longer assignments quite well. In such a case, assignments may be suggested as follows: pp. 482–489, 492–494, 494–502, 504–511, 511–520, 520–527. In either of these systems the investigations come at appropriate intervals.

## TEACHING NOTES

### INVESTIGATION 14.1

#### ANIMAL STRUCTURE AND FUNCTION (pp. 477–481)

The introduction (p. 477) sufficiently explains the intent of this investigation. Perhaps not a great deal of physiology is learned, but questions are raised that lead meaningfully into the following exploration of animal functioning. You will probably think of additional observations you would like your students to make. These—and questions relating to them—may be inserted at appropriate places. Any new questions may be accommodated by adding letters to the numbers already in use (e.g., 1a, 1b, 2a, 2b, etc.)

Each part of the procedure is intended for a laboratory period, but the periods need not be on consecutive days.

### Materials for Procedure A

If grass frogs (*Rana pipiens* and relatives) are to be used, an order for medium frogs will usually provide approximately equal numbers of both sexes; an order for large frogs will usually provide a preponderance of females.

If the frogs arrive two or three weeks **before** use, they can be stored in a dishpan **or tote** tray on the lower shelf of a refrigerator, a dozen or so per gallon-size container. A few bright pennies in each container may help to prevent "red leg," a fungus disease of frogs. The water should not be allowed to freeze and should be changed every two or three days. Frogs do not require feeding for several weeks, even months, under these conditions. The frogs should be removed from the refrigerator at least two hours (preferably two days) before the laboratory period. You or your lab assistants should tie the gauze to the frogs' legs before the animals are distributed to teams. The gauze, when used for one period at a time, does not seem to injure the animals. The frogs should be distributed in containers. Students should *never* be allowed to dangle the frogs on the cords. This is an excellent occasion for distinguishing between procedures necessary for legitimate learning and thoughtless or deliberate cruelty.

### Procedure A

This part of the investigation enlarges upon some aspects of Investigation 4.3. That investigation should be reviewed before work is started.

Encourage a calm atmosphere—but do not expect too much. Chances are that about half the frogs will escape temporarily sometime during the day. Your own calm will be more effective in keeping such occurrences at a minimum than will any amount of exhortation. Frogs may be covered with battery jars to hamper mobility, but this also hampers visibility.

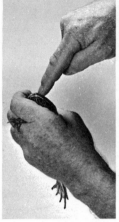  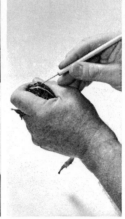 

1. Locating base of skull   2. Inserting needle into foramen magnum   3. Moving needle to destroy brain   4. Pithing the spine

**Figure T–18**

Steps in pithing anesthetized frog. The head is to the left in all pictures.

Two teams at a time should be assigned to the two aquariums to make the observations called for in the last paragraph (pp. 478–479), so that all teams do not try to do this simultaneously.

### Materials for Procedure B

Pith the frogs before the laboratory period begins—as shortly before as possible. If student assistants are employed to aid in pithing, be careful to select very stable and reliable ones with a serious interest in biology.

Anesthetize frogs by placing them, with a swab of absorbent cotton or gauze soaked in diethyl ether or chloroform, in a large plastic bag or screw-top jar. The frogs will be subdued in about five minutes. Grasp one of the frogs with its head between your first and second left-hand fingers. Bend the body down with your thumb (Picture 1, Figure T–18). Feel for the foramen magnum with the point of a sharp dissecting needle (Picture 2). Turn the point into the brain cavity and insert the needle two or three times (Picture 3). Reverse the direction of the needle so that it can be thrust down the spinal cord (Picture 4). The hind legs will extend straight back when a complete spinal pith has been performed.

To be useful, scissors must be sharp, with straight and sharp-pointed blades.

Use 1-ml pipettes.

The sugar solution is 2%. Dissolve 2 g of sucrose in 98 ml of distilled water.

The 0.7% salt solution is made by dissolving 7 g of NaCl in 993 ml of water.

### Procedure B

Inevitably the question arises: Are the frogs dead? This raises the very intricate question, What is death? To deal with such a question at the beginning of a period very full of work is impossible. Even if consideration were given to the question at this point, any discussion would be unconvincing, for reactions—which to most students are signs of life—are being sought throughout the period. But it is worth reviving the matter during the post-laboratory discussion, when it can be related to questions that have arisen as a result of human-organ transplants.

It *is* important to stress the results of pithing, so that students are not led to the mistaken belief that vivisection is being practiced on a conscious animal.

Before beginning, you may want to review the anatomical terms "anterior," "posterior," "ventral," and "dorsal." You will need to watch that each team follows directions carefully. The tendency is to rush through a dissection, always looking for something different but studying nothing. Emphasize methodical work and close observation. While avoiding inhibition of legitimate interest and enthusiasm, try to keep the workers serious.

If a specimen is large, it may be advisable to tie off its abdominal vein. This is done by making two posterior-anterior cuts in the body wall, one on each side of the vein that runs down the center of the abdomen. (The vein can be seen through the body musculature.) The center strip is then tied with thread in two places about 2 cm apart. Then lateral cuts through the vein and strip of muscle in between the two threads allow the upper and lower portions of the vein to be lifted away from the body. This technique has the advantage of allowing blood to continue flowing.

Observations recommended in Procedure B are rather few because a considerable amount of time is required for carrying out dissection procedure. You may, however, wish to set up at this time — or during Procedure C — a demonstration of capillary blood flow. See pp. T209–T210.

Success in all operations should not be expected from all teams. It will probably be necessary to have the successes of some teams shared with members of unsuccessful teams.

If the frogs are small, students may not be able to find the glottis. Some teachers order one large bullfrog for each class so that this operation and a few others requiring large size may be demonstrated.

If refrigerator space is not available for storage, the dissected frogs, properly tagged for identification, may be placed in a formaldehyde solution, made by mixing 1 part of commercial formalin with 7 parts of tap water.

## Materials for Procedure C

If frogs have been stored in formalin, they should be washed for at least one hour in running water before the laboratory period. Exposure to formalin changes the colors of some organs.

## Procedure C

If frogs have been stored in a refrigerator, heart action is often still perceptible twenty-four hours later.

A manikin that can be dissected should be used during this part of the investigation to bring out comparisons of frog and human structure. This is not only instructive in itself; it also carries along the comparative approach adopted in the remainder of the chapter.

Disposing of frogs in waste jars may be offensive to some students. At the conclusion of the investigation, you may have the frogs wrapped in paper toweling and collected. Then store them out of view until the custodian can pick them up after school.

## Discussion

Probably the most effective discussion will take place as you visit the teams during their work. But at least a major part of a period should be spent discussing the questions and the comparisons students have made in Item 35. This should uncover many individual differences among frogs (as well as among observers) and should do much to weaken a Platonic conception of *the* frog, which is, unfortunately and unintentionally, fostered by the careless language of almost all biological authors.

You may wish to review frog anatomy and physiology before leading this discussion. Moment (reference: p. 574) has a brief treatment, as do many other college zoology texts. But remember, it is not what authorities *say* but what students *see* that is important.

- (1): Frogs are essentially neckless.
- (2): We are tailless!
- (6): A frog's skin is loosely attached and relatively thin. A frog's skin quickly shrivels on drying out, but this should not be observed; related to it, however, is the common student observation that it is wet and slippery.
- (7): A frog has the same bony limb divisions that we have.
- (8): Several good points may be made, but the basic one is the lack of nails (or claws) on the digits.
- (10): The attachment of the legs to the pelvic girdle is such that the legs cannot be brought under the body and the knee joint cannot be rotated to give support from beneath.
- (11)– • (15): These questions all revolve around the coordination of movements of the nares and throat muscles. Air is drawn into the mouth through the nares by enlargement of the mouth cavity; then the nares are closed and the muscles of the mouth and throat force air into the lungs. Closure of the mouth is necessary for this series of actions. A frog lacks the ribs and diaphragm by which our thoracic breathing motions occur.
- (20): This question is related to the observations made in connection with • (11)– • (15).
- (21): The transparent nictitating membrane is frequently, but not always, observed during this procedure.
- (23): Contractions begin at the sinus venosus (anterior), next travel to the atria, and end with the ventricle (posterior). But students do not always see it this way.
- (25): Quivering of the intestinal wall is brought about by increase of $Na^+$ and $Cl^-$ ions in the surface water. This ion concentration affects nerve endings in the walls of the intestine, causing abnormal efferent impulses to contract muscles spasmodically.
- (26): One explanation for any contractions noted is that calcium is withdrawn by the distilled water. An inbalance in calcium-ion concentration in the interstitial fluid causes convulsive muscular contraction. This is referred to obliquely on p. 514, ¶ 1.
- (29): A frog's gall bladder seldom appears green. It is more often reported by students as bluish.
- (31): The rugosity of the inner stomach wall is sometimes overlooked as a student concentrates his attention on remains of his frog's last meal.
- (32): Very difficult. A frog's kidneys are almost shapeless.
- (33): Depending on the recent history of specimens, fat bodies vary from large to practically imperceptible. In the spring, when this investigation is usually conducted, fat bodies are usually more noticeable in males than in females.
- (34): The tubules leading to the bladder (called ureters but not strictly homologous to the ureters of mammals) are difficult to see; frequently no team in a class successfully makes this observation.

---

## ACQUIRING ENERGY AND MATERIALS (in part)
(pp. 482–489)

**p. 482, note 4:** Tapeworms (p. 792) and *Oncicola* (p. 793) have no digestive systems. Note that these are both intestinal parasites. In a sense the specialized leaves of pitcher plants are digestive cavities, but they can hardly be said to ingest food. Leaves of Venus's-flytrap, however, really engender a problem of definition reminiscent of "individual," pp. 37–38.

**p. 483, Fig. 14·2:** Somewhat like an animated strip of flypaper. But students today are unlikely to be familiar with fly-paper; they are more likely to be acquainted with the anteater in the comic strip "B.C."

**p. 484, Fig. 14 · 3:** A comparison of body plans reveals that only one figure shows an anus. Some students may antici-pate a problem of waste disposal; a little research in zoology books can clear up this matter. Here—and in discussing subsequent systems—stress the physiological relation-ship between successive levels of organiza-tional complexity. And point out that all existing levels of organization have been successful from the viewpoint of the survival of species.

**p. 484, ¶ 4:** Once the function of the gizzard is understood, students can under-stand the reason for placing sand and other grit in bird cages and poultry yards.

**p. 486, Fig. 14 · 5:** Most of the fiber digestion in the rumen is by numerous anaerobic bacteria—up to a billion per milliliter of rumen contents. Presumably the bacteria benefit and the cow obtains much of its nutrition from the bacterial products, so the relationship is usually adjudged mutualistic. No sectional diagram can dis-play the complexity of the digestive ap-paratus of a cow; only a three-dimensional model can do so.

**p. 486, note 1:** See Investigation 14.1, Item 31.

**pp. 486–489:** Much of the anatomy of the human digestive system should be re-view matter for many students. Dwell on the physiology, especially enzyme action.

**p. 488, ¶ 1:** Peptide bonds are broken by enzymatic hydrolysis—essentially the reverse of dehydration synthesis. (The same enzymes are used.) A look back to pp. 424–425 may be useful here. It is worth taking the time to picture hydrolysis, since all the digestive enzymes work in the same way.

**p. 488, note 3:** Vomit tastes sour or bitter depending on the origin. In violent spasms some material from the duodenum may be vomited; this is bitter because of the highly alkaline bile. If, however, only stomach material is regurgitated, it is sour because of the hydrochloric acid content.

**p. 489, Fig. 14 · 9:** The enzyme no-menclature is that currently used. It is well to let "ptyalin," "trypsin," "steapsin," etc., die.

## INVESTIGATION 14.2

### THE ACTION OF A DIGESTIVE ENZYME (pp. 490–491)

The teaching objective of the investiga-tion is to have students understand some factors influencing enzyme action and how enzymatic activity can be studied. In Investi-gation 12.2, students saw a factor that de-stroys enzyme activity.

Though the use of saliva may be con-sidered messy, it has the advantage of clearly relating enzyme action to a living organism. In the minds of students, diastase (which might be substituted) is divorced from life; if it were used, the investigation would become a purely chemical—not a bio-chemical—one. Of course some attention must be given to establishing a proper in-vestigatory attitude, and good judgment must be used in selecting the students who contribute saliva.

### Materials

Plain starch can be substituted for un-sweetened cracker, but it is difficult to chew.

For preparation of iodine—potassium-iodide solution, see p. T30.

Use either Benedict's or Fehling's solu-tion in testing for maltose. It is easiest to use commercially available solutions, but you can prepare your own if you wish.

Fehling's solution is made of two parts, A and B.

A. Dissolve 34.66 g of copper sulfate, $CuSO_4 \cdot 5 H_2O$, in 500 ml of distilled water.

B. Dissolve 173 g of potassium so-dium tartrate (Rochelle salts), $KNaC_4H_4O_6 \cdot 4 H_2O$, and 50 g of sodium hydroxide, NaOH, in 500 ml of distilled water.

For a combined Fehling's solution, mix equal volumes of the two solutions when you are ready to test.

Benedict's solution is made by heating 173 g of $C_3H_4(OH)(COONa)_3$, sodium citrate, and 100 g of $Na_2CO_3$, sodium carbonate, in 800 ml of distilled water. Filter if necessary and dilute to 850 ml. Dissolve 17.3 g of copper sulfate, $CuSO_4 \cdot 5\,H_2O$, in 100 ml of distilled water. Pour this copper sulfate solution, with constant stirring, into the carbonate-citrate solution and add distilled water to make one liter.

A 3% starch solution is made by boiling 3 g of soluble starch (laundry starch or cornstarch will do) in 97 ml of distilled water.

Hydrochloric acid of pH 3 is made by first diluting 0.86 ml of concentrated HCl (36%) to 100 ml with distilled water. Add 10 ml of this 0.1N HCl solution to 990 ml of $H_2O$.

To make HCl of pH 6, put 1 ml of the pH 3 dilution in 999 ml of $H_2O$.

You can make sodium hydroxide solution of pH 11 by first dissolving 0.42 g of solid NaOH in enough water to make 100 ml of solution. Add 10 ml of this 0.01N solution to 90 ml of $H_2O$.

To make NaOH of pH 8, put 1 ml of the pH 11 solution in 999 ml of $H_2O$. Because NaOH reacts somewhat with carbon dioxide in the air, stale NaOH may need a bit stronger concentration to equal the desired pH's. Adding the concentrated stock solution dropwise to the final dilutions should bring about the desired hydrogen-ion concentration. Test with wide-range pH paper. Store in tightly sealed bottles until ready for use.

The exact pH's of these solutions are not critical. One acid and one base should be rather close to neutral, and the others should be rather far from neutral.

## Procedure

The whole of Procedure A can be done as a demonstration, following which seven teams may each perform one of the operations in Procedure B. If students providing the saliva have been chewing gum, their saliva will produce a positive sugar reaction.

Teacher demonstration: Make up a 5% solution of maltose by dissolving 5 g of maltose in 95 ml of distilled water. To about 10 ml of this solution in a test tube, add about 10 drops of either the combined Fehling's solution or the Benedict's solution. Heat gently until a red or yellow color shows (cuprous oxide). Boiling is not required.

Neither Fehling's solution nor Benedict's solution is specific for maltose (both give the same results with glucose and other reducing sugars), but that does not matter here. They *do* indicate that something happens to the starch after it is subjected to the action of saliva—if, as the procedure indicates, they give negative results with starch itself.

## Discussion

- (1): A negative test indicates a lack of action by saliva on starch. A positive test indicates the action of saliva on starch. On the basis of Figure 14 · 9 this can be translated into the action of salivary amylase on starch to produce maltose. Students should be aware of the point at which interpretation from direct observational evidence ends and interpretation from other—more or less trustworthy—information begins.

- (2): *In vivo* conditions for action of salivary amylase are a temperature of 37°C and a pH of 7 or a little more.

- (5) and • (6): In general, data show that the closer conditions come to the normal *in vivo* conditions, the greater is the activity of amylase.

- (7): In a human mouth both temperature and pH are probably much more variable than they are inside cells. Therefore, a wider tolerance for environmental vicissitudes might be expected of a salivary enzyme than of an intracellular one.

## ACQUIRING ENERGY AND
## MATERIALS (cont.)
(pp. 492–494)

**p. 492, ¶ 2:** Recall Problem 3, p. 440.

**p. 493, note 2:** A frog has neither diaphragm nor ribs.

**p. 493, ¶ 3:** In mammals, control of breathing movements is a function of the concentration of $CO_2$ in the blood (see p. 515, ¶ 5). A student can experience this regulation. He hyperventilates by taking several deep breaths of fresh air, then times the interval he can hold his breath. After breathing normally for five to ten minutes, he again times the interval he can hold his breath. Usually the time is longer after hyperventilation than after normal breathing. The increased ventilation does not increase the oxygen content of the blood, but it does remove more than the usual amount of $CO_2$ from the blood. It then takes longer to build up the concentration of $CO_2$ to the point where the respiratory center is switched on. But the physical and chemical control of respiration is intricate, and the details still challenge physiologists. Some students might enjoy doing some research on the mechanics, as they are now understood, or on the unsolved problems. Start with D'Amour (reference: p. 533).

## TRANSPORTING MATERIALS
## IN THE BODY (pp. 494–502)

**p. 496, note 1:** Refer to p. 157, note 4. By this time students should be rather familiar with the term "vascular" as applied to tracheophytes.

**p. 496, note 2:** An earthworm can easily be set up under a stereomicroscope. Place it in a moist petri dish and check from time to time to see that it remains moist. Students may then observe the pulsing of the dorsal blood vessel.

**p. 497, Fig. 14·14:** The diagram of the circulatory system of an earthworm is somewhat misleading, because the connections between vessels in the dorsal and ventral body walls cannot be shown in a longitudinal section.

**p. 497, ¶ 2:** Among reptiles there is a wide variation in the amount of ventricular septation; it is complete in the crocodilians.

**p. 498, Fig. 14·15:** Heart structure is simplified in these diagrams, the sinus venosus and conus arteriosus being ignored. The "four chambers" of the comparative anatomist can only lead to confusion here.

**p. 499, Fig. 14·16:** Auriculoventricular valves (called "tricuspid" on the right side, "bicuspid" or "mitral" on the left) point into the ventricle. When intraventricular pressure rises (ventricular systole) the auriculoventricular valves are driven closed. Heart action can be adequately visualized only in motion: See film loop *The Heart in Action* (p. T211).

**p. 499, Fig. 14·17:** 55 percent.

**p. 500, ¶ 2:** The striking similarity between heme and the porphyrin part of chlorophyll has been the subject of some interest and speculation among biologists. It sometimes interests students. At the least it points up the biochemical unity of living things.

**p. 500, note 5:** The reasoning is: Activity requires an energy source; this energy derives from cellular respiration; cellular respiration requires oxygen; oxygen is delivered through oxyhemoglobin — thus deficiency of hemoglobin leads to deficiency of activity.

**p. 501, ¶ 4:** To most students blood clotting appears to be a simple process; upon investigation it turns out to be a complicated biological phenomenon. A chalkboard diagram of the clotting mechanism will help to straighten out the complex of terms. One such diagram will be found in Schmidt-Nielsen, *Animal Physiology* (reference: p. 534). Some students may seek information on phlebitis and internal blood clotting.

## INVESTIGATION 14.3

## A HEART AT WORK (pp. 502–504)

### Materials

*Daphnia* may be collected from ponds and lakes during most months of the year. They can be ordered from biological supply houses and quite often may be obtained at aquarium supply stores or at fish hatcheries. *Daphnia magna* is the largest and, therefore, the species of choice. *D. pulex* and *D. longispina,* though smaller than *D. magna*, are also quite satisfactory for this investigation.

A *Daphnia* culture can be maintained for one or two weeks in pond water at 22° to 26°C. The culture should be kept out of direct sunlight. If the culture is to be maintained for a longer period, a culture medium must be provided. Many types of media are suggested in literature, particularly in Needham (reference: p. T73).

A 50-ml beaker is a good container for the *Daphnia.* It must be made of heat-resistant glass, since it will be transferred from ice water to hot water. A 250-ml beaker provides a good water jacket.

If depression slides are not available, make a ring of wax dripped from a burning candle onto a clean slide. Place the drop of water containing the *Daphnia* within the ring; this will prevent the animal from being crushed when the cover slip is added.

If stereomicroscopes are not available, the low power of a monocular scope may be used, but considerable difficulty in keeping the specimen within the field of view may be encountered.

### Procedure

The counts must be made quickly. Therefore students should be familiarized with *Daphnia* in advance. At the same time assign temperatures to teams and have teams decide which members are to perform each task during the laboratory period.

Two members of a team should make and record a count; then the other two members should verify the rate. Alternating students through the counting and data-recording routines provides maximum participation and instills greater responsibility for the results.

Give some practice in counting rapidly by making pencil dots on paper in rhythm with the heartbeat. The dots should be made in a continuous line, back and forth in this manner:

................................................
................................................ :
:................................................

Assuming that room temperature is about 20°C, suggested temperatures are: 15°, 10°, and 5°C (ice water); and 25°, 30°, and 35°C (hot water).

It is not necessary to have a separate hot-water supply for each team. One large container can be maintained at about 90°. If one laboratory assistant is made responsible for distribution of the hot water, movement about the room can be reduced and safety enhanced.

### Discussion

The first point of this work is the variability of physiological data. Students are often unduly impressed by various "normal" values for physiological measurements, such as body temperature and blood pressure. You can make a comparison between the heartbeat rate of *Daphnia* at room temperature and that of man by having students count their own pulses. These data, assembled on the chalkboard, will not only provide a comparison with *Daphnia* but will also emphasize the variability of data and lead to a better understanding of the many "normal" values found in textbooks of human physiology.

The second point to be stressed—if the data allow you to do so—is the effect of temperature on the physiology of a "cold-blooded" animal. The normal heartbeat rate of *Daphnia* is 300–350 per minute. The rate usually declines with lowered temperatures and rises with raised temperatures, but at about 40°C a decline occurs, and the heart-beat usually ceases at about 45°C.

- (2): By the time Chapter 14 is reached, this question should be routine.
- (3): Inaccuracy of counting, temperature variation during the period of positioning the specimen, and variation in age and physical condition of specimens are all likely suspects.
- (4): The more data collected, the greater the range is likely to be, because the larger the number of counts, the greater is the chance that aberrant counts may have been made.
- (6): The class average is probably likely to be nearer the "true" rate—the rate likely to be obtained from a second series of comparable data (see Investigation 7.1, Item 7, p. 217) —because errors or differences noted in Item 3 are compensated as data are averaged. In statistical terms, the more data, the greater the range (Item 4) but the less the standard deviation.
- (9): "Warm-blooded" (homeothermic) vertebrates (dogs) are able to keep a steady rate of heartbeat despite wide changes in environmental temperatures, because the regulation of heartbeat occurs in the little-changing internal environment. "Cold-blooded" (poikilothermic) vertebrates (frogs) are similar to *Daphnia* in that their internal processes, including heartbeat, are little insulated against fluctuations in environmental conditions such as temperature.

## For Further Investigation

1. In addition to snails, you may use mosquito larvae and *Tubifex* worms for comparisons.

2. Besides the suggested drugs other substances that might be tried are aspirin, tea, phenobarbital, carbonated beverages, coffee, and tobacco.

## REMOVING MATERIALS FROM THE BODY (pp. 504–511)

**p. 506, note 2:** Anything that an organism gets rid of *may* be a waste. It *is* a waste if the organism has too much of it. But our only criterion for "too much" of a substance is that an organism habitually gets rid of it.

**p. 508, Fig. 14·22:** Fifty molecules of $CO(NH_2)_2$ contain as much nitrogen as 100 molecules of $NH_3$.

**pp. 508–510:** The removal of nitrogenous wastes is complex, and it is likely to be new to most students. Take some class time to go over this function. Stress the fact that the flow of blood through kidneys is controlled by nervous and endocrine systems, and in this way water content of the body is kept in balance. Students can generalize from this that the action of the kidney is correlated to ecological conditions by means of the coordinating systems.

**p. 509, Fig. 14·23:** This is a good example of the complementarity of structure and function.

**p. 510, note 2:** The drinking of seawater is not merely a matter of salt excretion. It involves also water diffusion from the lumen of the alimentary canal into the wall. Man's physiology, of course, includes the rudimentary ability to use tear glands as excretory organs. Among other points that might be made is the lack of a handy way to deal with increased tear flow. Presumably sea turtles and seabirds can wash away their tears conveniently.

## MAINTAINING A STEADY STATE (pp. 511–527)

The idea of steady state (and its maintenance by homeostatic mechanisms) underlies the whole *Green Version*. The idea is first referred to on pp. 4–5, and Chapter 20 is a great fugue on that theme. If the student has truly caught this idea, he will easily see the artificiality of the heading to this part of the chapter: it could just as well be the title to the chapter as a whole.

T 206

**p. 512, ¶ 5:** Students frequently confuse the functions of enzymes, animal hormones, and plant hormones. This is a good place to discuss their similarities and differences.

**p. 514, Fig. 14·25:** Refer students to Figure 14·24, p. 510, for structural relation of adrenal glands to kidneys.

**p. 514, note 1:** Clotting of blood and coagulation of milk are dependent upon calcium ions. Some nervous disorders are associated with calcium imbalance. The permeability of cell membranes is calcium-dependent. So is the coalescence of cells; cells tend to fall apart from each other if calcium ions are lacking in the surrounding medium.

**p. 515, ¶ 3:** The adrenal cortex also contains hormones associated with sex. Preadolescents—even genetic females—having diseases of this gland may develop male secondary sexual characteristics.

**p. 515, note 2:** Development of knowledge concerning the thymus gland has been rapid in recent years. A student might begin with M. Burnet, "The Thymus Gland," *Scientific American* (November, 1962) and follow up with J. F. A. P. Miller, "The Thymus and the Development of Immunological Responsiveness," *Science* (June 26, 1964).

**p. 516, Fig. 14·26:** Some biologists believe the nerve network of coelenterates to be a staining artifact. See H. M. Lenhoff and W. F. Loomis, *The Biology of Hydra and of Some Other Coelenterates* (Miami, Fla.: University of Miami Press, 1961).

**p. 518, Fig. 14·27:** Neuroanatomists do not seem to agree on axon-dendrite terminology. Therefore, these familiar terms have been omitted from this figure.

**p. 519, Fig. 14·28:** Be sure students note the amount of reduction or enlargement the artist has used in each drawing. Only then will it become apparent that the more recently evolved animals have larger cerebrums. Students may also note the association of olfactory bulbs with cerebrums, the tendency of the cerebrum to cover other brain sections, the maintenance of relative position of parts, etc. The pituitary, partly derived from nerve tissue, serves as a topographical marker.

**p. 521, ¶ 3:** Among many time-honored topics omitted from the *Green Version* is consideration of structure and function of special vertebrate sensory organs. Even in the unlikely event that your students have not studied the structure and functioning of human eyes and ears, pausing to do so here might be unwise, because the point of "Adjustment to the External Environment" might then very easily be overlooked.

**p. 521, note 1:** By using instruments.

**p. 524, Fig. 14·31:** Muscles work in pairs, one in opposition to the other. Muscles only pull, never push.

**p. 524, note 2:** In general, "warm-blooded" animals require more food than "cold-blooded" animals do. In extreme environmental conditions "warm-blooded" animals may perish through inability to control their internal environments, whereas "cold-blooded" animals under the same conditions may escape death through dormancy. Of course, some "warm-blooded" animals in such circumstances abandon warm-bloodedness temporarily.

**p. 526, Fig. 14·32:** This kind of heat-conserving behavior occurs also among many nontropical birds.

**p. 526, Fig. 14·33:** By exposing a maximum of body surface—especially nose, inner surface of ear, and the bottom of feet—to the surrounding air, the cat dissipates a maximum amount of heat. This indicates the air temperature is high. In cold air a cat usually depresses the ears and lies with feet tucked under the body and tail curled over the nose.

## INVESTIGATION 14.4

### CHEMORECEPTORS IN MAN
(pp. 527–531)

If time is pressing, one or more parts of this investigation may be omitted. If all materials are ready, Procedures A and B can be accomplished in one period. If you wish to combine Procedures B and C in a second laboratory session, then in the first session Procedure A can be repeated, with students of each pair alternating. This gives each student experience with all four tastes. Another alternative is to assign Procedure C as homework.

In all parts of this investigation, the power of suggestion is great. Students should be warned about it. Most will try to be objective if they are cautioned. This may be a good time to discuss the difficulty of experimentation that involves a report from the subject—the opposite to the difficulty mentioned in the introduction (p. 527). Such a discussion provides a good transition to Chapter 15, especially to pp. 536–540.

### Materials

For Procedure A weigh out a number of grams corresponding to the percentage and dissolve in enough water to make 100 ml of total solution. The 1% acetic acid solution can be made by mixing 1 ml of concentrated (glacial) $CH_3COOH$ and 99 ml of $H_2O$.

The toothpick swabs should be prepared before the laboratory period, because students tend to make them too large and loose. The pledgets of cotton should be wrapped very tightly and should not be more than 3 mm in diameter. The prepared swabs may be wrapped in paper and sterilized in an autoclave.

Small battery jars or 1-gallon pickle or mayonnaise jars (available from restaurants and cafeterias) make convenient waste jars. If plenty of sinks are available, waste jars may not be needed.

Make the sugar solutions for Procedure B by mixing the most highly concentrated one first and then diluting appropriately. Prepare the 0.5% solution by putting 0.5 g of sucrose in 99.5 ml of $H_2O$.

20 ml of 0.5% solution + 80 ml of $H_2O$ = 0.1% solution
10 ml of 0.5% solution + 90 ml of $H_2O$ = 0.05% solution
20 ml of 0.05% solution + 80 ml of $H_2O$ = 0.01% solution
10 ml of 0.05% solution + 90 ml of $H_2O$ = 0.005% solution
20 ml of 0.005% solution + 80 ml of $H_2O$ = 0.001% solution

Follow the same procedure for making up the salt solutions.

Suggestions for additional solutions in Procedure C: grapefruit juice, garlic salt. All of the solutions should be dilute.

### Procedure

Student assistants are very useful in this investigation. In Procedure A, for example, only one or two stock bottles of the solutions are required if student assistants deliver the solutions as needed.

A simple method for assigning solutions in Procedure B is to have all students who were designated $A$ (in Procedure A) work with the sugar solutions and all students who were designated $B$ work with salt solutions.

In Procedure C a system for labeling the "unknowns" must be devised, so that the discussion following the experiment will be meaningful.

The students should have an opportunity to discuss the procedure with you before they begin. The instructions may seem complicated at first.

### Studying the Data

Most of the answers to questions depend upon the nature of the data collected during the investigation. The distinction to be stressed is not between "right" and "wrong" answers, but between more or less carefully obtained data.

- (5): The assumption is that the nerve endings in the nose have a great deal to do with sensations reported as taste.

PROBLEMS (pp. 532–533)

Most of the problems can be answered —at least to some degree—by consulting standard books on physiology. Two that are most useful are D'Amour (reference: p. 533) for matters of human physiology and Prosser and Brown (reference: p. T212) for matters concerning other animals.

1. The general procedure for studying any hormone action is to remove the suspected source of the hormone; observe function in comparison with the functioning of intact animals and then inject the purified hormone—if available—to observe return to normal function.

2. The hormones of mammals are in many cases the same in all or a wide variety of species, and the antibodies are similar enough to provide immunity. Whole blood, however, is a vastly complicated biochemical mixture, and its proteins are highly specific. Blood even from one individual within a species may be incompatible with blood from another individual of the same species. This problem leads to the idea of blood types, though many more factors are involved.

3. Gaseous wastes are diffused away, commonly through leaves, and water is lost constantly by terrestrial plants. This much students already know. Some excess materials may be stored in parts that are discarded, such as leaves. But the problem of plant excretion still remains and occasionally is discussed by botanists. As one wrote recently, "Why do not plants urinate?"

4. $CO_2 + H_2O \xrightarrow{\text{carbonic anhydrase}}$ carbonic acid ($H_2CO_3$);
$H_2CO_3 + KCl + NaCl \longrightarrow$
$KHCO_3 + NaHCO_3$;
$KHCO_3 \longrightarrow K^+ + HCO_3^-$, and
$NaHCO_3 \longrightarrow Na^+ + HCO_3^-$.

Thus, most of the $CO_2$ is carried in the bloodstream as bicarbonate ions. And about 20 percent is apparently carried as carbamino-hemoglobin.

6. Iodine deficiency results in the production of fewer molecules of thyroxin. This results in symptoms of thyroxin deficiency. See D'Amour. And in compensation for deficiency, the thyroid gland enlarges, forming a simple goiter.

7. Students should encounter hemocyanin, chlorocruorins, and hemerythrins in researching this problem. Most of the respiratory pigments contain one or more divalent metal atoms (iron, copper, vanadium), and it is thought that these atoms are the sites of oxygen attachment. In general there is a greater variety of respiratory pigments in primitive phyla than in more recently evolved phyla. The chemical relationship between heme and chlorophyll was discussed on p. T203. The occurrence of hemoglobin in *Rhizobium* nodules is at present considered to be a biochemical accident or coincidence similar to the occurrence of cellulose in tunicates.

8. Both flushing and blushing result from vasodilation affecting the capillaries in the skin.

9. The sandwich contains carbohydrates, fats, proteins, mineral nutrients, and cellulose. The student need merely consider the enzymes affecting (or failing to affect) these substances and the general story on pp. 486–489. But he might produce an account with greater detail by consulting the discussions of alimentary physiology in a text on human physiology, such as D'Amour.

10. Calcium is essential to the conversion of prothrombin into thrombin, but just how it acts does not seem to be known. Vitamin K is somehow essential to the production of prothrombin.

11. Carbon monoxide poisoning is essentially suffocation. Treatment is fresh air forced into the body by artificial breathing. In extreme cases, air containing 40% oxygen and 7% $CO_2$ is used. The high oxygen tension liberates hemoglobin from the CO, and the $CO_2$ stimulates breathing action.

**12.** Material for a superficial answer to this problem is contained in Chapter 14, but good students should be encouraged to delve further.

**13.** Again, there are various levels at which this problem might be answered. The basic point is that different methods of successfully maintaining life functions depend upon living in different environments. A sponge's methods are not successful where a mountain goat's are — and vice versa.

## SUPPLEMENTARY MATERIALS

### Additional Investigation

#### EFFECTS OF CHEMICALS ON CAPILLARY CIRCULATION

There are numerous methods of demonstrating capillary circulation to students. This one may be used during work on Investigation 14.1. When all students have observed normal circulation, the experimental part can be turned over to special teams who may report their findings to the rest of the class.

### Materials and Equipment

frog, pithed
dissecting tray
scissors
dissecting needle
medicine dropper
glass plate
paper towels
stereomicroscope, 40X to 60X
solutions of drugs
finger bowls

### Procedure

Using scissors, make an incision through the skin and body wall parallel to the midline of the frog, along the ventral margin of pigmentation. The incision should extend about 2 cm from a point about 1 cm anterior to the hind leg. Apply pressure on the body wall on the side opposite the incision. By holding aside the intestines and ovary (if present) with a wooden handle of a dissecting needle, you can press the urinary bladder through the incision.

If the bladder is not well filled, gently force physiological saline solution into the cloaca, using a medicine dropper. Avoid introducing air into the bladder during this operation. It may be necessary to fill the bladder in this manner before it can be pressed from the body cavity.

Place the frog on a glass plate in such a position that light from below is transmitted through the bladder without obstruction. Cover the rest of the frog with a wet paper towel. Every two or three minutes place a drop or two of physiological saline solution on the bladder.

• What is the ratio of the diameter of the smallest visible blood vessel to the diameter of the largest? (1)  • How can you distinguish between *arterioles* (small arteries) and *venules* (small veins)?(2)  • Which vessels, if any, can be seen to pulsate?(3)  • Is the speed of blood flow the same in all vessels? If not, is it faster in the smaller or the larger vessels?(4)  • Red blood cells average 22 $\mu$ long, 15 $\mu$ wide, and 4 $\mu$ thick. What is the approximate diameter of a capillary?(5)

You will be provided with solutions of one or more substances that are used as drugs. Using a medicine dropper, apply two drops of one drug to the surface of the bladder in place of the physiological saline with which you have been bathing it. One member of the team should apply the solution while another closely observes the capillaries through the microscope *before*, *during*, and *after* the application. Look for *dilation* (widening in diameter) or *constriction* (narrowing) of the capillaries. The dimensions of the red blood cells and the rate of flow are two standards for determining dilation or constriction. Observation should be continuous for at least three minutes to allow time for the drug to diffuse into tissues.  • Record the name of the drug and the effect (if any) on the capillaries.(6)

Before applying a second drug, wash the bladder thoroughly with physiological saline solution, using a medicine dropper to apply the solution and a finger bowl to catch it.

### Summary

• Write a brief description of capillary circulation.(7)

Assemble the data from the drug tests on the chalkboard. • To what extent are the results obtained by teams using the same drug in agreement?(8) • What factors may have caused any lack of agreement that exists?(9) • According to the data, which drugs act as *vasodilators* (vessel dilators) in frogs?(10) • Which act as *vasoconstrictors?* (11) • For which are your data inconclusive?(12) • Do you think these drugs would have the same effects on your own capillaries? Why or why not?(13)

---

### For the Teacher

If stereoscopes with sufficient magnification are not available, ordinary monocular microscopes can be used, especially if they can be equipped with 5X objectives.

Physiological saline solution for this investigation can be made by dissolving 7 g of NaCl in 1000 ml of water. Or you can use the Ringer's solution prepared for Investigation 11.1 (p. T159). Suggested drugs are ethyl alcohol, sodium nitrite, adrenaline chloride, acetylcholine bromide, and nicotine sulfate. The first two are readily available from the usual suppliers of chemicals; the others may be obtained from pharmacies, sometimes with the aid of a physician. Good results have been obtained with nicotine extracted from cigarette filters. Acetylcholine, alcohol, and sodium nitrite are vasodilators; nicotine and adrenaline are vasoconstrictors.

About a half hour before beginning the work, inject 3 to 6 ml of physiological saline solution into the dorsal lymph sinus. This usually results in a well-distended bladder. It is not uncommon in a pithed frog for circulation in the bladder to stop temporarily. The frog usually recovers in about fifteen minutes, but if it does not, another specimen must be used.

• (2) This question depends upon distinguishing capillaries. Blood flows into capillaries from arterioles and from capillaries into venules.

• (4) This is an application of Bernoulli's theorem and a good example of simple biophysics.

• (13) This is not a matter of yes or no, but of greater or lesser confidence. We might have more confidence in application to human beings if the work had been done on rats instead of frogs, still more if done on chimpanzees, and rather less if done on goldfish.

### Invitations to Enquiry

*Invitation 12*, **pp. 84 – 86 of *The Biology Teacher's Handbook*.** (Reference: p. T35). Through the investigation of vitamin deficiency, this invitation develops the role of hypothesis in experimentation and the difficulty of achieving control.

*Invitation 15*, **pp. 96 – 103 of the *Handbook*.** A long invitation that uses neurohormones of the heart as a means of exploring the formulation of scientific problems.

*Invitation 17*, **pp. 108 – 112 of the *Handbook*.** Thyroid function is used to introduce the concept of causation in biological inquiry.

*Invitations 21 – 24*, **pp. 116 – 130 of the *Handbook*.** A series of invitations, dealing with various aspects of causation and all concerned with the endocrine system of mammals.

*Invitations 32 – 36*, **pp. 173 – 184 of the *Handbook*.** This series of invitations makes use of animal structure—chiefly muscle structure—to develop reasoning about function.

### Audiovisual Materials

**Models:** Just as models are very useful in developing ideas of plant structure, they are also useful in developing ideas of animal structure. Of course, experience with models is not as good as firsthand acquaintance with the structures of living and recently deceased specimens. But if Investigation 14.1 is done thoroughly and proper emphasis is placed upon physiology, time seldom permits detailed anatomical investigations of other animals. Nor will other considerations permit much anatomical investigation of the most interesting of animals — man. Therefore, a good manikin should at least be available — preferably one with interchangeable reproductive systems, so that it may also be used in connection with Chapter 16.

**Phonograph records:** *Heart Recordings,* Columbia Records, KL 4967, and *Stethoscopic Heart Sounds,* Columbia Records, KL 4240. The sounds of normal heartbeat and of abnormalities.

**Filmstrips:** *William Harvey.* Encyclopaedia Britannica Filmstrips. Color. For the most part, historical content has been crowded out of Chapter 14. This filmstrip may help to restore the balance.

*Metamorphosis.* LIFE Filmstrips. Color. Too often endocrine control is taught exclusively from a mammalian or (at most) a vertebrate viewpoint. This filmstrip deals with the hormones of insect metamorphosis; furthermore, it is a beautiful example of the way in which experimental procedure can be explicated on a filmstrip.

*Circulation.* McGraw-Hill Text Films. Color. Ties other systems to the circulatory and has good summarizations of clotting.

*How the Nervous System Works.* McGraw-Hill Text Films. Color. Good supplement to Chapter 14: all-or-none principle, acetylcholine at synapse, proprioceptors and enteroceptors.

**Motion-picture films:** *Frog Skeletal Muscle Response.* Thorne Films, Boulder, Colo. 16 mm. Color. 8 min. Shows use of the kymograph in studying normal muscle response, tetany, and fatigue.

*Human Body: Skeleton.* Coronet Films. 16 mm. Color. 10 min. A good supplement to Chapter 14; shows (by fluorography) human skeleton in action.

*The Blood.* Encyclopaedia Britannica Films. 16 mm. Color. 20 min. Probably too much, but has good sequences that can be selected: blood-cell types and counting procedures, illustrations of capillary circulation, clotting.

*Digestion, Part 1 (Mechanical).* United World Films, Inc. 16 mm. Color. 17 min. The mechanical processes, absorption, function of the liver.

*Digestion, Part 2 (Chemical).* United World Films, Inc. 16 mm. Color. 19 min. Structure and function of digestive glands, distribution of digested foods.

*The Kidney and Homeostasis.* BSCS Inquiry Film Loop. Super-8. Color. (Rand McNally #11–2980). Presents data from which students can derive the homeostatic function of kidneys. Best used before the textbook material is assigned.

*Comparison of Teeth in Mammals.* International Communications Films. Film loop. 8 mm. Color. 3 min., 51 sec. Complementarity of structure and function in ingestive action among mammals.

*Water and Desert Animals.* BSCS Inquiry Film Loop. (Rand McNally #11–2967).

*Temperature and Activity in Reptiles.* BSCS Inquiry Film Loop. Color. (Rand McNally #11–2964). This and the preceding film are excellent means for keeping ecological implications of physiology before students. Both raise problems for which students suggest hypotheses as data are presented.

*Fundamentals of the Nervous System.* Encyclopaedia Britannica Films. 16 mm. Color. Good for review.

*The Heart in Action.* Encyclopaedia Britannica Films. 8 mm. Color. Illustrates the complex motions of the human heart.

*The Animal and the Environment.* McGraw-Hill Text Films. 16 mm. Color. 28 min. The self-regulating mechanisms (homeostasis) involved in breathing, heartbeat, and kidney function are described and illustrated.

*The Senses.* McGraw-Hill Text Films. 16 mm. Color. 28 min. Sight, hearing, and taste and the nervous and chemical operations involved in these processes. Includes a good sequence on the experimental determination of taste in houseflies. Can serve well as a link with Chapter 16.

*Pithing the Frog.* Ealing. Super-8. Color. 3 min. For the teacher.

*How Animals Breathe—Fresh Water.* Ealing. Super-8. Color. 4 min., 10 sec. Good for extending students' ideas of breathing beyond themselves.

## Teacher's References

ADOLPH, E. F. "The Heart's Pacemaker," *Scientific American*, March, 1967, p. 32.

BAKER, P. F. "The Nerve Axon," *Scientific American*, March, 1966, p. 74.

BEST, C. H., and N. B. TAYLOR. *The Human Body.* 4th ed. New York: Holt, Rinehart and Winston, 1963. (A good reference for quickly locating information on human anatomy and physiology.)

DEBRUL, E. L. *Biomechanics of the Body.* Boston: D. C. Heath & Co., 1963. (A BSCS pamphlet that discusses the biophysics of the gross structure of the human body.)

HEILBRUNN, L. V. *An Outline of General Physiology.* Philadelphia: W. B. Saunders Co., 1952. (This advanced text gives useful comparisons of plant and animal physiology.)

MAYER, W. V. *Hibernation.* Boston: D. C. Heath & Co., 1964. (A BSCS pamphlet that discusses in some detail the physiology of dormancy, particularly that of "warm-blooded" animals under conditions of cold.)

PROSSER, C. L., and F. A. BROWN, JR. *Comparative Animal Physiology.* 2nd ed. Philadelphia: W. B. Saunders Co., 1961. (The basic reference for Chapter 14; rich in detail and broad in its coverage of the animal kingdom.)

ROMER, A. S. *The Vertebrate Body.* 3rd ed. Philadelphia: W. B. Saunders Co., 1962. (Principally concerned with anatomy from a comparative viewpoint.)

SMITH, H. W. *From Fish to Philosopher.* New York: Doubleday and Co., Inc., 1961. (The problems of water balance in vertebrates, presented in an informal way.)

STORER, T. L., and R. L. USINGER. *General Zoology.* 4th ed. New York: McGraw-Hill Book Co., Inc., 1965. (An encyclopedic college text; very useful for a quick check of anatomical and physiological details of all phyla.)

TURNER, C. D. *General Endocrinology.* Philadelphia: W. B. Saunders Co., 1960. (This text treats of endocrine function in both vertebrates and invertebrates.)

WOOD, I. E. "The Venous System," *Scientific American*, Jan., 1968, p. 86.

# 15

## Behavior

---

## MAJOR IDEAS

1. The ability to detect and respond to stimuli from the environment (irritability) is a basic characteristic of living things.

2. Irritability undoubtedly involves complicated biochemical and biophysical actions at the molecular level—indeed, it must involve the whole physiology of the individual. But as a matter of convenience, behavior is usually understood to consist of responses that are visible. In this view plants and protists exhibit behavior, but it is debatable whether much clarity is gained by separating behavior from the rest of the physiology of these organisms.

3. The scientist's observing and reporting are themselves examples of animal behavior; hence, complete objectivity in the study of behavior is extremely difficult to achieve. Furthermore, since different animals perceive different environmental stimuli, only the most painstaking analysis can determine to which of myriad possible environmental stimuli an organism is responding—and in some cases the stimuli may be completely unknown to the observer.

4. No completely satisfactory classification of behavior exists. However, increasing levels of complexity can be distinguished—from simple tactic and tropic responses to reasoning ability.

5. Two approaches are common in behavior research. In one, attention is principally directed to the mechanism of behavior; in the other, attention mainly focuses on the way in which behavior affects the life of individuals and populations. The former approach is physiological, the latter ecological.

6. From the viewpoint of mechanism, behaviors can be conveniently divided into two classes: innate and learned. While some behaviors are undoubtedly determined genetically, the way in which genes bring them about—especially the complex ones called instincts—is not clear. Learned behavior has been intensively investigated in conditioning experiments, but much remains unexplained—from the problem of defining it to the phenomenon of insight (which is almost, but not quite, a monopoly of *Homo sapiens*).

7. From the viewpoint of ecological function, classifications are at present protean; investigators adopt the classification that is most convenient for the purposes of the investigation at hand. However, some fairly prevalent behavioral patterns can be recognized, such as territorial phenomena, social interactions, and so on.

## PLANNING AHEAD

You need to make final plans now for the investigations in Chapter 16. By this time you should have obtained enough coleus plants to supply the number of teams you plan to use in Investigation 16.1. Your plan for handling the schedule of events demanded by Investigation 16.3 should be complete; and while work on Chapter 15 is proceeding, incubations of the eggs needed for the later stages should be started. You should check on the availability of poppit beads for Investigation 16.2 and plan a substitute if you cannot obtain them.

If you required experience in rearing, handling, and examining fruit flies, you should now be in the midst of this. If not, and if you have not been maintaining cultures, order them now. At the same time, order tobacco seeds for Investigation 17.3. These must be seeds that are expected to produce a 3:1 green-albino ratio in the seedlings. Corn or sorghum seeds that show a 3:1 green-albino ratio may be used, but if you plan either of these substitutions, be sure that you have the space and equipment to use it.

Seeds for Investigation 17.5 (round and wrinkled peas) should be obtainable locally in the spring. Many more wrinkled varieties are available than round, but "Alaska" can usually be obtained. You may need to order glucose-1-phosphate (Cori ester) from a specialized supplier of biochemicals rather than from one of the usual biological supply companies.

## GUIDELINES

Students come to biology with certain ideas about the word "behavior." Whatever those ideas may be, they probably do not coincide with the concept that is encountered in Chapter 15. For the most part they are likely to be too narrow. Broadening the student's viewpoint must be one of the principal aims of the teacher. On the whole this is easier than narrowing a definition (as in the case of "food"), but it requires constant attention.

No doubt most of the students' ideas of behavior have human implications, and certainly major interest lies in human behavior. But here the authors' views are similar to their views on sex education: the social-science teacher can better handle the details of acceptable human behavior in contemporary civilization; and the biology teacher can best contribute to the student's development by providing a broad biological perspective, which has value in itself and also provides a basis for a rational grasp of psyche and mores.

Undoubtedly every specialist feels that his field is slighted in high school textbooks — but none with more justification than a behavioral scientist. By devoting a special chapter to behavior in 1963, the authors of the BSCS *Green* and *Blue* versions pioneered in bringing an increasingly important area of biological research into the high school curriculum. But it must be kept in mind that Chapter 15 is not *the* chapter on behavior in the *Green Version*, just as Chapter 18 is not *the* chapter on evolution. Behavior is treated, at least implicitly, throughout Sections One and Three, and in parts of Chapter 14. Be sure your students realize also that Investigations 1.4 (Part C), 4.3 (in part), 9.2, 14.1 (in part), and 14.4 have already involved them in the study of behavior.

Today, even more than in 1963, the study of behavior represents one of the major frontiers of biology. Therefore, even though the year is on the wane and you see many important matters ahead, you should not bypass this chapter. For good students who are learning to handle long assignments, it can readily be broken into two parts—one consisting of "The Study of Behavior" and "Levels of Behavior," with two associated investigations (pp. 535–556), and the other consisting of "Some Patterns of Animal Behavior," also with two investigations (pp. 556–575). If time is running short, Investigation 15.3 can be carried out as a homework assignment, with discussion of questions in class. Some aspects of Investigation 15.4 could also be carried out by students outside of school hours. For very slow students an opposite extreme of assignments might be pp. 535–540 (guide questions 1–4); pp. 540–547 (guide questions 5–8—include here also Investigation 15.2, pp. 554–556); pp. 547–556 (guide questions 9–14); pp. 556–564 (guide question 15); and pp. 564–572 (guide questions 16–20).

In the past, investigators of both human and nonhuman behavior have often

been hampered by inadequate knowledge of neurology and endocrinology, while investigators of nerve and gland function have suffered from a laboratory myopia that restricted the meaning of their researches. With increasing attention to interdisciplinary research, this old dichotomy is disappearing. Placement of the study of behavior immediately after the chapters devoted to plant and animal physiology has been our way to emphasize the mutual interdependence of these fields of study. Nevertheless, we urge you and your students to refer frequently to Dethier and Stellar (reference: p. 574) for assistance in integration.

## TEACHING NOTES

### THE STUDY OF BEHAVIOR
(pp. 535–540)

**p. 535, ¶ 2:** One of Darwin's most delightful books, and indeed the last book which he wrote, described his work on earthworms—*The Formation of Vegetable Mould through the Action of Worms, with Observations on Their Habits.* A popular article dealing with this research is Georg Zappler's "Darwin's Worms," *Natural History* (Nov., 1958), pp. 488–495.

**p. 536, ¶ 3:** See last paragraph of "Guidelines" above.

**p. 538, ¶ 1:** You may wish at this time to discuss fashions in scientific investigation. For thirty years *Drosophila* and maize were (not without good reason) *the* organisms of genetics. For an even longer period, experimental knowledge of learning in animals was basically a knowledge of learning in the white rat. Only recently have biologists begun to assess the probable bias by employing other animals—especially individuals from wild populations—in their researches (see J. L. Kavanau, *Science* **143:** 490, Jan. 31, 1964).

**p. 539, Fig. 15 · 3:** In controlling rodents, advantage has been taken of their color blindness. Poison grain is colored with hues that birds (which can distinguish colors) dislike. Thus, rodents indiscriminately eat the poisoned grain while birds in the area avoid it. What does the knowledge that most mammals are color-blind do to the idea that bulls are incited by seeing "red"?

**p. 540, note 1:** Dogs are stimulated by harmonics that are too high for our ears to detect. Studies indicate that while the upper limit of hearing for man is around 20,000 cycles per second, for dogs it is 40,000 CPS, and for dolphins (porpoises) it is at least 130,000 CPS. Young children can hear higher notes than their elders; and older ornithologists can in some cases no longer hear many of the spring birdsongs, a shortcoming which affects their ability to carry out breeding-bird population studies (see Investigation 15.3). An interesting sidelight on dolphin hearing: A researcher was rewarding a dolphin for whistling. The dolphin began at a higher pitch each time it whistled, being rewarded for each whistle until the sounds were too high for the researcher to hear. At this point, not receiving a reward, the dolphin came back down the scale until its pitch was within the range of the investigator, thus prompting rewards again.

**p. 540, Fig. 15 · 4:** "Avoiding reaction" is not only a good description of the behavior of the paramecium but happens, actually, to be the behavioral term applied to this type of reaction. It is clearly a random, trial-and-error kind of behavior.

## LEVELS OF BEHAVIOR (in part)
(pp. 540–542)

**p. 541, ¶ 3:** Plants, for example, exhibit what are called "nastic movements," involving such things as opening of flowers, drooping of or changing the angle of leaves, and so on, responses which may be stimulated by light, temperature, etc., but which are not directly related to directional stimuli. The prayer plant (*Maranta*), a common household ornamental, can be used to demonstrate nastic movements; its leaves are folded together at night. And wild buttercup blossoms in a vase open during the day and

close at night, while evening primroses in the field do just the opposite. Among Charles Darwin's many published works was one on *The Movements and Habits of Climbing Plants*.

**p. 541, ¶ 6:** Not all biologists distinguish clearly between tropisms and taxes. "Tropism" is properly restricted to non-motile organisms, principally plants. "Taxis" applies to motile organisms and is not necessarily restricted to organisms that lack nervous systems; the term is also employed by entomologists.

**p. 541, Fig. 15 · 6:** Students may come up with numerous interesting explanations but probably few correct ones. At the base of each petiole, on the underside, are enlarged cells that ordinarily are turgid. Stimuli of various kinds—sudden contact, rapid temperature change, electricity, ether—cause release of some diffusable chemical substance that stimulates these cells to lose liquid. The loss of liquid reduces their turgor to a point at which the cell walls collapse and this results in the folding of the leaf. Although folding is almost instantaneous, recovery of the plant may take some minutes. *Minosa pudica*, incidentally, is fairly easy to grow; seeds may be obtained from biological supply companies.

**p. 542, Fig. 15 · 7:** Since paramecia are motile organisms, their responses are obviously taxes. In $B$ and $C$, the response is positive; in $D$, response is positive to the bubble of $CO_2$ but neutral to the bubble of air. Interpretation of $A$ is somewhat tricky; although the organisms respond positively to the drop of salt solution, they respond negatively to the high concentration in the center of the drop. The textbook's terminology will not permit further description, but the teacher can provide additional descriptive terms. For example, since three of the situations involve chemical stimuli, the prefix "chemo-" could be applied (as in chemotactic), while "thigmo-" (touch) or "stereo-" (solid) could be applied to the filter-paper stimulus.

## INVESTIGATION 15.1

### TROPIC RESPONSES IN PLANTS
(pp. 542–544)

In its usage here, the word "tropic" is usually pronounced with a long *o*.

It is not necessary to have each team set up each part of this investigation. If a class is divided into six teams, for example, each part may be set up by two teams; every team then has another with which to check its results.

### Materials

Corn grains should be soaked for three days before the investigation is set up.

The larger the petri dishes, the better.

Use nonabsorbent cotton to pack the grains.

Paper toweling can be used instead of blotting paper, but the grade of paper in desk blotters forms a better support for seeds and cotton. However, colored blotters sometimes contain dyes that are harmful to the corn grains.

Various substitutes for flowerpots can be used. Milk cartons, with holes for drainage punched in the bottoms, are good. Any kind of small cardboard box, lined with sheet plastic or aluminum foil to keep the moisture from softening the cardboard, will serve.

Unless you plan to grow the seedlings further for some other purpose, the soil may be plain sand or fine vermiculite. Avoid a clay soil.

*Zebrina* (wandering Jew) is the preferred material for this procedure, but coleus may be substituted.

### Procedure

If taping the dish to a table seems unsatisfactory, try mounting the edge of the dish in a wad of modeling clay.

Since radish seeds germinate quickly, not more than a week is needed to obtain results. The radish seedlings should be allowed to grow for only two or three days after they break through the soil.

### Discussion

It is most important that the data obtained be the basis for discussion. This, of course, has been emphasized throughout, but Investigation 15.1 seems a good place to reiterate it. A corollary of this principle is that students should not be permitted to generalize on the basis of one experiment: if the radish seedlings in Procedure B turn away from the light, and if students can find reports of many other experiments in which the converse was reported, then students should be permitted to entertain some doubts concerning the validity of their own results.

- (1): Appropriate hypotheses might be statements concerning expected effects of gravity (Part A), of color of light (Part B), and of a combination of white light and gravity (Part C). In the second and third cases students are likely to put the hypotheses in the form of questions.

- (7): Light may affect the shoots to some extent, and under the conditions of this experiment its effects cannot be separated from negative geotropism.

- (8): It is quite possible for individual differences among seedlings to occur. If so, this might be kept in mind for reference in Chapter 18. On the whole, however, cultivated plants show more uniformity than wild, as their breeders have artificially selected them for the characteristic of uniformity.

- (14): Least preciseness is likely to be encountered in formulating a conclusion to Part C.

### For Further Investigation

There is a discussion of centrifugal force related to plant growth, as well as other comments and other illustrations of plant-growth patterns encountered in Parts B and C, in Richard G. Beidleman, *Dynamic Equilibrium* (Patterns of Life Series). Chicago: Rand McNally & Co., 1966, pp. 44–48.

## LEVELS OF BEHAVIOR (cont.)
(pp. 545–553)

**p. 545, ¶ 5:** The construction of nests in a characteristic form by each bird species is often regarded as an example of instinct. Yet carefully controlled observations on the role of heredity in this process have been few. Modern procedure in such study is presented in an article by E. C. and N. E. Collias in *The Auk* **81**: 42–52, Jan., 1964. They found that, in a weaverbird, "practice, channelized by specific response tendencies, but not necessarily tuition by example, is needed for development of the ability to build a normal nest."

**p. 546, Fig. 15 · 12:** This is a famous demonstration of a "releaser." A parent herring gull has a yellow bill with a red spot on each side of the lower mandible, the contrasting spot representing a "releaser" of tapping behavior on the part of nestlings. On the models the less the contrast between spot and bill, the less the response on the part of the nestling gulls. Students who show particular interest in bird behavior, including this research on releasers, might enjoy reading Tinbergen's book *The Herring Gull's World* (New York: Basic Books, Inc., 1961).

**p. 547, Fig. 15 · 13:** Here merely a tuft of red feathers acts as a releaser, eliciting from a male a response that is associated with territorial behavior (see p. 559). A whole, mounted immature robin, which has a *brown* breast, and a silvery model of a whole robin did not act as releasers. This study is included in David Lack, *The Life of the Robin* (London: H. F. & G. Witherby Co., 1943).

**p. 547, note 1:** The plane apparently had a "hawk" silhouette. A helicopter might appear to have such a shape, but a balloon almost certainly would not. Of course, we cannot look through the eyes of the birds, so observation of behavior during tests with helicopters and balloons is necessary. Red-winged blackbirds are pictured on p. 68.

**p. 550, note 2:** These questions raise the problem of statistically significant dif-ferences. With most students you need only emphasize that 100 percent *v.* 0 percent is very infrequent in behavioral studies (and, indeed, in most other biological studies) and suggest that some way must be found to decide at what point a difference is to be accepted as meaningful. If you do have such a discussion, you should recall it when tackling chi-square in Investigation 17.2.

**p. 550, Fig. 15 · 15:** The data are from E. C. Tolman and C. H. Honzik, *University of California Publications in Psychology* **4**: 257–275, 1930. The results seem to indicate that the rats used in this experiment learned faster when rewarded with food than they did without a food reward. The group that received no food reward until the eleventh day bears this out, but the record does not go far enough to indicate whether the apparent advantage of withholding the food reward is permanent.

**p. 552, Fig. 15 · 17:** The structuring of a situation to solve a problem, *if* the situation has not been encountered before, is certainly an example of insight. The "if," however, is very important and very difficult to control. Lack of such control gives rise to many tales involving popular animals such as dogs and horses.

**p. 553, Fig. 15 · 18:** Although learning *per se* may not involve a high degree of intelligence, there seems little doubt today that porpoises are highly intelligent mammals. Considerable behavioral research involving porpoises and their relatives (the mammalian order of whales) is currently being carried out; and a good though somewhat dated paperback book on some of this research is John C. Lilly, *Man and Dolphin* (New York: Pyramid Publications, 1961).

## INVESTIGATION 15.2

### BEHAVIOR OF AN INVERTEBRATE ANIMAL
(pp. 554–556)

Considerable criticism can be leveled at an animal behaviorist who doesn't know

Key to North American Terrestrial Crustacea*

Outer branch of uropods pointed
  Flagellum of antenna 2-segmented (Porcellionidae — sow bugs)
    Abdomen abruptly narrower than thorax . . . . . . . . . . . . . . . . . . . . . . . . . . . . *(Porcellionides)*
    Abdomen not abruptly narrower than thorax
      Body flattened and incapable of being rolled into ball
        Two pairs of pleopods with respiratory sacs (white bodies) . . . . . . . . . . . *(Porcellio)*
        Five pairs of pleopods with respiratory sacs (white bodies) . . . . . . . . . . . *(Trachelipus)*
      Body convex and capable of being rolled into ball . . . . . . . . . . . . . . . . . . *(Cylisticus)*
  Flagellum 3-segmented (Oniscidae — sow bugs)
    Abdomen not abruptly narrower than thorax
      In eastern and central states . . . . . . . . . . . . . . . . . . . . . . . . . . . . . . . . . *(Oniscus)*
      In California . . . . . . . . . . . . . . . . . . . . . . . . . . . . . . . . . . . . . . . . . . . . *(Alloniscus)*
    Abdomen abruptly narrower than thorax . . . . . . . . . . . . . . . . . . . . . . . . . . . . *(Philoscia)*
  Flagellum 4- or 5-segmented (Trichoniscidae) — . . . . . . . . . . . . . . . . . . . . . . . *(Trichoniscus)*
Outer branch of uropods broadly truncate ("cut off")
                      (Armidillidiidae — pill bugs)
  Exopod of uropod very small; California . . . . . . . . . . . . . . . . . . . . . . . . . . . . . *(Cubaris)*
  Exopod large . . . . . . . . . . . . . . . . . . . . . . . . . . . . . . . . . . . . . . . . . . . . . . *(Armadillidium)*

*Generic names are in italics.     From pp. 440–443 of *A Manual of the Common Invertebrate Animals,* by H. S. Pratt. Copyright © 1935 by McGraw-Hill Book Co. Used with permission of McGraw-Hill Book Co.

what organism he is working with. Students should be made to appreciate this (What difference does proper identification make?) and thus might feel the urge to identify their experimental animals, at least to genus, before carrying out this investigation. Figure T–19 will permit them to accomplish this. The key might be written on the blackboard or duplicated for members of the class. Students will need to know the following terms:

*Uropods:* the last paired appendages, projecting at the posterior end

*Flagellum:* the outermost section of the antenna, made up of several separate segments

*Pleopods:* paired abdominal appendages (the uropods are the last of these)

*Exopod:* the outer terminal segment of each uropod

Materials

Sow bugs and pill bugs are very easy to keep in the laboratory; you may want to set up a colony early in the school year.

Large finger bowls of 8 1/2" diameter make excellent containers. Half fill each one with garden soil, scatter leaves on the surface of the soil, keep soil moist by pouring in some water every few days, cover dish with a piece of cardboard, and place in a fairly dark spot. Feed the crustacea as suggested in this investigation. The sow bugs reproduce readily in their vivarium; and with a little ingenuity, you should be able to put them to use in other sections of your course — population ecology, life-history studies, reproduction, development, and so on, not to mention the soil ecosystem, since other organisms will be present as well.

Procedure

• (1): The animals usually scatter haphazardly in all directions.

• (2): Over a period of time, the majority move to the blotter end of the pan. If any remain at the dry end, they usually cluster in one corner.

• (3): Most seek shelter beneath the blotter.

- (4): The animals tend to move faster in the dry section. More detailed observations have indicated that sow bugs react to higher relative humidity with a slowing down of their movements. This tends to cause the organisms to congregate in moist areas, since they move more slowly there; in dry areas they tend to disperse, since they move more rapidly in such situations. Sow bugs prove very responsive to humidity (or lack of humidity). It is easy to demonstrate (and it often happens unintentionally) how short an exposure to a low relative humidity is required to incapacitate a sow bug.

- (5): Usually the organisms tend to congregate in clusters.

- (6): This may prove difficult to set up. If it is done properly (and the specimen performs "properly"), the animal pursues an almost-straight-line path equidistant from the two lamps. This is because the organism is receiving equal stimulation from each lamp.

- (7): Again, if the animal behaves "properly," it circles around to its left in a pattern called "circus movement."

- (8): Presumably the light; in their normal habitats sow bugs shun direct sunlight — an advantageous behavior because of the drying effect. In this situation the animal turns left, away from the light, because the left eye is being stimulated by the light.

- (9): The sow bug moves up the T away from the light.

- (10): There should also be a lamp at the base of the T, as before. The sow bug should turn down the arm away from the second light — that is, in a direction opposite to its normal turning.

Discussion

- (11): The answer has been intimated before. In a dry environment sow bugs and pill bugs become desiccated quite rapidly.

- (12): Again, this answer has been suggested before. Light = sunlight = drying effect.

- (13): Behavioral adaptation. Students who have thoroughly understood structural adaptation should have little difficulty suggesting this new, analogous term.

- (14): This would seem to be an example of innate behavior (see pp. 545, 547). If one does not restrict the term "taxis" to animals without a nervous system, then one could say that the sow bugs exhibit complex, negatively phototactic behavior.

- (15): If one is actually maintaining a colony of the crustacea, it would be possible to try the investigation (or some modification) on very young individuals that have been separated from adults. Other ideas may also occur to you and your students.

- (16): Trial-and-error learning.

- (17): If, after the light at the end of the T arm was no longer used, the sow bugs still turned in a direction opposite their original turning direction, then their new behavior was "learned."

- (19): This is a speculative question at this time, but it paves the way for Chapter 18.

For Further Investigation

There is a familiar man-and-weather saying that "It's not the heat; it's the humidity." Essentially, that is what we are talking about here. For example, is it the light, or the heat of the light, or the low relative humidity near the light that the sow bug is avoiding? Imaginative students should come up with numerous approaches to the problem: using a heat source without light, using light wavelengths not at the heat end of the spectrum, using dry heat *v.* wet heat, and so on. This might make a good project for an eager student.

---

## SOME PATTERNS OF ANIMAL BEHAVIOR (pp. 556–561)

**p. 559, note 1:** New York and Santiago de Chile are at approximately the same longitude and in approximately the same time zone. One might wonder, however, how being in the Southern Hemisphere and hence in an opposite season might affect a person's biological clock.

**p. 559, note 2:** Eliot Howard's classic is now available in a paperback edition: Eliot Howard, *Territory in Bird Life* (New York: Atheneum Publishers, 1964).

**p. 559, note 3:** "Defending" and "warning" certainly can have anthropomorphic connotations. But they can also be used to describe behavior that has certain observable effects in other organisms. Your students may be quite ingenious in suggesting substitute terms, but on examination they are likely to have as many anthropomorphic connotations as the words they are intended to replace.

## INVESTIGATION 15.3

### A METHOD FOR STUDYING TERRITORIALITY (pp. 561–564)

### Background Information

The data in this investigation are derived from a study of a brushland, grassland, and ponderosa-pine ecotonal area adjacent to one of Colorado Springs' high schools. Parts of both the fieldwork and the analysis of data were carried out by high school students in a National Science Foundation summer science-training program. The study concerned sizes of breeding-bird populations, determination of which is largely dependent upon territoriality. The complete study was published in *Audubon Field Notes*, Dec., 1964, pp. 567–568. An interesting population comparison is a five-year analysis of winter studies in the same plot (*Audubon Field Notes*, June, 1968, pp. 494–496).

In three of the five species—flicker, robin, and rufous-sided towhee—the sexes can be distinguished in the field even when birds are not singing.

### Procedure

In reading the data, students should be cautioned not to confuse the capital "I" with the lowercase "l."

When students have finished plotting the dates, the clusters of different numbers represent the bird territories. A circle should be drawn around clusters to indicate the territories. In some cases, deciding which group of numbers represents which cluster will prove somewhat arbitrary. In the actual study, more field data were, of course, available. And in actual practice, an ornithologist, after determining what he thinks are the territories, would check his decisions by further field observations. You should encourage the students to make as reasonable a choice of numbers for territories as possible. Probably not all will agree, but neither might two professional ornithologists.

### Discussion

- (1): Different species may have territories of different sizes. Generally, larger birds tend to have larger territories. Also, since the carrying capacity of the ecosystem for different species varies, this has an effect on territory size. If, in a particular locality, the carrying capacity for a species is low, a pair of that species generally holds a larger territory there than a pair of the same species in a more favorable locality.

- (2) and (3): Since different species generally occupy different ecological niches, it is not surprising to discover that territories held by individuals of different species ordinarily overlap—or may even coincide—in a particular ecosystem.

- (4): The red-tailed hawk, a large second-level consumer, requires a large territory; and this particular ecotonal area represents merely a small part of it. The hawks nest elsewhere in their territory.

- (5): Brushland, with pine woodland next.

- (6): There might be a limited number of nest trees available. In actuality, there is only one good nest tree in the entire plot, a large pine with a dead top, and over the years this is where the flickers have nested.

- (7): Students should find about 25–27 territories wholly or mostly within the area. Since there are two adult birds per territory, the carrying capacity is approximately fifty birds.

- (8): There is less variety and abundance of food in the winter, not to mention less shelter. For the past five winters the average number of rufous-sided towhees has been only four, all males.

- (9): The carrying capacity of the area is obviously not the same for the two species. This is not surprising, because the two species are of different sizes and occupy different niches, though both occur in brushland. Based upon what one can determine here, it would be difficult to decide if the population of either was less than the carrying capacity, since carrying capacity is governed by a number of limiting factors. More intensive and extensive studies would be needed to determine this.

- (10): Since some of the territories exist on the boundaries of the plot, one would expect that in such locations similar habitat would occur outside of the plot.

- (11): These may be individuals from outside which on occasion "invaded" the area. Another possibility is that these birds, noted on the first field date, failed to establish territories for one reason or another. Still a third explanation is that the observer failed to record the particular birds on later field trips, neither seeing nor hearing them.

- (12): The locations of nests should, and indeed do, fall within some of the postulated territories. Some students might think that locating nests would be an easier way to work out territories than recording singing males. In the case of the rufous-sided towhees, however, though the breeding density was high, only one nest was found. This is a common—and frustrating—experience.

For Further Investigation

1. Although scrub jays emit several different notes, it is only on rare occasions that the male could be said to produce a song. As indicated earlier, the sexes cannot be distinguished by sight in the field.

---

## SOME PATTERNS OF ANIMAL BEHAVIOR (cont.—pp. 564–571)

**p. 565, note 1:** This is a matter on which there can be much discussion, mostly centering around the term "communication." One view might certainly be that the meaning the poet obtains from the singing is foreign to the motivation of the singing by the bird, and therefore no meaning has passed from bird to poet—hence no communication has occurred.

**p. 565, note 2:** The male moth seeking out the female by scent is a good example (p. 545). It is also suggested (pp. 539–540) that dogs do some communicating by scent. Many mammals, including dogs, have urination posts which serve as a means of communication through scent.

**p. 566, Fig. 15·26:** You might raise the question of how such a color pattern might have originated. This can bring up the matter of purposive action on the part of the caterpillar and again pave the way toward Chapter 18.

**p. 568, Fig. 15·28:** See Shaw, "The Schooling of Fishes" (reference: p. 575).

Shaw postulates a number of advantages: confusing predators, locating food more readily, stimulating feeding, facilitating movement through the water as a group, and possibly giving some reproductive advantage.

**p. 568, Fig. 15 · 29:** For all their social "virtues," ants have a very restricted nervous system, and as mentioned in the student's book (p. 569, ¶ 2), their behavior is essentially innate. Man makes heavy use (ideally) of his cerebral hemispheres in his learning and reasoning; ants possess no such complex structures and certainly do no reasoning. However, a number of interesting behavioral investigations can be carried out with ants, an imaginative reference being S. H. Skaife, *The Study of Ants* (London: Spottswoode, Ballantyne and Co., 1962).

## INVESTIGATION 15.4

### PERCEPTUAL WORLDS
(pp. 571–572)

This is a relatively unstructured investigation. Although, on a class-wide scale, there are serious difficulties involved in such investigations, and although the values to be derived from experience in developing hypotheses and devising appropriate experiments can probably best be achieved through individual and small-group work, something can be gained by occasionally setting up an open situation before an entire class.

After the students have grasped the nature of the investigation, you should present a list of suitable organisms. This might be supplemented with student suggestions, passed upon by you. Animals already living in the laboratory and somewhat familiar to the students are perhaps best—for example, *Daphnia*, brine shrimp, mealworms, planarians, frogs, and (after doing Investigation 15.2) sow bugs. Easily obtained organisms come next—for example, earthworms, crayfish, pond snails, crickets. But there is some gain in interest when less familiar animals

are used—for example, silkworms, cockroaches, salamanders, the lizard *Anolis*, parrakeets (budgerigars).

A day should be allowed for consideration before choices are made. To avoid duplication, obtain first and second choices. Of course, all teams might use the same organism, but variety is desirable.

After the specimens have been obtained, allow each team at least ten minutes to become generally acquainted with the behavior of the species it chose. If the organism is a quite unfamiliar one, time should be increased. The remainder of the period may be used for team planning.

You then need several days to review the plans and the equipment lists. Several more days are required for gathering the materials and equipment before a laboratory period can be scheduled. Whether one or two periods are needed will depend, of course, upon the plans. However, elaborate plans requiring more time should be avoided. Encourage simplicity and ingenuity. A delightful book pertinent to this particular investigation is Dethier's *To Know a Fly* (reference: p. T227). And the Magna Vision Corporation (Seattle, Wash.) produces a helpful kit (Micro Bio Chamber System) for studying behavior of small organisms.

It is essential that you guide students away from all inhumane procedures, even —if necessary—employing your veto power. Before beginning this investigation, you might consult the publications of the Animal Welfare Institute, P.O. Box 3492, Grand Central Station, New York, N.Y. 10017.

## PROBLEMS (pp. 573–574)

1. Attempting to distinguish between "reflex" and "instinct" should introduce the student to the problem of definition in behavior. If a reflex is a *direct* and immediate response to an environmental stimulus, as some suggest, then the human infant's grasping reaction is a "reflex." Yet the case of a young squirrel "instinctively" burying a nut (p. 545) may be no different from a young child

grasping, except perhaps in degree and situation. Certain behaviorists conclude that "instincts" are "mere bundles of reflexes," while others feel that instincts *per se* must be accompanied by consciousness. Students should be made to appreciate that the search for terminology must not become more important than the phenomenon being investigated. The past adaptive value, from an evolutionary survival standpoint, will be apparent to anyone who has watched movies of primates in the wild or has observed them in zoos. Young primates grasp their mothers, to be carried. Arboreal primates must early be able to grasp branches, to keep from falling out of trees. It is interesting to observe female monkeys in zoos pushing their very young infants against the cage bars and leaving them hanging by their own hands. This behavior strikes zoo visitors as being "heartless" (or some such anthropomorphic term), but it is of adaptive advantage to the monkeys. The adaptive value of this behavior for human infants today is presumably negligible.

2. One obvious approach would be to isolate a specimen of each of these organisms from others of its kind at "birth" and see if the particular behavioral pattern becomes apparent in the isolated animal. Many investigations of this type *have* been carried out. In most cases the basic "talent" would seem to have an instinctive foundation, with refinement being added through learning. For example, with respect to the singing of European chaffinches (illustration: p. 548), individuals raised by themselves can produce a very generalized "chaffinch song," one which lacks, however, the detailed pattern of the typical song.

3. An excellent source of information on care given young of various species of animals and on number of offspring produced is Philip L. Altman and D. S. Dittmer (eds.), *Growth* (Washing-

ton, D.C.: Federation of American Societies for Experimental Biology, 1962), pp. 187–225 (vertebrates) and pp. 230–238 (invertebrates). Similar information is to be found in *Biology Data Book* (edited by the same men and published by the same federation in 1964), pp. 57–68. These two books also contain information on life-span. Students should be able to generalize that the greater the care of the young, the fewer the number of offspring. If the above references are not available, there are, of course, many other sources of pertinent information, including biology textbooks and encyclopedias; but the information may be scattered.

4. The birth of a mammal introduces it to an entirely new set of environmental stimuli. Up until birth the fetus has been receiving oxygen from its mother, and its lungs are nonfunctional. At birth the oxygen supply from the mother is cut off. Then carbon dioxide builds up in the blood of the offspring and activates the respiratory center in the brain, causing respiratory movements. Meanwhile, the respiratory muscles associated with the ribs and diaphragm may have become more responsive with the changed temperature and gas content of the new environment, facilitating the breathing movements. It would seem, thus, that the new respiratory behavior is not learned. On the other hand, there has been an extended dialogue about the status of a baby chick's pecking behavior. As soon as baby chicks hatch, they begin pecking at the ground. Is this behavior learned, or is it innate? A baby chick uses a pecking movement of the head to crack the eggshell during hatching. This certainly couldn't have been learned, since the unhatched chick apparently has no way to learn it. Yet there are those who suggest that the embryo chick has picked up this pecking movement of the head from the beating of the embryonic heart, near which the head rests during embryonic development.

Whatever the explanation, it *is* true that baby chicks learn *what* to pick up by trial and error, at first pecking at anything and not until later, through experience, pecking only at food.

5. There is limitless information on the migration of birds both in books and in periodical articles. Farner deals with the topic in a format suitable for high school students (reference: p. 574). Any ornithological text will have a good discussion, while excellent and comprehensive coverage is to be found in A. J. Marshall (ed.), *Biology and Comparative Physiology of Birds* (New York: Academic Press, 1961), Vol. 2, pp. 307–339; and in A. Wolfson (ed.), *Recent Studies in Avian Biology* (Urbana: University of Illinois Press, 1955), pp. 198–237. Actually, the discussion in the textbook (pp. 557–561) represents a good starting point for this particular problem; and if students have access to a college or university library, pertinent and current research articles can be looked up in the following ornithological journals: *Auk, Condor,* and *Wilson Bulletin.* A more comprehensive listing can be compiled from *Biological Abstracts,* if this publication is available.

6. If students, by this stage in their biological educations, can appreciate that the human being is related to other living things, then they may believe that studies of nonhuman behavior might have some relevance to the study of human behavior. An old book by Vance Packard (*Animal IQ.* New York: Dial Press, 1950) touches in a very popular way on aspects of the topic, while three new (and in some respects controversial) books relate the behavior of other organisms very strongly to human behavior: Ardrey's *The Territorial Imperative* (reference: p. T226), Lorenz's *On Aggression* (reference: p. T227), and Morris' *The Naked Ape* (reference: p. T302). These three, by the way, have been best sellers, which emphasizes the amount of human interest in the subject.

7. Butt order in cows, peck order in chickens and pigeons, status seeking in people —all are examples of social hierarchy. There is much literature, both popular and technical, on the subject. Two good periodical references are A. M. Guhl, "The Social Order of Chickens," *Scientific American*, Feb., 1956, pp. 42–46; and S. L. Washburn and Irven DeVore, "The Social Life of Baboons," *Scientific American*, June, 1961, pp. 62–71. Among pertinent and readable books are H. Munro Fox, *The Personality of Animals* (London: Penguin Books, 1952), pp. 104–110; Ruth C. Noble, *The Nature of the Beast* (Garden City, N.Y.: Doubleday, Doran and Co., 1945), pp. 98–110; and J. P. Scott (reference: p. 575). Vance Packard's *The Status Seekers* relates the phenomenon specifically to man. Although we usually think of social hierarchy with respect to members of a single species, there are also examples in nature of social organization between members of different species that group together—for example, small winter birds and, in zoos, large wading birds, penguins, and monkeys. Indeed, if students have access to a zoo, they might ask keepers about existing social hierarchies among some of the captive mammals and birds. Any student who pursues the problem of social hierarchy will turn up all sorts of interesting information: injecting male hormones into a low-order chicken will raise her in the social hierarchy, but female house finches, in winter, are higher in the peck order than males; a good milk cow at the top of a butt order in one dairy herd may quit giving milk if moved to another dairy's herd; lion tamers in a circus assume the top of the hierarchy in the lions' cage, if luck remains with them; and schoolchildren who move to other schools in midyear have to work their way into the existing hierarchies, often (for the boys) at the expense of black eyes.

## SUPPLEMENTARY MATERIALS

### Audiovisual Materials

**Filmstrips:** *Behavior of Living Things* ("Principles of Biology," Part 6). McGraw-Hill Book Co., Inc., 1955. Employs a terminology somewhat different from that used in the *Green Version* (and confuses tropism and taxis). Of some use for a review.

*Symbiosis* (Darwin's World of Nature Series). LIFE Filmstrips. Concentrates on interspecific behavior.

**Motion-picture films:** *Social Behavior in Chickens.* BSCS Inquiry Film Loop. (Rand McNally #11-2966). Observation of behavior leads to the concept of social hierarchy.

*An Example of the Biological Significance of Color.* BSCS Inquiry Film Loop. (Rand McNally #11-2965). Leads to design of an experiment to determine the role of color in food selection by tortoises. Useful to lead up to Investigation 15.4.

*Mating Behavior in the Cockroach.* BSCS Inquiry Film Loop. (Rand McNally #11-2977). The student develops hypotheses from observation of male and female behavior. Illustrates the study of communication behavior.

*Temperature and Activity in Reptiles.* BSCS Inquiry Film Loop. (Rand McNally #11-2964). Relates the study of physiology to the study of behavior.

*Plant Tropisms and Other Movements.* Coronet Films. 16 mm. Color. 11 min. Uses time-lapse photography to show a variety of kinds of movements in plants.

*Courtship in Birds.* Ealing. Film loop. Super-8. Color. Behavior of four large species is shown: black-footed and laysan albatrosses, whooping crane, and wild turkey.

*Behavior* (AIBS Film Series). McGraw-Hill Book Co., Inc. 16 mm. Color. 28 min. Good for introducing the topic.

### Teacher's References

This is a lengthy list, but behavior is a relatively new and rapidly growing field that has not been well represented in college biology courses or general college textbooks.

Starred items (*) are suitable for students with better-than-average reading ability.

*ARDREY, R. *The Territorial Imperative.* New York: Atheneum Publishers, 1966. (A highly readable, popular, and controversial treatment of the phenomenon of territoriality among animals, with many even more controversial implications for humans.)

BARNETT, S. A. *Instinct and Intelligence.* Englewood Cliffs, N.J.: Prentice-Hall, Inc., 1967. (A popular consideration of the roles of instinct and intelligence in the animal kingdom, including man.)

BONNER, J. T. *Cells and Society.* Princeton, N.J.: Princeton University Press, 1955. (A somewhat different approach to behavior, dealing with the manner in which a variety of plants, animals, and protists meet the biological necessities of life.)

*BROADHURST, P. L. *The Science of Animal Behavior.* Baltimore: Penguin Books, Inc., 1963. (Small but provides an excellent survey of the field. The teacher who lacks background in animal behavior might very well begin with this book.)

*CARRIGHAR, S. *Wild Heritage.* Boston: Houghton Mifflin Co., 1965. (A popularized account of animal behavior in relation to human behavior by one of the best fictionalizers of animal behavior for young people.)

*CARTHY, J. D. *The Study of Behaviour.* New York: St. Martin's Press, 1966. (A short and stimulating consideration of animal behavior; in paperback.)

CHAUVIN, R. *The World of an Insect.* New York: McGraw-Hill Book Co., Inc., 1967. (Paperback, mainly on insects of agricultural interest. Provides a tremendous number of intriguing suggestions for behavioral studies as well as relating results of such studies.)

CLOUDSLEY-THOMPSON, J. L. *Microecology.* New York: St. Martin's Press, 1967. (The latter half of this paperback book has some good suggestions for behavioral studies of small invertebrates.)

DAVIS, D. E. *Integral Animal Behavior.* New York: The Macmillan Co., 1966. (Paperbound. Summarizes anatomical and physiological foundations for behavior, ending with consideration of the behavior of some individual organisms.)

*DETHIER, V. *To Know a Fly.* San Francisco: Holden-Day, Inc., 1962. (Not for information, but a highly amusing account by a perceptive biologist of his efforts to understand the behavior of a common invertebrate.)

DEVORE, I. (ed.). *Primate Behavior: Field Studies of Monkeys and Apes.* New York: Holt, Rinehart & Winston, 1965. (An excellent review of some of the provocative behavioral studies of primates.)

ETKIN, W. (ed.). *Social Behavior and Organization among Vertebrates.* Chicago: University of Chicago Press, 1964. (This compendium includes many recent developments in the study of social behavior, written by active researchers in the field.)

FOLLANSBEE, H. *Animal Behavior.* Boston: D. C. Heath & Co., 1965. (BSCS Laboratory Block which contains much information on methods of studying behavior in the high school laboratory.)

*FRISCH, K. VON. *Bees: Their Vision, Chemical Senses, and Language.* Ithaca, N.Y.: Cornell University Press, 1956. (Not only a fine account of behavior, but also a record of ingenious experimentation.)

HINDE, R. A. *Animal Behaviour.* New York: McGraw-Hill Book Co., Inc., 1966. (This book represents a definitive synthesis of ethology and comparative psychology.)

*HUXLEY, J., and L. KOCH. *Animal Language.* New York: Grosset & Dunlap, 1964. (This easy book on how animals communicate includes a long-playing record of actual animal sounds.)

JESSOP, N. M. "Animal Behavior—a Bibliography," *BioScience,* Feb., 1967. Pp. 125–132. (This is an excellent reference list, arranged by subjects.)

KLOPFER, P. H. *Behavioral Aspects of Ecology.* Englewood Cliffs, N.J.: Prentice-Hall, Inc., 1962. (This will help the teacher relate the subject matter of Chapters 2 and 3 to that of Chapter 15.)

———, and J. P. HAILMAN. *An Introduction to Animal Behavior.* Englewood Cliffs, N.J.: Prentice-Hall, Inc., 1967. (An excellent survey of the developments in ethology during the past century.)

*LORENZ, K. *On Aggression.* New York: Harcourt, Brace & World, 1966. (A popular book on the nature of animal aggression by a famous and literate ethologist.)

McGAUGH, J. L., N. M. WEINBERGER, and R. E. WHALEN (eds.). *Psychobiology.* San Francisco: W. H. Freeman and Co., 1967. (This excellent publication brings together many articles published in *Scientific American* that deal with the biological bases of behavior.)

McGILL, T. E. (ed.). *Readings in Animal Behavior.* New York: Holt, Rinehart & Winston, 1965. (An excellent compilation of articles providing a good review of many aspects of the subject.)

MARLER, P., and W. J. HAMILTON III. *Mechanisms of Animal Behavior.* New York: John Wiley & Sons, 1966. (This deals with physiological bases for behavior.)

MILNE, L., and M. MILNE. *The Senses of Animals and Men.* New York: Atheneum Publishers, 1962. (Good for developing ideas of perceptual worlds.)

PORTMANN, A. *Animals as Social Beings.* New York: The Viking Press, 1961. (This is a popular treatment of the subject, including many different examples.)

RHEINGOLD, H. (ed.). *Maternal Behavior in Mammals.* New York: John Wiley & Sons, Inc., 1963. (Includes papers by biologists who use diverse approaches to the subject; studies on both confined and wild species of five different orders.)

ROE, A., and G. G. SIMPSON (eds.). *Behavior and Evolution.* New Haven, Conn.: Yale University Press, 1958. (A symposium volume that should do much to relate Chapters 15 and 18.)

SCHALLER, G. B. *The Year of the Gorilla.* New York: Ballantine Books, 1964. (A classical field study of gorilla behavior.)

SOUTHWICK, C. H. *Primate Social Behavior.* Princeton, N.J.: D. Van Nostrand Co., Inc., 1963. (Good reference for Chapter 15 and background for Chapter 19.)

THORPE, W. H. *Learning and Instinct in Animals.* Cambridge, Mass.: Harvard University Press, 1958. (A scholarly and comprehensive work which deals with various aspects of learning and instinct, including a lengthy discussion of learning abilities of the main animal groups.)

*TINBERGEN, N. *Curious Naturalists.* New York: Basic Books, Inc., 1958. (A personal account of twenty-five years of behavioral study, by one of the world's great ethologists.)

*———. *The Herring Gull's World.* New York: Basic Books, Inc., 1960. (A nontechnical book, but one that illustrates the kind of results that emerge from studies by ethologists.)

———. *Social Behavior in Animals.* London: Butler & Tanner, 1965. (A well-written coverage of the subject by an authority; also available in a paperbound edition.)

———. *The Study of Instinct.* New York: Oxford University Press, 1951. (A book that did much to rehabilitate the term "instinct.")

*VAN DER KLOOT, W. G. *Behavior.* New York: Holt, Rinehart & Winston, Inc., 1968. (A new paperbound book succinctly dealing with the analysis of the behavior of animals.)

WYNNE-EDWARDS, V. C. *Animal Dispersion in Relation to Social Behaviour.* London: Oliver & Body, Ltd., 1962. (Elaborates a theory of population homeostasis through the development of social behavior. The theory leaves much to be desired, but the material used in explanation is most informative.)

**CONTINUITY
OF THE
BIOSPHERE**

William H. Amos

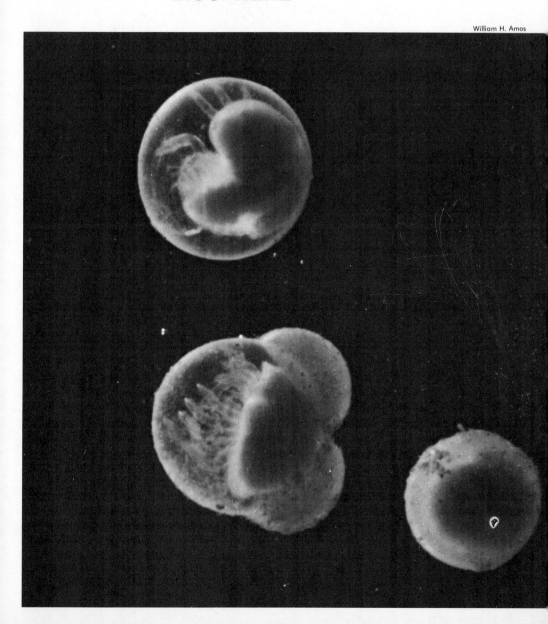

Abundant evidence points to the conclusion that even on the time scale of earth history, life is not a recent phenomenon. Even within their own short span of observation, tenth-grade students have seen how mortality and natality are constantly changing the players as the play continues. And from this it is not difficult to extrapolate both backward and forward in time. The resulting concept of biological continuity is one of the most valuable acquisitions for a developing human mind. It is not only a key concept in the structure of modern biology; it is also a firm basis for a system of ethics. In a biology course that has a humanistic bias, this latter is a permissible consideration.

Perhaps the most important task in working with Section Five is to maintain the sweep of ideas through the three chapters without becoming entangled in detail. Reproduction implies heredity, and the mechanisms of heredity form the basis for evolution. No other section of the course has such a tight scenario. But without care this can be lost in the details of chick development or the manipulation of fruit flies.

Nevertheless such live materials are needed to maintain reality in the biology course, for the ideas are increasingly abstract. In Chapter 18 firsthand experience becomes very difficult to achieve. Everything possible should be done to mobilize visual aids in defense of credibility.

Section Illustration

Development of eggs of *Limulus*. Lower right: new-laid egg. Lower left: as the embryo develops, the outer covering splits and is cast off while the inner membrane expands. Upper: the clear membrane will be ruptured by abrasion of sand grains during the next spring tide.

# 16

# Reproduction

## MAJOR IDEAS

1. Every individual organism has one or two precursors
   —parents. The discrediting of the spontaneous-generation
   theory left only reproduction to account for the addition
   of new individuals to populations.

2. Reproduction (here considered as a process involving whole
   organisms as opposed to replication of molecules within
   individuals) is characteristic of living things but is not essential for the existence of any single individual. Yet, because individuals die, it is a process essential for the survival
   of the species and for the continued existence of the biosphere.

3. Asexual reproduction is found in all three kingdoms; it is
   most common among protists and least common among
   animals. Because the process does not allow for random
   recombination of chromosomes (an idea to be more fully
   developed in Chapter 17), organisms that reproduce only
   asexually are essentially in evolutionary blind alleys.

4. The basic point in sexual reproduction is the union of two
   cells (gametes), each normally from a different parent individual and usually morphologically distinguished as sperm
   cell and ovum. Upon these gamete distinctions rests the distinction between male and female.

5. Because chromosome number is constant in a species and
   fertilization doubles the number in the gametes, there must
   be some mechanism that reduces the number of chromo-

somes at some time between successive fertilizations. This mechanism is meiosis.

6. Characteristically a plant alternates a sexually reproducing gametophyte generation with an asexually reproducing sporophyte generation.

7. Such an alternation of monoploid and diploid generations is unknown among animals. Further, most animal species have definite, separate sexes.

8. In both animals and multicellular plants, an adult organism develops from a zygote not merely by a proliferation of cells through mitosis but by a process of cellular differentiation. Thus embryonic development is basically a study of growth and differentiation of cells.

9. Adaptations such as timing mechanisms that maximize the chances of fertilization, internal fertilization, and protection and nourishment of the young are correlated with the production of fewer eggs as the chances of development to adulthood are increased.

10. Human reproductive patterns afford maximum opportunity for fertilization and provide for highly developed prenatal and postnatal care. The complex regulation of the menstrual cycle indicates a hormonal feedback system that is an excellent example of regulation.

## PLANNING AHEAD

All should now be in readiness for the genetics investigations. And with those preparations completed you have surmounted most of the difficulties of planning for the year. The principal preparations for the remaining chapters require not so much the obtaining of materials as the thinking through of procedures. All of the investigations in Chapter 18 are "dry runs"; that is, the data have already been collected (or, in Investigation 18.1, hypothesized), and the work of the investigations involves the manipulation of ideas rather than of equipment. If you are to be of maximum effectiveness as a teacher, you must understand the investigations so thoroughly that you can guide the thinking of your students, not merely provide answers.

## GUIDELINES

The introduction to Section Five places the process of reproduction in the setting of species continuity. If Flask 7 from Investigation 6.4 has been saved (as was suggested), it can now be brought forth as a silent witness against abiogenesis. Establishing the special place of reproduction among life processes is probably the best approach to the work of this chapter.

Throughout the work on reproduction, it is important to have in the laboratory an abundance of living materials illustrating reproductive processes.

It is easy to assemble collections of organisms displaying the phenomena of asexual reproduction. Strawberry plants, *Sanseveria*, *Bryophyllum*, and potatoes demonstrate various kinds of vegetative reproduction. Budding yeasts, fissioning paramecia, and even budding hydra are not difficult to obtain. Spores from bread molds are easy to demonstrate. Among plants sexual processes are not very obvious, and recourse to prepared slides may be necessary, but flowering plants can certainly be provided in variety. For animals the problem of timing is difficult to overcome, but guppies and pregnant rats or mice can always be obtained. And in most places this chapter is likely to be undertaken at a season when frogs in amplexus can be secured; any fertilized eggs obtained from them can be used as a supplemental study of embryological development.

The primary aim of the chapter is to establish a rational, objective, and integrated view of reproduction as a basic (perhaps *the* basic) process in biology. Secondarily, the chapter provides a background for later development of concepts of heredity and evolution.

In pursuing these aims, students will undoubtedly gain perspective on their own personal interests in reproductive processes. During the last parts of the chapter, they may be encouraged by the scientific atmosphere to seek answers to personally perplexing questions. You should do what you can within your competency to deal with such questions. But this is a *biology* course. Just as the authors have stressed ecology rather than conservation, nutrition rather than dieting, and the dynamics of host-parasite relationships rather than "health habits," so they insist that the biology of reproduction — not sex education — is the proper emphasis for the biology course. A liaison with social-studies teachers is desirable; usurpation of their role is not.

A suggested division of the chapter for assignments is as follows: pp. 578–582 (guide questions 1–5), 584–589 (guide questions 6–10), 591–599 (guide questions 11–14), 599–607 (guide questions 15–23), 614–620 (guide questions 24–31). Fairly short assignments are desirable in this chapter, partly because Investigations 16.1 and 16.3 are long and must overlap several topics

if not each other. However, an alternative assignment scheme might be: pp. 578–591, 591–603, and 603–620.

## TEACHING NOTES

### WHY REPRODUCTION?
(pp. 578–579)

**p. 579, Fig. 16·1:** Redi's experiment is not difficult to duplicate in warm weather. The conclusion derived from the results pictured seems very obvious, but it passes over the heads of some students unless you have other students explain it.

### KINDS OF REPRODUCTION
(in part — pp. 579–582)

**p. 580, ¶ 2:** Asexual reproduction of potatoes is easy to demonstrate. But watch out for market potatoes that have been treated to inhibit sprouting.

**p. 580, Fig. 16·3:** *Bryophyllum* is easy to grow in the laboratory. The related *Kalanchoe verticillata* also produces foliar plantlets and is equally easy to grow where there is plenty of light.

**p. 581, Fig. 16·4:** Note the amitotic division of the macronucleus. Stained slides of other microorganisms in fission can be obtained from biological supply houses.

**p. 581:** Not only are slides of budding hydra available for demonstration purposes from biological supply houses, but living hydra kept in aquariums in the classroom can frequently be observed undergoing budding.

**p. 582, note 1:** Budding and vegetative reproduction are similar in that the offspring in each case is essentially the same in its inherited characteristics as the single parent.

**p. 582, ¶ 2:** Note that the "spores" of bacteria do not conform to this description. Bacterial spores are not really reproductive structures at all, but rather a means of circumventing unfavorable environmental conditions.

**p. 582, ¶ 3:** If "fruiting" plants of such species of *Lycopodium* as *L. obscurum* or *L. complanatum* are collected in the autumn and dried in a plant press, in spring the specimens will release visible showers of spores when tapped lightly. The spores can then be observed under the microscope. Or bread mold (*Rhizopus*) may be used to demonstrate sporangia and spores.

## INVESTIGATION 16.1

### VEGETATIVE REPRODUCTION
(pp. 582–584)

This investigation is concerned primarily with the concepts of experiment, observation, control, and conclusions. The students should be able to explain the rationale behind the experimental design and to discuss the concept of control. Some students may think that the original plant is the control in this experiment. Why isn't it? Does every experiment require a control? Recall Investigation 1.2, Item 7. (Cutting A is as near to being a control as any cutting in this investigation.) The ability of the student to observe will largely determine the quality of his conclusions. The conclusions should relate directly to coleus as an organism capable of vegetative reproduction but one that does not normally use it as a mechanism for perpetuation of its species. Observations will lead to conclusions regarding regeneration.

### Materials

Almost any container that allows good drainage may be used. The saucer permits watering from below, so that the plastic bag need not be disturbed.

Vermiculite may be substituted for sand. If possible the medium should be heat-sterilized in an oven before use.

Coleus is a common plant, easily obtained and likely to give good results. The household geranium (*Pelargonium*) may be used, but results appear more slowly, and there is likely to be more difficulty with molds. The plants from which cuttings are taken should be young and vigorous, with several side branches. The directions must be modified slightly if plants with alternate leaves are used.

### Procedure

Good comparisons can be made if different species of plants are used by different teams, but replication should also be provided. One scheme is to have all teams in a class use the same species but have different classes use different species.

If teams must be large, each pair of students on a team may be made responsible for setting up one of the cuttings.

A quantitative aspect can be introduced into this experiment by having the students measure the growth, if any, on various cuttings and graph the data.

- (1): Coleus and most other plants heal wounds quite quickly unless the damage has been extensive. At the terminal portion of the branch, not just one but several new branches may grow.

- (2): In all probability, all four cuttings will still be alive; D is more likely to die than is either A or B. Student evidences for whether the part is alive or not will be varied and will form the basis for an interesting classroom discussion.

- (3): If roots develop, they come either from the callus (a mass of poorly differentiated cells covering a wound) at the bottom of the branch or from the stem immediately above it. They first appear as somewhat shiny swellings on the stem and later break through the epidermis and resemble ordinary roots.

- (4): The cut surface at the bottom of the branch is most likely to be covered with a layer of callus.

- (5): Depending on the situation, the tip of the cutting may have wilted or be in the process of growth.

- (6) and • (7): See • (3) and • (4) above.

- (8): The cut surface will probably be dried out, and the cut tip may even shrink back to the node where the leaves arise. Any new growth of stem or branches occurs from axial buds, but this growth does not usually occur until well-developed roots have formed.
- (9)_ •(14): See comments above. Root development is unlikely in Cuttings C and D.

Discussion

- (15): The healing of a wound (callus formation) on the surface of a living plant involves regeneration. This may not be very obvious to students; but if new branches have grown (as usually occurs in Cutting B), this should be obvious evidence for regeneration.
- (16): This question must be answered with respect to the experimental cuttings. Which types of broken branches have the best chance of survival if they become imbedded in the earth?

  Present the following statement to students for discussion: Vegetative reproduction as a result of accidental fragmentation is probably not important to the coleus population, but it is of importance to streamside willows and to many plants that grow in shallow water.

KINDS OF REPRODUCTION (cont.)
(pp. 584–589)

p. 584, Fig. 16 · 7: A demonstration of the sexual reproduction of *Rhizopus nigricans* by plus and minus strains can be performed by the students. The necessary living materials can be obtained from biological supply houses.

p. 585, Fig. 16 · 8: In *Ulothrix*, gametes are morphologically all of one kind. Therefore, they cannot be considered either ova or sperm cells; they are simply gametes.

p. 585, ¶ 3: The mention of mitosis as a means of increasing cell number is not accidental here. This is a good time to review the material on mitosis, beginning on p. 394, before introducing the process of meiosis.

p. 587, note 1: The branch of human knowledge in which truth is established by reasoning alone is mathematics. Such branches of human knowledge as theology and philosophy must be excluded because of the difficulties of establishing what is "truth" in these areas.

p. 588, Fig. 16 · 10: The diploid number of chromosomes is four.

p. 588, Fig. 16 · 11: Crossing-over has little significance at this point. But since it occurs regularly in meiosis, it deserves to be mentioned as part of the process. Throughout the course students have encountered facts that were not immediately explainable. And if they are getting the spirit of the course, they may quickly ask, "Why does crossing-over occur?" Put in that very common form (and better students may no longer be using such a form), the question is, of course, basically unanswerable. Historically, crossing-over was at first merely a cytological curiosity—as it must be here to the students. But it did turn out to have significance; and in the next chapter it will have significance for your students.

INVESTIGATION 16.2

A MODEL OF MEIOSIS
(pp. 589–591)

If you have used the model technique in connection with mitosis in Chapter 11 (see pp. T166–T167), the general scheme of the procedure will already be familiar to the student. Otherwise some time will be required to establish the identity of the model materials.

Materials

Pipe cleaners may be used as substitutes for poppit beads, but they are not as suitable as they were for simulating mitosis, because they have to be cut and the pieces twisted together to show crossing-over. Further, when the "chromosomes" are grasped at the "kinetochores" and pulled toward the poles, pipe cleaners do not assume characteristic shapes. If pipe cleaners must be used, they may be dyed to obtain two colors.

If enough materials are available, three pairs of homologous "chromosomes" may be constructed. A very short pair will clearly show the relationship between chromosome length and the probability that crossing-over will occur.

## Procedure and Discussion

In this investigation the manipulation of the materials achieves the purpose, but a number of points can be made in discussion, either during the procedure or afterward. One worth considering (because of its bearing on matters in Chapter 17) is the random distribution of paternal and maternal chromosomes during synapsis. Since no directions are given for arranging the colors, there is likely to be considerable variation among teams when the "chromosomes" are placed in homologous pairs. The consequent separation of paternal and maternal chromosomes may be pointed out—without necessarily developing any genetic implications at this time.

When work with this model of meiosis has been completed, students should be able to contrast and compare the processes of mitosis and meiosis as well as to review the usefulness of biological models.

Note: This investigation may be repeated when recombinations are dealt with (Chapter 17). The beads then represent genes. If the beads are marked with washable ink, the genetic effects of crossing-over can readily be seen. For example, the events shown in Figure 17 · 19 can be duplicated; or crossing-over can be demonstrated at different distances from the kinetochore; or, with strands of 15 or more beads, double crossing-over can be shown.

- (2): The size of the model and the ability to manipulate it allow for easy viewing of the events under consideration. The action can be stopped at any stage, reversed, or repeated for complete comprehension. This would not be the case with living material.

- (3): The model has the disadvantage of all models: it is not the real thing. A model is a form of analogy and has, in some degree, all the advantages and disadvantages attached to the verbal form. (Refer to Investigation 2.1 and p. 60.) A simulated series of events cannot anticipate the variations in a living system, and by its very nature the model takes some liberties and shortcuts to illustrate aspects of the process under consideration. At every point where a model differs from the biological reality—for example, size, color, materials, metabolic activity—danger of misunderstanding lurks.

## PATTERNS OF REPRODUCTION
(in part—pp. 591–607)

**p. 591, note 1:** Primarily, because they are basically stable within the genetic complements of the organism and can be used to categorize organisms with similar features. But, further, if a classification is to reflect ideas of genetic relationship, characteristics associated with evolutionary history are the materials from which a phylogeny can be constructed.

**p. 592, Figs. 16 · 13 and 16 · 14:** These provide a basis for a discussion of relative advantages of motile and nonmotile gametes.

**pp. 592–599:** The three examples of plant reproduction used in this section are designed to communicate two ideas: (1) the alternation of monoploid and diploid, sexually and asexually reproducing generations in plants, and (2) the reduction, in the course of evolution, of the monoploid gametophyte generation and the concomitant dominance of the diploid sporophyte generation. The second of these purposes dictates the choice of *Selaginella* as an example in place of the more familiar ferns. Nevertheless, some suggestions for work with ferns are given on pp. T244–T247.

**p. 593, Fig. 16 · 15:** You should not expect the details of this figure or of the similar Figures 16 · 18 and 16 · 23 to be memorized. They should be compared and used to establish the evolutionary decline of the gametophyte generation.

**p. 593, ¶ 3:** *Selaginella* is not likely to be familiar to students. But it is fairly easily cultured in a terrarium or greenhouse, so living material should be available in the classroom. Biological supply houses provide stocks of some species.

**p. 596, note 1:** In angiosperms the distinctions between ovum and sperm (p. 585) are not clear because both gametes are reduced to mere nuclei. On the basis of motility, the nuclei produced by the pollen grain can be considered male. However, the chief basis for distinction lies in the homology of pistil structures with megaspores of more primitive tracheophytes and of pollen grains with microspores, which (in *Selaginella*, for example) produce undoubted sperm cells.

**p. 597, ¶ 2:** Refer to Figure 5 · 6. The diversity in pollen grains may provide an interested student with a fine topic for microscopic investigation. This can be started now with house or greenhouse plants; it can be extended to wild flowers later in the spring.

**p. 597, note 1:** Plants benefit from insect visitation through pollination; the insects benefit by obtaining food (nectar). This form of mutualism has been investigated extensively with respect to mechanisms, but little quantitative assessment of "benefit" has been made in the sense discussed on pp. 88–89.

**p. 600, note 2:** An oyster's sex is perhaps best described as "indeterminate."

When the gonads produce ova, the animal is female; when they produce sperm, male. The reason for this question, however, is not the specific matter of the American oyster, but the attempt to get students to thinking about maleness and femaleness in a fundamental way.

**p. 600, ¶ 3:** Interested students may investigate the processes of spermatogenesis and oogenesis, which help to explain why sperm cells are smaller and more numerous than eggs. But they should be cautioned that the usual description—in close association with meiosis—does not apply to these processes in most plants.

**p. 601, ¶ 3:** To most students hermaphroditism and parthenogenesis (pp. 602–603) are highly abnormal. But what is abnormal in one group of organisms may be normal in another. A definition of "normal" may be necessary.

**p. 601, note 1:** Actually the complete separation of ovule-bearing and pollen-bearing in individual plants is rare in angiosperms and gymnosperms. It occurs in willows, poplars, ginkgo, and American holly (*Ilex opaca*). More frequently (and botanical terminology often does not clearly separate this from the condition just discussed), separate pistillate and staminate flowers occur on the same individual plant —for example, maize, oaks, hickories. But this latter condition would still be hermaphroditism from a zoological standpoint.

**p. 601, ¶ 6:** The contrast between internal and external fertilization provides examples of the correlation of structural adaptations and function, such as the reduced production of eggs and behavioral changes that increase the efficiency of fertilization.

**p. 602, Fig. 16 · 26:** Timing may be occasioned by moonlight itself. Many animals are known to receive from the environment visual clues that influence their pituitary glands and, thus, the entire sexual cycle. However, a critical factor for the success of spawning is the high tide. Particularly high tides (spring tides) occur when the moon is in conjunction with the sun (new moon) or in opposition to it (full moon).

**p. 603, note 1:** Parthenogenesis occurs in the context of sexual reproduction and can be described meaningfully only as a variation of it. However, in parthenogenesis the basic point of sexual reproduction, the union of two cells to form a new individual (p. 584), is lacking. Thus, there is room for your students to debate, but be sure that they realize that it is a verbal, not a scientific, issue.

**p. 603, ¶ 3:** Hydras in the high school laboratory seldom produce sexual structures; the stimuli for sexual reproduction seem to be the relative concentrations of oxygen and carbon dioxide in the water. Prepared slides of hydras bearing gonads and of budding hydras can be obtained from biological supply houses.

**p. 604, note 2:** *Hydra oligactis*, as pictured in Figure 16 · 28, always has two parents because the sexes are separate. But (p. 604, line 1) most other hydra species are hermaphroditic; thus a student can reasonably conclude that a sperm cell might fertilize an ovum on the same individual from which the sperm cell came, producing a zygote that had a single parent.

**p. 605, note 4:** The accompanying paragraph indicates that an earthworm zygote results from the union of a sperm of one individual with an ovum of another individual, even though the individuals are hermaphroditic.

**p. 605, ¶ 3:** Earthworms kept in a terrarium can occasionally be found in copulation. Earthworm cocoons, resulting from the secretions of the clitellum, can be purchased from biological supply houses.

**p. 606:** You may find in your classes one or two students who are tropical-fish fanciers. If so, they may be able to set up aquariums with breeding fish.

## INVESTIGATION 16.3

### CHICK EMBRYOLOGY
(pp. 608–612)

This investigation is a good test of the extent to which (1) a class has developed team coordination, and (2) individuals have developed manual dexterity and the habit of careful attention to directions. The investigation requires a considerable degree of skill, and it is to be expected that some teams will be unsuccessful.

You must become familiar with all techniques before attempting to lead a class through them.

### Preparations

Fertile eggs may be obtained from hatcheries or from poultry farmers who keep roosters in their flocks. In ordering, make some allowance for infertile eggs.

To secure embryos that correspond in development to those seen in the standard illustration of chick embryos at 24 hours, 33 hours, 48 hours, etc., keep the eggs cool (*but not below 10°C*) until they are incubated. When eggs are stored for more than a week after they are laid, viability of the embryos is greatly reduced. During incubation of the eggs, temperature should be kept between 37° and 39°C; and humidity, 50 percent or more. Because sufficient oxygen must pass through the shells to the embryos, some air-space must surround each egg. Using a soft pencil, mark each egg with the date and time at which incubation is started. To prevent the embryos from sticking to the shells, rotate the eggs daily. The marks will enable you to keep track of the rotation.

Set up a schedule for incubating the eggs. In the 48-hour eggs, variations of even a few hours can produce considerable differences in the appearance of the embryos. Therefore, when putting eggs for this stage into the incubator, consider the hour when each class meets. The exact hour at which incubation starts is less important for later stages, however. Note that incubation of some eggs must begin *twenty-one* days before use.

Suggestions for improvising an incubator may be found in R. E. Barthelemy, J. R. Dawson, Jr., and A. E. Lee, *Equipment and Techniques for the Biology Teaching Laboratory* (Boston: D. C. Heath & Co., 1964). Before use, thoroughly test the incubator (whether improvised or purchased) for its ability to maintain a steady temperature over the required time.

## Materials

Plastic refrigerator dishes may be substituted for finger bowls.

For the opening of early-stage eggs, cotton batting forms a better nest than paper towels; but it is more expensive.

Scissors must have fine points. Ordinary dissecting scissors are not satisfactory.

Petri dishes may be substituted for Syracuse watch glasses.

The chick physiological saline is different from that used for frog material. To prepare it, dissolve 9 g of sodium chloride in 991 ml of distilled water. Assign a student laboratory assistant to maintain the solution at a temperature of 37°C and to deliver it to teams as needed.

## Procedure

Part A can be done as a demonstration. Two or three eggs, set up around the room, can be observed by small groups of students while other work is in progress. Parts B and C each requires a full laboratory period. Or both can be done in one period if Part B is assigned to some teams and Part C to others; the materials are then exchanged between teams for observation by all.

- (1): Albumen is nearly homogeneous in appearance except for the chalazae, two stringy masses projecting from the yolk along the long axis of the egg. An especially observant student may also note that near the yolk the albumen is somewhat more dense than it is peripherally.

- (2): If the student has an unincubated egg, he will see nothing much more than the blastoderm itself, which appears as a whitish circular area surrounded by a somewhat darker marginal area. If the egg has been incubated for a short time, the primitive streak may be visible in the center of the blastoderm.

- (4): This space between the membrane and the shell is occupied by air.

- (5): The middle of a laboratory investigation is not the time for book research. The answer to this question —albumen, shell membrane, and shell—should be deduced from observation.

- (6): The student is not in a position to provide detailed answers, so accept any reasonable function. Protection, for example, is an acceptable answer for all three layers. The albumen is not a food source, although many students may suggest this. Some may guess it to be a water source. For the most part problems of respiration, dehydration, etc., will probably not occur to students at this time.

- (7): If development is normal, approximately the top half.

- (8): Students may have a number of ideas; but because the yolk sac is highly vascular, many should suggest that it transfers food material from the yolk to the embryo.

- (9): Normally, the heart begins regular contractions after about 44 hours of incubation. The actual rate must be determined by the student.

- (10): The answer varies with observational ability, but most students should be able to see most of the structures in Figure 16 · 33.

- (11): In the 33-hour egg, the embryo is oriented more or less in a straight line. By 48 hours the anterior end has greatly enlarged and there is a flexing of the body to one side, the heart being prominent in the concavity of this flexure.

• (12): It is difficult for students to trace the path of the blood. It passes from the heart into the ventral aortas, along the dorsal aortas, and out through the omphalomesenteric arteries to the plexus of vessels on the yolk. It then returns to the heart from the extra-embryonic vitelline circulation.

• (13): At two days the amnion is incomplete; there is a head fold and the beginning of a tail fold. By the fifth day, however, the head fold has grown backward and the tail fold forward, and they have fused to form a complete covering for the embryo.

• (14): It should not be difficult for a student to ascertain that the amnion is liquid-filled.

• (15): Normally at five days the entire yolk is covered by the sac.

• (16): The relatively large eyes in avian embryos are a mark of distinction from embryos of other vertebrates. Refer students to Figure 18 · 6.

• (17): The wording of this question may encourage more imagination than observation. At this stage, the limb buds have just become visible and appear as somewhat flipper-like appendages, like neither wings nor legs. The only real basis for distinction is position.

• (18): Students can make a wide variety of observations. One should concern the increased torsion and flexure of the five-day embryo. The somites have become much more numerous, better defined, and larger in the anterior half of the body; the arterial arches have increased from two to four; the arteries and veins are better defined; and, in addition, students should notice both size and position changes.

• (19): Primarily, oxygen and carbon dioxide.

• (20): The yolk sac is connected to the embryo in the abdominal region by means of a yolk stalk. The yolk sac becomes progressively smaller, finally being drawn into the body and incorporated into the small intestine, where it is still present several days after hatching.

• (21): The food in the yolk is absorbed by the blood vessels on the surface of the yolk sac and carried by blood vessels through the yolk stalk, the liver, the heart, and ultimately the rest of the developing embryo. There is an opportunity here for students to go into some detail by recalling ideas from Chapter 14.

• (22): Obviously, students' lists will differ depending upon the development stage of the egg examined.

Students frequently wish to preserve their specimens. This can be done in 70% alcohol. The small embryos on the filter-paper rings can be preserved in vials; larger embryos, in wide-mouth jars. Because water in specimens dilutes the preservative, drain out the alcohol after two days and replace.

Discussion

This investigation constitutes the principal attention to embryology in this course. Consequently discussion should be thorough, and the points scattered through pp. 603– 620 should be woven into it. Opportunities for discussion should occur after each of the parts of the investigation, and a concluding comparative discussion should be based on the written summaries, Item 25. Following are some comments on the questions that precede that item:

The extraembryonic membranes allow the chick egg to develop on land. The shell and albumen would be of less consequence if the egg developed within the hen. The circulatory system must develop early in order to carry food through the entire embryo and to remove waste products. Segmentation is seen primarily in the somites and in the nervous system. Students should have seen a dorsal hollow nerve cord but probably did not recognize the notochord. The aortic arches indicate the presence of pharyngeal pouches. However, any reasonable combination of ideas that indicates the student has synthesized his observations should be acceptable.

## PATTERNS OF REPRODUCTION
(cont. — pp. 614–620)

**p. 613, Fig. 16 · 37:** Do not overlook this illustration. It serves as a focal point for discussing mating behavior and secondary sexual characteristics, two very important aspects of reproduction. Further, it relates Chapter 15 to Chapter 16; a large amount of behavioral research has centered on reproductive behavior.

**p. 614, note 1:** The eggs of ovoviviparous animals develop internally, utilizing only food in their yolks, and the young are essentially hatched within the body of the female before encountering the environment. This is common among fishes and reptiles. Encourage your students to get examples and details, not merely dictionary definitions.

**p. 614, ¶ 2:** Just as the development of social hierarchy (see BSCS film loop *Social Behavior in Chickens*, reference: p. T226) conserves energy within a closely associated group of animals, so also does seasonal sexual behavior. The behavioral patterns associated with cyclic reproduction are well developed in birds that fly to high-latitude breeding grounds in spring and, after raising their young, fly equatorward again in fall.

**p. 614, ¶ 5:** Emphasize the extirpation experiment as a common way to elicit data about the physiological processes of specific organs.

**p. 615, Fig. 16 · 38:** This and Figure 16 · 41 are better than nothing, but much more detailed anatomical illustrations should be available. The Frohse Anatomical Charts, A. J. Nystrom & Co., are excellent. Better still is a manikin with interchangeable inserts of reproductive parts.

**p. 615, ¶ 3:** The interactions discussed in this and subsequent paragraphs are excellent examples of homeostasis. The hormonal relationships among the pituitary gland, the ovary, and the uterus should be tied to what students already know about regulation from their study of Chapter 14.

**p. 616, Fig. 16 · 40:** These diagrams illustrate the text description, but you will probably have to provide most students with some help in interpreting them.

**p. 617, note 2:** Cf. pp. 525–526 and 559–560.

**p. 617, note 6:** Since students have learned (pp. 559–560) that male white-crowned sparrows have a cyclic reproductive pattern, they can surmise that some kind of hormonal feedback mechanism exists in these birds. In this case, however, the mechanism is strongly influenced by environmental factors.

**p. 618, ¶ 1:** The events of fertilization and implantation institute a new sequence of controls, which cause the cessation of the menstrual cycle and the maintenance of pregnancy.

**p. 618, ¶ 3:** Abundant materials on descriptive human embryology are available. Student interest is high, so you should at least take time for some presentation such as the filmstrips referred to on p. T254. Comparisons should be made with features that the students have themselves observed in chick embryos.

**p. 619, Fig. 16 · 44:** Occasionally a physical break occurs within the placenta, between the two circulatory systems, and then there may be direct contact between the bloods of mother and infant. This is of considerable importance if the blood types differ, particularly in the case of the Rh types. Some student might want to investigate this and report to the class.

**p. 619, note 2:** The lack of a fully formed placenta prevents the development of marsupial embryos to the extent attained in placentals. When nourishment becomes critical, the young are born in a fetal condition. However, muscles of limbs and mouth are developed enough for the young to crawl into the mother's pouch and attach themselves to the teats. From this time on they are nourished with milk.

**p. 619, ¶ 3:** If students ascertain the gestation periods of various mammals, an interesting classroom discussion can ensue. Correlations between birth size and length of gestation period can be made. Generally, the smaller the animal, the shorter the period of gestation, but there are exceptions that can challenge students' ingenuity in providing possible explanations.

### PROBLEMS (pp. 622–623)

1. One way would be to remove the placenta and analyze it for the presence of progesterone. The student might ask, however, "Could not the progesterone found in the placenta have originated somewhere else and been stored there?" Students should be encouraged to provide an answer for that question. They might be led to suggest that if all other known sources of progesterone were extirpated and progesterone were still found in the placenta, this would be evidence of its production there. Students should then be asked what tissues would have to be extirpated. Obviously, the ovaries would be the first to consider.

2. A student might come up with the suggestion that sperm cells of birds have more resistance to high temperatures than those of mammals. Most students probably do not know that birds have extensions from the lungs, air sacs. A pair of these air sacs extend abdominally and lie close behind the testes. Undoubtedly, they cause some reduction in testicular temperatures.

3. Principally, propagation by cuttings insures offspring that have the same traits as their parent. Because of genetic recombination, this is not necessarily

true with seeds, which are produced sexually, even if both parents have the desired traits. In addition, most plants produced by cuttings mature faster than those produced from seeds. In grafting, man takes advantage of established root stocks to further quicken early growth of cuttings from plants with desirable characteristics. Frequently varieties that have excellent root growth have poor fruit or flower characteristics, and vice versa. Grafting combines the desirable traits. For example, most citrus varieties are budded (a kind of grafting) on sour orange stock. This is a large subject, and an interested student can carry it far, both in the library and in the greenhouse or field.

4. Whether a paramecium presents a special case of sexuality or not depends upon one's definition of sexuality. If sexuality is an exchange of nuclear material that provides genetic variability, then conjugation in paramecia is certainly included. If, however, the student defines sexuality in terms of sperm and ova, then in paramecia, as in *Rhizopus* and *Ulothrix*, there is no way to distinguish mating types as male and female.

5. This can be a very extensive investigation. Some examples: the stigmas becoming receptive before the pollen matures; the anthers maturing and shedding their pollen before the stigmas are receptive; the flower being constructed so that there is little chance of its pollen being deposited on the stigma; the pollen failing to germinate or the growth of the pollen tube being inhibited.

By this time the students should be aware that the inclusion of the word "always" in a question makes it somewhat difficult to answer. However, most cereals (except rye and corn), garden peas, tobacco, and cotton are normally self-pollinated.

If a plant is self-pollinated normally, it is almost certain to produce seeds. An isolated plant of this type can propagate its species, but it could not if it were an obligatory cross-pollinator. On the other hand, cross-pollination introduces a larger degree of variability into a population, allowing genetic changes that may permit survival under quite adverse conditions; self-pollinated species in the same situation might become extinct.

6. Apomixis is the formation of seed in the pistil of a flowering plant without fertilization. It is thus comparable to parthenogenesis and has the same genetic implications. The families Compositae, Rosaceae, and Gramineae have species that reproduce apomictically. In some species it seems to be the only method of reproduction.

7. (a) Yuccas are insect-pollinated plants depending upon pronuba moths for fertilization. (b) In the hollies usually planted for ornament, male and female plants are separate. Fruits are developed only if a male and female plant are relatively close together. In a pair, no berries develop on the male plant; if both plants are of the same sex, neither bears fruit. (c) Apomixis is called into play to answer this question. (d) Night-blooming plants are usually pollinated by night-flying insects such as moths. (e) Bees kept near flowering plants insure maximal fertilization for insect-pollinated species. (f) Peas are normally self-pollinated. Obviously, any plant dependent upon wind pollination or some other mechanism independent of insects might produce seeds when grown in an insect-free greenhouse.

8. Students will find that vertebrates can be divided into amniotes (reptiles, birds, and mammals) and anamniotes (amphibians and fish). Embryonic membranes are basically an adaptation to a land environment. Amnion and chorion are usually the best developed of all membranes; yolk sac and allantois vary in extent of development, but in some groups are quite rudimentary.

## SUPPLEMENTARY MATERIALS

### Additional Investigations

### ALTERNATION OF GENERATIONS IN FERNS

This is a predominantly observational investigation using a combination of fresh plant materials and prepared microscope slides. It provides comparisons with the descriptions of alternation of generations in *Selaginella* and in flowering plants.

#### Introduction

Ferns are of no great economic importance. But the importance of an organism is not established on the basis of its economic value alone. Some forms of life may be more worthy of study than others, but all are products of a long, slow process of change and evolution; each form presents unanswered questions about ancestry, biochemical processes, and behavior. When you look at a fern, it may be a good idea to remind yourself that before you is a modern descendant of plants that dominated the earth for millions of years before man arrived to appreciate—or ignore—them.

#### Materials and Equipment
(for each team)

Intact specimen of fern sporophyte, fresh or dried
Living fern sporophytes in pots, 2 or 3 per class
Hand lens
Scalpel
Microscope slide
Medicine dropper
Cover slip
Monocular microscope
Fern gametophyte
Stereomicroscope

#### Procedure

Examine your specimen of a fern sporophyte, comparing it with a living plant

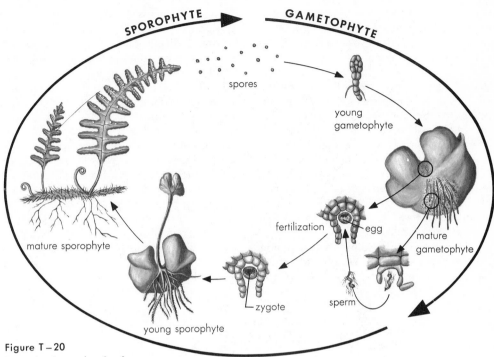

Figure T–20
Reproductive cycle of a fern.

growing in a pot. • Where is the stem located in the growing plant?(1) With a hand lens observe the leaves (fronds). The veins are neither netted nor parallel but are said to be *dichotomous* (refer to p. 139). • What does this term mean?(2) Notice that some of the leaves have small, brown dotlike or elongated structures, called "sori" (singular, "sorus"). • On which surface of the leaves do they occur—upper or lower?(3) • Do the leaves that bear sori look like those that do not?(4)

With a scalpel, scrape off a few of the sori. Deposit them in the middle of a clean slide; add a drop of water and a cover slip. Examine with a microscope, using low power. The small stalked structures you may see are spore cases. If you find any, examine one closely and notice the row of thick-walled cells across the top and around one side. Draw the whole spore case. If some of the cases have been broken in handling, spores may be scattered on the side; other spores may be observed inside the broken cases. Draw two or three spores as you see them under high power.

As a spore case reaches maturity, its cells begin to dry out. The row of thick-walled cells straightens, tearing the case open and exposing the spores. As the case continues to dry out, the row of thick-walled cells acts as a spring and snaps back, throwing the spores into the air. This is one of the fastest movements found anywhere in the plant kingdom. The spores are so small that they may float in the air for a long time. Volcanic islands and lava flows are frequently populated by ferns and mosses well in advance of the appearance of seed plants. • Explain.(5)

Spores that settle from the air in favorable locations germinate and develop gametophytes. Examine a fern gametophyte under the stereomicroscope. • Describe the size and shape of the gametophyte.(6) Observe the threadlike structures on the lower surface; these are not vascular, so they are called rhizoids rather than roots.

T 246

Although it is small and relatively inconspicuous, the gametophyte is important in the fern reproductive cycle, for it produces both male and female gametes. The male organs (*antheridia*) appear as small, dome-shaped, multicellular structures among the rhizoids on the undersurface of the gametophyte. Antheridia generally develop before the female organs (*archegonia*) appear. The archegonia are also produced on the undersurface of the gametophyte—but near the notch. They are flask-shaped, with enlarged basal portions buried in the tissues of the gametophytes and necks projecting about the surface. Each basal portion of an archegonium contains an egg.

Remove an antheridium and crush it in a drop of water on a clean slide. Add a cover slip and examine under low power of the monocular microscope. • Can you see any released sperms? What kind of movement, if any, do they show?(7)  Sperms liberated from the antheridia swim to the archegonia; fertilization takes place in the archegonia. • In what kind of habitat must gametophytes grow for fertilization to occur?(8)  In most ferns both antheridia and archegonia are produced on the same gametophyte, though sperms and eggs do not ordinarily mature at the same time. • How is this likely to affect the parentage of the offspring?(9)

The zygote divides repeatedly to form a young sporophyte, which generally grows for several years before it begins to produce spores. Soon after the roots and leaves of the young sporophyte are well developed, the parent gametophyte dies and decays —in other words, the sporophyte remains

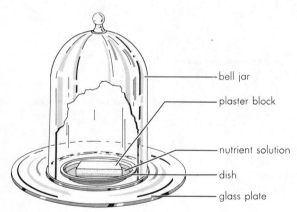

bell jar
plaster block
nutrient solution
dish
glass plate

Figure T–21

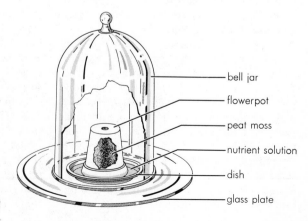

bell jar
flowerpot
peat moss
nutrient solution
dish
glass plate

Figure T–22

dependent upon the gametophyte for a very short time. • How does this compare with the relationship between gametophyte and sporophyte in mosses?(10)

## For the Teacher

The investigation is written for use with a species of fern that has moderately dimorphic fronds — *Polystichum acrostichoides* or *Polypodium virginianum*, for example. But almost any fern of a convenient size can be used. The specimens for each team should be of the same species as the potted plants, which are included so that the position of the rhizome (underground stem) can be shown.

Ejection of spores from sporangia may be demonstrated if mature sporangia are available. Test sporangia from different individuals until some are found at the proper stage; keep these plants in a plastic bag until class time. Place a sorus under a stereomicroscope and focus a hot, bright light on it, which will cause the sporangia to dry out. They first dehisce; then, as drying continues, the annuli snap back, ejecting the spores.

Fern gametophytes may be grown by several methods. One involves planting spores on blocks of plaster of Paris. Mix plaster of Paris with water until it attains a viscous, but easily stirred, consistency. Pour it into a small aluminum pie pan (smaller in diameter than the dish you will use). When it hardens, wash it thoroughly with a nutrient solution. The solution may be made from a commercial fertilizer such as Hyponex (1 g dissolved in 1 liter of water) or from the materials supplied for hydroponics experiments (General Biological Supply House or Carolina Biological Supply Co. — addresses: p. T 326). Set up the apparatus shown in Figure T–21. Lay fern fronds bearing mature sporangia on a piece of white paper, and place under a lamp to dry. The spores that collect on the paper may then be blown gently onto the moist surface of the plaster block. Place the apparatus in indirect but not dim light. Young gametophytes should appear in about ten days; mature antheridia and archegonia should develop in about two months.

A similar method of growing fern gametophytes involves use of a clean, preferably new flowerpot stuffed tightly with fibrous (not granulated) peat moss (Figure T–22). Collect and sow spores on the surface of the pot in the manner described for the plaster block.

## FROG EMBRYOLOGY

### Background Information

You have learned how pituitary hormones function in the reproductive cycle of human females. In general the pituitary glands of vertebrates influence the activity of the gonads by means of hormones called *gonadotrophins*. In female frogs the seasonal changes of spring stimulate the pituitary to secrete large quantities of gonadotrophins into the bloodstream. Reaching the ovaries, these hormones cause eggs to be released into the oviducts. After the eggs are laid, the ovaries build up a new crop of eggs during the summer. When female frogs go into hibernation in the autumn, the eggs to be laid the following spring need only the stimulus of gonadotrophins to be released from the ovaries. Therefore, if gonadotrophic hormones are injected into a female frog during late fall or winter, eggs can be obtained long before the frog's own gonadotrophic hormones are secreted from its pituitary.

In male frogs, also, pituitary hormones stimulate the gonads by secreting gonadotrophins. This results in normal mating behavior and release of sperm cells over the eggs as they are laid by the female. Gonadotrophins may be secreted by the frog's own pituitaries in spring, or they may be injected into the frog. But active sperm cells may be obtained — even in winter — by removing the gonads (testes) from a male frog and chopping them up in a little water.

T 248

CONTINUITY OF THE BIOSPHERE

## Materials and Equipment
(for each team)

*A. Inducing ovulation*
   Live female frog, at least 8 cm from snout
      to anus
   Hypodermic syringe, 2 ml or larger
   Hypodermic needle, #25
   Pituitary suspension
   Battery jar with weighted-screen cover

*B. Fertilizing frog eggs*
   Pithed male frog
   Scissors
   Scalpel
   Forceps
   Petri dish
   Pond water
   Graduated cylinder (25 ml or 100 ml)
   Female frog (from A, above)
   Syracuse watch glass
   Medicine dropper
   Stereomicroscope
   Finger bowls or plastic dishes, approxi-
      mately 10 cm in diameter and 4 cm deep,
      3 or 4
   Glass-marking crayon
   Frog eggs, fertilized several hours before
      the laboratory period
   Temperature Gradient Box, 1 per class

*C. Observing frog embryos*
   Developing frog eggs (from B, above)
   Stereomicroscope
   Centigrade thermometer
   Medicine dropper
   Forceps
   Graph paper, 1 sheet per student
   Pencils, 4 or 5 colors

## Procedure

*A. Inducing ovulation.* Part A can best be done by three members of the team (Students A, B, and C); the other members can assist by keeping all materials ready for use as needed.

Student A: Grasp the frog gently in the left hand. The dorsal surface of the frog should rest against your palm. The posterior legs should be held firmly between the fingers of your right hand.

Student B: Grasp the frog's ventral skin between your thumb and forefinger and lift it away from the body wall.

Student C: Draw into the hypodermic syringe the amount of pituitary suspension recommended by the teacher. Attach the needle and insert it through the frog's skin and into the muscle of the body wall. (CAUTION: Do not insert the point of the needle *through* the body wall!) Inject the pituitary suspension.

Put the frog into a battery jar. Add water to a depth of about 2 cm and cover the mouth of the jar with a weighted screen. Place the jar where the frog will not be disturbed and will have an even room temperature (20° to 22°C). In two or three days the frog should be ready to release eggs.

*B. Fertilizing frog eggs.* When the female frog is ready to ovulate, open the abdominal cavity of a pithed *male* frog quickly, using the technique described in Investigation 14.1. Move the internal organs aside and locate the testes. These are two whitish, oval organs located on each side of the backbone and just ventral to the kidneys. Using scissors and forceps, remove both testes and put them in a petri dish containing about 2 ml of pond water at room temperature. With a scalpel cut the testes into fine pieces; use the flat side of the blade to mash the pieces against the bottom of the dish. Add 20 ml of pond water and set the dish aside for ten minutes. During this time, sperm cells released from the testes will become active and form a sperm suspension.

While this is happening, place a few milliliters of pond water into a Syracuse watch glass. Grasp the ovulating female frog in one hand, dorsal side against the palm, and extend the hind legs with the other hand. Hold the frog in this position over the watch glass. Squeeze the frog's abdomen gently, applying pressure gradually from the anterior part of the abdomen toward the posterior part. In this manner strip a few eggs into the watch glass. When the sperms have had ten minutes to become active, use the squeezing technique again to strip 100–150 eggs from the female frog into the petri dish containing the suspension. Bathe the eggs with the sperm suspension, using a medicine dropper; leave the eggs in the suspension for ten minutes.

Meanwhile, observe the eggs in the Syracuse watch glass, using a stereomicroscope. Note whether the eggs are floating dark side up, light side up, or without regard to color. Note the thickness of the eggs in relation to the thickness of the jelly that surrounds them.

When the eggs have been in the sperm suspension ten minutes, gently pour the sperm suspension from the petri dish, disturbing the eggs as little as possible. Use a medicine dropper to remove the last few milliliters of the suspension, picking up any remaining pieces of testes as you do so. Pour about 20 ml of pond water over the eggs and again allow them to stand—this time for fifteen minutes.

While you are waiting, number some finger bowls (your teacher will designate the quantity needed). Label the bowls with your team symbol and pour 100 ml of pond water into each one.

Place in the watch glass a few of the frog eggs that were fertilized before your laboratory period began. Observe with the stereomicroscope. In your data book, record the time at which these eggs were fertilized (obtain this from the teacher) and the time at which you observe them. Study the stages of development shown in Figure T–23 and record the number of the stage that most resembles the eggs you are observing. Also compare these eggs with the ones just fertilized and with the unfertilized eggs, noting any differences.

When jelly has swelled around the eggs in the petri dish, it is safe to handle them. Use a scalpel to free any eggs that stick to the dish. With scissors, cut the ribbon of eggs into groups of 5 to 10 eggs each. (CAUTION: Be careful to avoid stretching or squeezing the eggs.) Using forceps, gently transfer 25–30 eggs into each finger bowl. Put the bowls in the Temperature Gradient

Box or in other places designated by your teacher.

*C. Observing frog embryos.* On each succeeding day, for as long as your teacher directs, observe the embryos in each bowl. During the first few days watch for eggs that are not developing. Using a medicine dropper and forceps, remove any dead eggs. In your data book, record the day of observation (if the eggs were fertilized on Monday, Tuesday is recorded as "Day 1," and so on). Next to this, record the number of the bowl observed. Next, record the temperature of the water in the bowl at the time you begin observation. Finally, record the number designating the stage in Figure T–23 that most closely resembles the majority of the embryos.

In Figure T–23 the eggs and embryos are shown without the surrounding jelly. In your own observations (through Stage 19) the jelly will look something like a halo. You will probably have particular difficulty seeing the differences among Stages 15, 16, 17, and 18, since at those stages the embryos are somewhat folded in the jelly covering. As you refer to Figure T–23, keep these points in mind: (1) The drawings and the ages given are those of embryos developing at a *constant temperature* of 18°C. (2) The notes under the drawings will help you to identify stages in the embryos you are observing. (3) The drawings show stages at which the embryos can be clearly distinguished; the embryos, of course, gradually change from one stage to another. Many of the embryos you observe will be at intermediate stages and will not look exactly like any one of the drawings. Indicate intermediate stages by using decimals (6.5, 10.5, etc.).

After each day's observation, return each finger bowl to its place, so that its temperature may be kept as stable as possible.

## Studying the Data

Plot the data from your team's bowls on a single grid, using a different color for each bowl. Show stages of development on the vertical axis and time on the horizontal

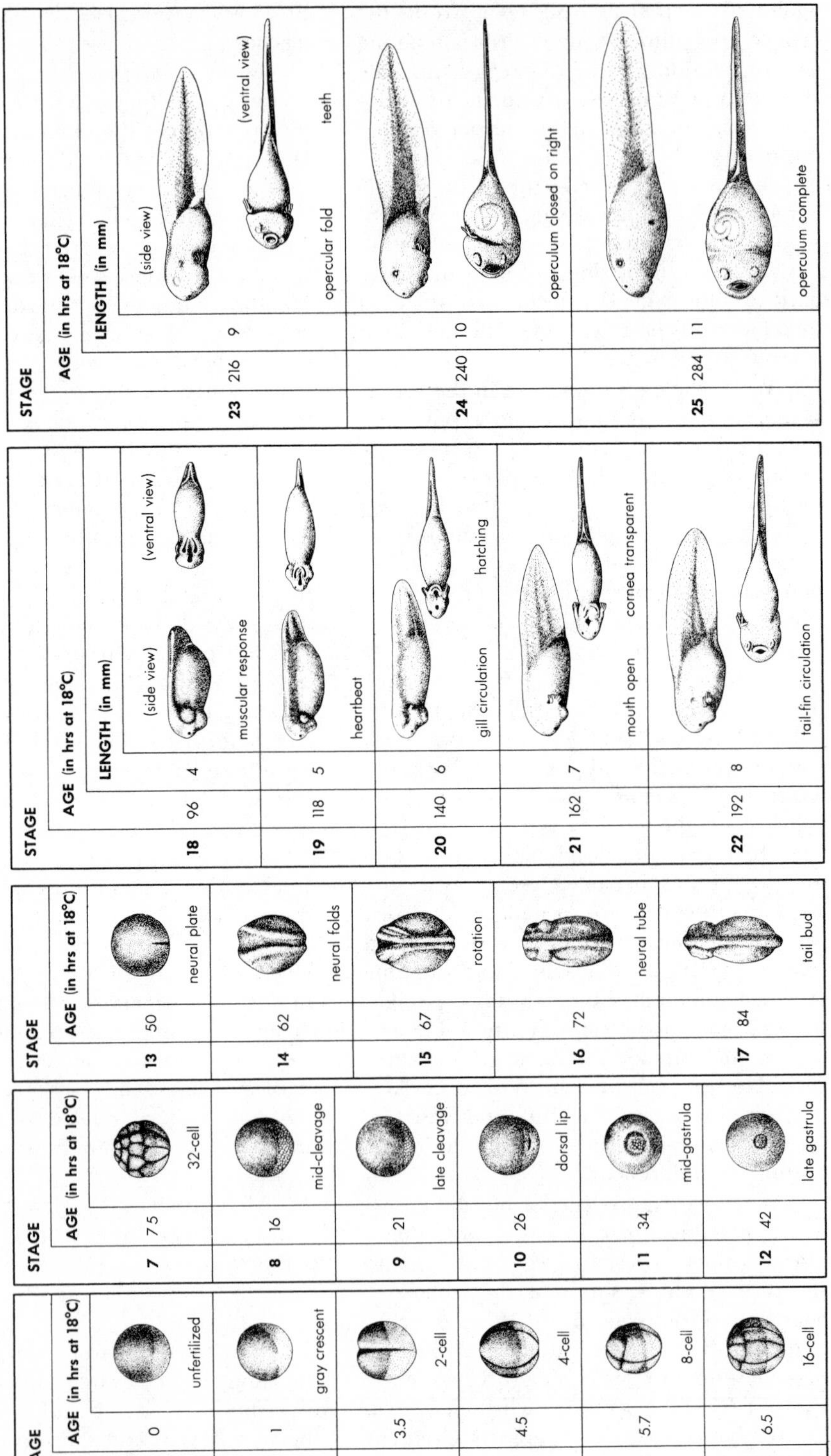

Figure T-23
Stages of development of *Rana pipiens*. (From Shumway's chart, Waldo Shumway, *The Anatomical Record*, Vol. 78, pp. 143-147.)

axis. Compute the average temperature maintained in the water of each bowl; in the key to the graph, write each average next to the appropriate color. Finally, use another color to plot the data from Figure T–23; write "Constant 18°C" next to this color in the key. • Which line shows the most even development?(1) • How can you explain this?(2) • Which line shows the most rapid development?(3) • The least rapid development?(4) • Explain.(5)

## Summary

• From the results, what general statement can you make about the influence of temperature on the rate of embryonic development in a frog?(6)

---

## For the Teacher

It is now not uncommon for students to have some experience with chick development in the early grades. And your students may have done much of the work outlined for Investigation 16.3 in junior high school or middle school. If so, the work on frog embryology may be a desirable substitute.

This investigation has been adapted and simplified from one part of the BSCS Laboratory Block *Animal Growth and Development*, by Florence Moog (Boston: D. C. Heath & Co., 1963), which should be consulted for broader background and fuller procedures.

You may be initiating this investigation at a time when frog eggs are naturally available. If this is the case, Parts A and B may be omitted. Keep a pond under observation each morning; try to collect only the freshest eggs. Eggs that were not present on the previous day were probably laid during the night. Or collect pairs of frogs in amplexus and bring them into the laboratory. The species of frog is not important; but be sure to keep in mind that Figure T–23 applies to *Rana pipiens*, and considerable deviation can be expected with the use of other species.

The omission of Parts A and B greatly simplifies the work, but it also bypasses some excellent experiences with hormonal control. If the investigation is scheduled after the normal egg-laying season and you still wish to have Parts A and B done, keep a few frogs in a refrigerator, which will delay ovulation and mating by several weeks.

*Part A.* The teams for this part may be larger than for the other two. However, some allowance should be made for treated frogs that may die or that may, for one reason or another, fail to respond to the treatment. (Immaturity is a common cause of failure; be sure the frogs equal or exceed the minimum size.)

The simplest method of getting equipment to demonstrate ovulation and fertilization in the frog is to purchase from a biological supply house a kit that contains male frogs, a female frog, and a bottle containing a suspension of pituitaries. To cover the possibility of failure, order several kits. However, you can arrange a better learning experience by dissecting out whole pituitaries and injecting these between the skin and body wall of the abdomen, using a #18 hypodermic needle. This procedure emphasizes the fact that gonadotrophins are not just present or absent, but vary in quantity. The number of pituitaries required to induce ovulation in a female varies with the sex of the donors and the season. Pituitaries from female frogs are approximately twice as potent as those from males. The suggested dosage of female pituitaries from September to January is 5; from January to March, 4; in March, 3; in April, 2.

Dissecting out the frog pituitary is a difficult procedure. A BSCS Technique Film (*Removing Frog Pituitary*. 8-mm or Super-8 film loop. Color. 1 min., 50 sec. Thorne Films, Boulder, Colo.) shows the complete procedure. This may be shown to the class at your discretion, but the procedure itself should be attempted only by students especially adept and interested in biological techniques.

In lieu of the film, Figure T–24 and the following directions may be used: Anesthetize a frog with ether or chloroform.

Figure T–24

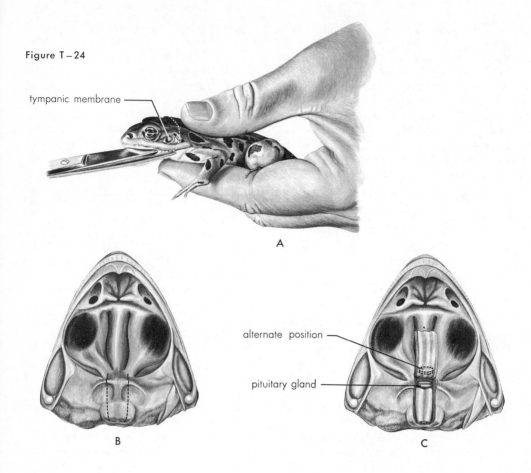

tympanic membrane

alternate position

pituitary gland

A

B

C

Insert the blade of a pair of strong, sharp-pointed scissors into the mouth at the angle of the jaw, cutting back on each side to extend the width of the mouth. Then make a transverse cut just posterior to the tympanic membranes. You have now cut off the upper jaw and skull as far back as the rear of the tympanum. Pith the body by inserting a dissecting needle into the spinal column and moving it about to destroy the spinal cord. Discard the carcass.

Wash the head and place it, ventral side up, on a dissecting pan. Cut away the skin on the roof of the mouth and expose the skull bones. Carefully insert the scissors in the opening at the base of the brain, and cut down one side of the bony floor of the cranium to a point even with the posterior margin of the eye socket; do the same on the other side. Each cut should be approximately 2.5 mm from the midline. Using forceps, carefully turn back the resulting flap of bone to expose the underside of the brain. The pinkish pituitary gland is attached to the brain just posterior to the crossed optic nerves and is about three times the size of the head of a common pin. Usually the pituitary adheres to the bony flap. Remove it with fine forceps, and place it in a small amount of amphibian saline solution (0.7% NaCl) in a watch glass.

Part A should be done on a Friday, if possible. The female frogs should be ovulating by Monday; development of the embryos can then be followed through the 96-hour stage before the next weekend.

*Part B.* This part of the "Procedure" is long. With good students it can be accomplished in a 55-minute laboratory period. If the period is shorter and the students are inept, it is well to dissect out the testes in one period and complete the procedure the next day. You may do this by stopping the procedure at the point of removal and continuing as follows: Rinse the testes in amphibian saline and gently blot with a paper towel. Fit a thin layer of cotton into a petri dish. Then remove the cotton, dip it in saline, squeeze firmly, and replace in the dish. There must be no standing water

in the dish! Place the testes on the cotton, cover with a second layer of moist cotton, put the cover on the dish, and store overnight in a refrigerator.

Pond water is the best medium for the eggs and developing embryos. Tap water, even when aged, is unsatisfactory. If pond water is not available, use a 10% Holtfreter's solution. First, prepare a stock solution by dissolving 3.5 g of NaCl, 0.05 g of KCl, and 0.2 g of $NaHCO_3$ in 1 liter of distilled water (a glass still must be used). To make 10% Holtfreter's, combine one part of the stock solution and nine parts of distilled water.

Frog embryos pass rapidly through the early stages of development. Students will

Figure T—25

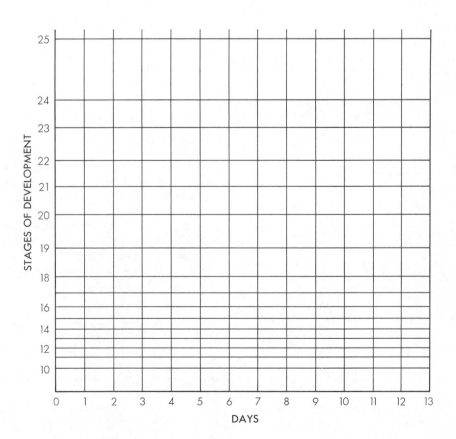

have an opportunity to observe at least a few of these stages if some frog eggs are fertilized early in the morning, before classes begin. These can be observed during the first class of the day. Then if a few dishes of fertilized eggs are saved from each class, later classes will be able to observe additional stages of development.

If stereomicroscopes are not available, some worthwhile observations can be made with hand lenses. In either case, a strong light source is important. Use a microscope lamp or the following improvisation: Place an incandescent bulb in a simple socket mounted on a board. Obtain a square piece of thin aluminum sheeting (such as that used in offset printing); each side of the square should be somewhat greater than the height of the bulb and socket. Bend the square so that two adjacent corners come together, and staple shut the folded edge between these corners. Open the free edges somewhat, and stand the resulting reflector on the board so that the stapled edge extends over the bulb. But take care that this device does not overheat the dish being observed.

The Temperature Gradient Box was discussed in connection with Investigation 6.2 (see Figure T–5). If such a box is not available, some dishes should be kept at room temperature; others should be kept at a higher temperature by being placed in a box that contains a lighted bulb (a thermostat is desirable but not essential if frequent checks are made); still others should be kept below room temperature in a refrigerator.

*Part C.* The daily observations should take no more than ten minutes of each period.

The principal object in this exercise is the observation of embryonic development; the experimental aspect is incidental. Therefore relatively little time need be devoted to the study of the data. However, if the data *are* obtained, they may be plotted on a grid such as that shown in Figure T–25. On this grid the standard rate of development (shown in Figure T–23) produces a straight line, which facilitates comparison of graph lines from experimental data.

## Invitations to Enquiry

*Invitation 3*, pp. 57–59 of the *Biology Teacher's Handbook*. (Reference: p. T35). If this invitation was not done in conjunction with Chapter 1, the topic of seed germination, which involves growth and differentiation, and the message of misinterpretation of data are both consequential. This invitation can be worked in nicely as a plant counterpart for Section D, p. 612, or as an extension of events subsequent to Stage D of Figure 16·22 on p. 598.

*Invitation 25*, pp. 130–135 of the *Handbook*. This invitation deals with the feedback aspects of pituitary-gonad mechanisms and is an excellent supplement to material on pp. 616–618, dealing with the human menstrual cycle.

*Invitation 37*, pp. 184–187 of the *Handbook*. This invitation is concerned with postnatal changes in the human embryo and indicates the capacity of the embryo to adapt to a new environmental situation.

## Audiovisual Materials

**Filmstrips:** *Development of Embryos.* Audio-Visual Division, Popular Science Publishing Co. Color. Development from cleavage of sea urchin, amphibian, reptile, and chick, with some attention to control factors.

*Ways of Starting New Plants.* Audio-Visual Division, Popular Science Publishing Co. Color. Both sexual and asexual methods are shown. The approach is practical.

**Motion-picture films:** *Mitosis and Meiosis.* Indiana University Films. 16 mm. Color. 16 1/2 min. Very good for recalling mitosis and contrasting meiosis with it.

*Asexual Reproduction.* Indiana University Films. 16 mm. Color. 10 min. Includes time-lapse photography of fission, budding, and spore formation.

*Theories of Development* (AIBS Film Series). McGraw-Hill Text-Film Division.

16 mm. Color. 28 min. Outlines history of theories and depicts development of frog.

*The Chick Embryo from Primitive Streak to Hatching.* Encyclopaedia Britannica Films. 16 mm. Color. 13 min. Includes time-lapse photography of the formation of the heart, beating of the heart, and circulating blood.

*Plants That Grow from Leaves, Stems and Roots.* Coronet Films. 16 mm. Color. 11 min. Presents many examples of vegetative reproduction.

*Flowers: Structure and Function.* Coronet Films. 16 mm. Color. Stamens, anthers, pistils, stigmas, ovaries, pollen, and fruit in both macroscopic and microscopic views. Pollination by insects and wind. Time-lapse sequence of pollen tubes growing from pollen grains.

*The Human Body: Reproductive System.* Coronet Films. 16 mm. Color. 13 1/2 min. Similarities and differences in male and female reproductive organs. Animation and photomicrography, including fertilization of the human ovum.

*The Liverwort: Alternation of Generations.* Coronet Films. 16 mm. Color. 16 min. Complete life cycle from gametophyte to sporophyte and back. Vegetative reproduction through gemmae. Transfer of sperm from antheridium to archegonium.

*Reproduction among Mammals.* Encyclopaedia Britannica Films. 16 mm. Black-and-white. Uses the domestic pig for illustrative purposes, including development of sperm and eggs, fertilization, and embryonic stages.

*The Fish Embryo: From Fertilization to Hatching.* Encyclopaedia Britannica Films. 16 mm. Color. 12 min. External fertilization and the tracing of the zygote from the first cell cleavage to the formation of the young fish.

*Meiosis: Sex Cell Formation.* Encyclopaedia Britannica Films. 16 mm. Color. 16 min. Explains the role of meiosis in gamete formation.

*Amoeba—Fission.* Encyclopaedia Britannica Films. 8-mm film loop. Color. 3 min. The process of binary fission in the ameba.

*Earthworm, Part 3, Reproductive System.* Ealing. Super-8 film loop. Color. 3 min., 10 sec. Chiefly anatomical, showing relation of male and female systems in a hermaphroditic animal.

*Algal Syngamy, Isogamy in Chlamydomonas.* Ealing. Super-8 film loop. 3 min., 30 sec. Fusion of gametes in an alga that has no morphological distinction between eggs and sperm cells.

*Pollen Tube Growth.* Ealing. Super-8 film loop. Color. 2 min. Excellent time-lapse photography of pollen-tube growth and formation of nuclei.

*Mating Behavior in the Cockroach.* BSCS Inquiry Film Loop. (Rand McNally #11-2977). Super-8. Color. Relates behavior to the reproductive process.

## Teacher's References

BALINSKY, B. I. *An Introduction to Embryology.* 2nd ed. Philadelphia: W. B. Saunders Co., 1965.

BULLOUGH, W. S. *Vertebrate Reproductive Cycles.* 2nd ed. New York: John Wiley & Sons, Inc., 1961. (Excellent review of the diversity of vertebrate reproductive patterns and their endocrinological basis.)

EBERT, J. D. *Interacting Systems in Development.* New York: Holt, Rinehart and Winston, Inc., 1965. Paperback.

JOINT COMMITTEE ON HEALTH PROBLEMS IN EDUCATION, of the National Education Association and American Medical Association. *Facts Aren't Enough.* Chicago: American Medical Association, 1962. (Primarily for adults who have responsibilities that may create a need for an understanding of sex education.)

PATTEN, B. M. *Foundations of Embryology.* 2nd ed. New York: McGraw-Hill Book Co., Inc., 1964. (New edition of a standard work devoted primarily to the standard vertebrate examples. Many other vertebrate-embryology texts are available.)

SUSSMAN, M. *Animal Growth and Development.* 2nd ed. Englewood Cliffs, N.J.: Prentice-Hall, Inc., 1964. Paperback.

TANNER, J. M., and G. R. TAYLOR. *Growth.* "Life Science Library." New York: Time, Inc., Book Division, 1965.

WILLIER, B. H., and J. M. OPPENHEIMER (eds.). *Foundations of Experimental Embryology.* Englewood Cliffs, N.J.: Prentice-Hall, Inc., 1964. (Eleven papers in the field of experimental embryology, originally published between 1888 and 1939. These were the years during which the foundations of the science were laid.)

# Heredity

## MAJOR IDEAS

1. Through a combination of fortunate mathematical background, native astuteness, and considerable luck, Gregor Mendel developed a fruitful inheritance theory that was fundamentally different from all previous theories.

2. The principles of probability theory are used by biologists to test various theories of heredity and to make predictions concerning future generations.

3. Mendel's experimental results led him to formulate a particulate theory of inheritance. By assuming that heredity is determined by particles transmitted from generation to generation through the gametes, he was able to explain the phenomena of dominance, segregation, and independent assortment. His choice of gene pairs clearly illustrates the scientific rule of parsimony.

4. Soon after their rediscovery, Mendel's principles were linked with nineteenth-century advances in cytology to form a chromosome theory of inheritance. Abundant experimental work during the first quarter of the twentieth century substantiated this theory.

5. The "proof" of a scientific theory consists in its continued ability to account for new evidence as it arises; a theory can never be finally proved.

6. Twentieth-century experimental work has revealed new principles of heredity: linkage, nondisjunction, nondominance, multiple alleles, continuously varying traits, etc. All of these phenomena were unknown to Mendel, but they proved to be explainable in terms of his theory.

7. The characteristics of an individual organism are the product of an inextricable interaction of heredity and environment.

8. Improvements in cytological and statistical technique have greatly increased knowledge of human heredity without resort to breeding experiments: human chromosomes have been accurately numbered and described; chromosome anomalies have been linked to clinical syndromes; and metabolic defects—traceable to gene defects—have been elucidated. Yet, many human "traits" of great interest still have not yielded to genetic analysis.

9. The origin of new traits in organisms has been traced to changes in nuclear materials—mutations. In recent years gene mutation has been linked to alterations in the structure of DNA molecules. These alterations occur "naturally," but they can be caused to occur at increased rates by treatment of cell nuclei with high temperatures, certain chemicals, or (especially) ionizing radiations.

10. During the last quarter century, genetic experiments with molds, bacteria, and other microorganisms have resulted in an understanding of the way in which genes function in heredity. The "coding" of nucleotide bases in DNA is transferred via messenger RNA to the assembly of specific sequences of amino acids to form proteins—including enzymes, which mediate biochemical reactions.

## PLANNING AHEAD

Because laboratory work and problems in Chapter 17 require a large amount of time, it is fortunate that the need to plan ahead is now considerably reduced. You should have reviewed the investigations for Chapter 18. If you can duplicate Figure 18·27, much tedious and unproductive student time can be avoided. The grid is a standard eight blocks to the inch; the map itself need only be drawn in outline.

Check your materials for the investigations in Chapter 19. It is possible to do Investigation 19.1 with but one cat skeleton and one human skeleton. For Investigation 19.3 you may find purchasing blood-typing kits more convenient than assembling the materials yourself. In either case, order the serums at this time and store in a refrigerator.

## GUIDELINES

The teacher who dives boldly into Chapter 17, assigning large blocks of material, setting up brief discussion periods, and passing quickly from one investigation to another, is doomed to disappointment. Genetics is a difficult subject. To lead students through Mendel's results is easy; to drill students in constructing Punnett squares is not much harder; to get students to memorize the definitions of "allele," "nondominance," "mutation," "lethal," etc., requires mere persistence. But to really understand genetics is difficult; the more fully you are aware of the difficulty, the greater the likelihood of a reasonable degree of success in teaching it.

The difficulty begins with a large terminology. It is compounded by frequent use of symbols. And it is made hopeless (in the eyes of some students) by mathematics. The teacher can alleviate the first difficulty by moving slowly from one set of terms to the next. He can cope with the second difficulty by repetition and an abundance of examples. But he cannot expect in any reasonable time to overcome native ineptness and perhaps ten years of mounting distaste for mathematics. He must be satisfied with bringing a degree of understanding to as many students as possible.

Several specific topics are troublesome and require extra teaching effort. Especially if you are somewhat inexperienced, be alert for signs of confusion in the following: the meaning of "proof" in science; the fact that many allelic genes may exist in a *population*, even though an individual normally carries only two alleles; the idea that most mutations are harmful. In addition, reasoning from data is difficult for many students; the following topics in Chapter 17 deserve considerable teacher explication: Mendel's reasoning, Sutton's reasoning, Morgan's reasoning about the Y chromosome, the reasoning involved in mapping genes, the reasoning in the *Neurospora* experiments, and the nature of the genetic code.

In view of these difficulties we suggest the following assignments: pp. 624–628 (guide question 1), 629–636 (guide questions 2–6), 636–641 (guide questions 7 and 8), 641–647 (guide questions 9–12), 647–652 (guide questions 13–16), 653–658 (guide questions 17 and 18), 659–664 (guide questions 19–23), and 664–669 (guide questions 24 and 25). With very good classes some advantage of logical organization might be gained by combining as follows: pp. 624–636, 636–641, 641–651, 651–658, 659–664, and 664–669. In this scheme the *Drosophila* work is still assigned by itself, but it is expected that you will expand considerably on "Mechanism of Gene Action" by using Chapter 7 of Simpson and Beck (reference: p. 672). This scheme incorporates each investigation in an assignment, which has not previously been the practice in recommending assignments. In this chapter, however, the investigations

contain a high degree of content and integrate directly into the text discussions — an ideal striven for, but less perfectly attained, in previous chapters. Investigation 17.2 deserves special assignment consideration not only because of its length but also because of the statistical content.

In chemistry and physics, solving problems is recognized as an important method by which students gain understanding. In biology, this principle has not been frequently adopted except in genetics. Most college genetics texts contain large numbers of problems. Select and adapt to secure series of problems that are commensurate with your students' abilities. It is more desirable to supply many simple problems that illustrate a limited number of principles through the use of different traits in different organisms than to cover a wide range of principles with a limited number of difficult or sophisticated problems.

A final point: Students have a natural interest in human genetics. It is well to capitalize on student interests, but they should not be allowed to capsize the course. It is easy to wallow without headway in an endless recital of human disorders and in vague speculation concerning the role of heredity in producing them.

## TEACHING NOTES

### INHERITANCE (pp. 624–625)

**p. 624, ¶ 1:** Suggestion: Introduce the topic by projecting a slide showing a human family — the more diverse the children, the better. Ask what characteristics have been inherited. Ask what inheritance is. Then, if you have slow readers, follow with a cooperative oral reading of the introductory paragraphs. Students may then be somewhat motivated to begin the arduous journey (29 pages!) back to their main interest — human genetics.

### THE WORK OF MENDEL (in part) (pp. 625–628)

**p. 625, ¶ 4:** The scientific study of heredity did not begin with Mendel. But so fundamental were the changes he wrought in biological thinking that attention to previous investigators serves no useful purpose in explaining genetics to high school students.

**p. 626, ¶ 6:** In this and succeeding paragraphs it is necessary to keep in mind that a pea seed *is* the next generation; the seed characteristics of the parental plants were those of the seeds from which they grew. This is most likely to cause difficulty when two traits are considered together. Observe a plant in the field. The height of the vine is a characteristic of one generation; the color of the seed on that vine is a characteristic of the next generation.

**p. 626, Fig. 17·3:** Being fresh from Chapter 16, students should grasp the caption without difficulty even though only the term "self-pollination" was used there.

**p. 627, Fig. 17·4:** Some books list flower color as a trait studied by Mendel. But this is not an additional trait. Mendel noted that white flowers regularly accompanied white seed coat and that colored flowers (plus a reddish tint on the stem in the axils of the leaves) regularly accompanied colored seed coat. This did not bother Mendel in his development of the idea of independent assortment. It might be considered an extreme example of linkage, and you might mention it when students come to that topic (p. 648), but it is regarded as an example of pleiotropism, which is not discussed in the *Green Version*.

**p. 628, Fig. 17·5:** This chart should be the focal point for the discussion of the first reading assignment. It is important that students know what a ratio is and be given an opportunity to struggle with the significance of the data. On the basis of later experimental work, some irreverent biologists have declared that Mendel must have "fudged" his figures. More charitable writers have suggested that Mendel intended his figures to be illustrative only. It really doesn't matter. Error of detail does not detract from the discovery of an in-

clusive principle; on the other hand, no degree of accuracy in figures would have compensated for faulty reasoning that might have led to unsupportable conclusions.

## INVESTIGATION 17.1

### PROBABILITY (pp. 629–630)

The ideas developed in this investigation are not only necessary for understanding Mendel's theory; they are basic to an understanding of modern science. Science deals largely (some scientists would say entirely) with probabilities—not with certainties. For example, the principles of probability are at work in the disintegration of radioactive atomic nuclei and in the collisions of molecules in gases—as well as in the distribution of genes from one generation to the next.

Both parts of the "Procedure" can be carried out in one period. "Studying the Data" requires the pooling of results—and some discussion—which can best be done cooperatively in class.

- (3): Increasing the number of tosses decreases the average size of the deviation. Point out the relationship between this conclusion about size of sample and the practice, in several past investigations, of combining team data.

- (4): Two columns: *Both H* and *Dull H/ Shiny T*.

- (5): It is best to use decimal fractions.

- (6): Analogous to • (4).

- (8): Only one: *Both H*. Note that the only use of *Both T* is to calculate the total.

- (10): The product. Make sure that students understand this as a generalization: the probability of two independent random events occurring simultaneously is the product of their individual probabilities.

## THE WORK OF MENDEL (cont.)
(pp. 630–636)

**p. 631, ¶ 3:** "In science the simplest explanation that *fits all the facts* is always preferred." You should make sure that this paramount principle of reasoning is not overlooked. The "Principle of Parsimony" far antedates modern science. Perhaps its most famous form is the statement by William of Occam: "Entia non sunt multiplicanda praeter necessitatem" ("Entities should not be multiplied beyond necessity" —Occam's razor), but as the doctrine of sufficient cause it can be traced to Anaximander at the dawn of Western philosophy.

**p. 632, "Testing the reasoning":** This section should be accompanied by an abundance of simple problems.

**p. 633, ¶ 2:** Here is where students should use the principles learned in Investigation 17.1. Try to avoid use of the Punnett square, which implies determinate slices of a pie, not probable events.

**p. 633, note 2:** With respect to an array of traits, self-pollination is *not* equivalent to crossing siblings, because siblings usually differ greatly not only in an array of traits due to recombination in the gametes from which they were formed but also in recombinations in the gametes they themselves form. But with respect to a single trait, 50 percent of all gametes in an $F_1$ generation have one allele, and 50 percent have the other, whether produced by one individual or by more than one. This is rather more explanation than a student is likely to give at this point.

**p. 633, "The theory applied to two traits":** This whole section requires much teacher explication. It is a rare student who can grasp this entirely on his own. Use problems freely. Ears of corn that graphically illustrate dihybrid ratios can be obtained from biological supply houses.

**p. 635, Fig. 17·7:** This modification of a Punnett square provides another approach to an understanding of a dihybrid cross. It is graphic but contains the danger (as does Figure 17·6, p. 631) that the student may *count* the gametes and peas instead of interpreting them as ratios. Note that the two characteristics are both of the embryo. Difficulty arises if one attempts to combine embryo and mature-plant traits, such as seed color and vine length. (See note to p. 626, ¶ 6).

## INVESTIGATION 17.2

### MENDELIAN MONOHYBRID CROSS IN *DROSOPHILA*
(pp. 636–641)

Work with *Drosophila* is highly desirable, but expect many difficulties. However, mastering the difficulties is eminently worthwhile because these little beasts, in addition to their starring role in genetics, have many nongenetic uses—for example, to show insect metamorphosis and to illustrate population growth under various conditions. If at all possible you should study the booklet by Demerec and Kaufman (reference: p. T274). However, if this is impossible the directions that follow should—with luck—suffice.

### Materials

*Etherizer.* Many types of etherizers are in use. For simplicity, economy, and ease of handling, the authors recommend the type shown in Figure 17·8. For each etherizer obtain a shot glass of heavy construction, a small aluminum funnel (about 6.5 cm), and 15 cm of heavy cotton string. Modify the funnel as follows (see Figure T–26): With a pair of tin shears, make cuts about 1 cm apart around the bottom edge of the funnel neck. Bend the resulting tabs outward 90 degrees. Lay the string along the neck, with about 5 cm extending beyond the tip. Hold the funnel horizontally in your left hand (if you are right-handed), with the thumb securing the end of the string. With your right hand extend the string along the outside of the funnel neck until it reaches the base of the cone. Wrap the free end of the

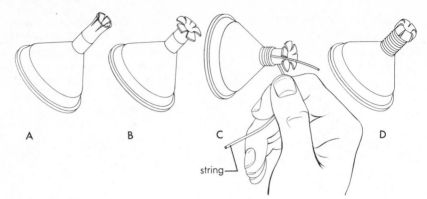

A       B       C       D

Figure T–26

string

string around the funnel neck, beginning at the cone. Wind the string in a single layer toward the end of the neck. When the tabs are reached, tie the two ends in a tight knot. Bend the tabs up over the tightly wrapped string. The string acts as absorbent material for the ether.

The cheapest technical grade of ether is quite adequate. CAUTION: When students are working with ether, the room should be well ventilated. Warn the students about dangerous explosive fumes: *No flames of any kind* should be allowed in the room.

If you do not wish to risk the use of ether, you can reduce temperature to immobilize fruit flies for examination. Place the fly containers in ice water for a few minutes, and then pour the flies on small metal plates resting on ice cubes in finger bowls. Some teachers have been quite successful with this substitute for etherization.

*Maintaining cultures.* Purchasing cultures to be used directly by your students is possible but expensive. It is much better to maintain stocks of the flies in your laboratory. After a little instruction, a small committee of students can handle the work as a long-term project.

For routine culturing of *Drosophila,* the following items of equipment are needed:

Culture bottles (1/2-pint milk bottles, 250-ml wide-mouth collecting bottles, or any wide-mouth jars of similar size), about 12 for five or six classes.

Glass vials (about 80 mm × 23 mm), for individual crosses, 1 gross for each cross.

Absorbent cotton (cheapest grade), 1 lb.

Cheesecloth (cheapest grade), for enclosing cotton plugs.

Pyrex flask (1000 ml or larger) with wicker covering. The cover allows you to pour directly from the flask while the medium is hot. (A kitchen saucepan may be substituted.)

Iron support stand.

Meeker burner (preferred) or Bunsen burner. (A gas or electric hot plate may be substituted.)

Wire screen (with asbestos), to prevent the medium from scorching while cooking.

Large Pyrex funnel with a 15–20 cm length of rubber tubing attached and closed with a pinch clamp.

Paper toweling (2- × 5-cm strips for each culture bottle and narrower strips for each vial).

Graduated cylinder (100 ml or larger).

Trip balance.

Glass-marking crayon, "Labelon" tape, or adhesive labels.

Filter paper (large), for weighing materials on the balance.

Pressure cooker, for sterilization.

Measuring cup.

Ring stand and clamp.

Many kinds of media have been used to culture *Drosophila,* and it is generally agreed that most are satisfactory if yeast is added. If you have only a small amount of laboratory assistance, it is best to buy premixed medium. But if you wish to prepare your own, the two formulas given below are recommended – one for its simplicity of measurement and storage and the other for its economical use of agar and its inclusion of a mold inhibitor.

The first medium is prepared from a dry mixture developed by W. F. Hollander, Genetics Department, Iowa State University. It may be kept in dry storage until needed, at which time water is added to make up the desired amount. No mold inhibitor is used by Hollander (though 5 to 6 ml of 0.5% propionic acid can be added).

> Sugar (sucrose), 3 parts by volume
> Cornmeal, 2 parts by volume
> Brewer's yeast, 1 part by volume
> Granulated agar, 1 part by volume

Mix these ingredients thoroughly. To make up the medium, add about 400 cc of the dry mix to 1 liter of cold water.

The second medium is a formula prepared by H. Bentley Glass at Johns Hopkins University. It is extremely economical in the use of agar, which is, by far, the most expensive ingredient in any medium.

> Water, 540 ml
> Cornmeal, 50 g
> Rolled oats, 25 g
> Dextrose, 50 g
> Brewer's dry yeast, 5 g
> Agar, 3 g
> 0.5% propionic acid, 3 ml

A 1/2-pint milk bottle filled to a depth of 2.5 cm requires about 45 ml of medium; therefore the quantities given above suffice for about 12 bottles.

Place the liquid mixture resulting from either the Hollander or the Glass formula over a burner, and bring to a boil. Boil gently for about five minutes or until the foaming stops. After boiling, transfer the mixture from the flask to the glass funnel mounted on the ring stand. Extend the rub-

ber tubing into a culture bottle or vial and regulate the flow of medium with the clamp. Dispense medium into each bottle to a depth of 2.5 cm and into each vial to a depth of about 2 cm. With a glass rod or a pencil, push one end of a doubled strip of paper toweling to the bottom of the container while the medium is still soft. It is sometimes necessary to gouge a fermentation vent through the medium to the bottom of the container; otherwise, when the live yeasts are introduced, $CO_2$ may build up rapidly under the medium and push it toward the top of the bottle or vial, trapping the flies. The vents may not be necessary if the paper strip is inserted deeply. The strips also provide additional surface for egg laying and for pupation. Plug containers with cotton stoppers wrapped in cheesecloth. (These stoppers may be used again and again if sterilized each time.)

After the culture containers have been filled and plugged, they must be sterilized in a pressure cooker or autoclave. The standard time for sterilization is fifteen minutes, at about 15 lb of pressure. This procedure will usually kill bacteria and mold spores in the medium. Then the culture containers may be stored for several weeks in a refrigerator or freezer. If a refrigerator or freezer is available, all the containers needed for Investigation 17.2 can be made up at one time.

About twenty-four hours before flies are to be introduced, inoculate the medium (thawed, if it has been frozen) in each container with 6 drops of a milky suspension of living yeast. The dry, packaged yeast obtainable in grocery stores is quite satisfactory for preparing this suspension.

Stock and experimental cultures may be kept on shelves or on the desks in the laboratory. They should not be kept in a refrigerator or near a radiator or on a window ledge in the sun. If the room is quite warm (25°C), *Drosophila* develop rapidly; if it is cool (15°C), they require a longer period of time to complete the life cycle. If the temperature of *Drosophila* cultures exceeds 28°C for much time, the flies become sterile.

In the southern states it has been found that some species of ants may crawl through the cotton plugs and chew up the developing flies. This can be prevented if culture bottles are placed on blocks in a shallow pan of water.

Change cultures every three or four weeks to avoid contamination by mites (minute parasites that live on flies) and molds. Medium should never be allowed to dry out, and water or yeast suspension should be added when moisture is required. At least two sets of each culture should be maintained in case one fails. Old culture bottles should be sterilized and cleaned when they are no longer needed.

*Obtaining stock.* Pure strains of *Drosophila* may be obtained from biological supply houses or, in some instances, from geneticists in nearby colleges or universities.

The flies are supplied in small vials. Use these to start your own stock cultures. Before transferring the flies from the vials to culture bottles, be sure there is no excess moisture on the medium or the sides of the bottles: flies can get stuck rather easily. Place a funnel in a bottle. Before removing the cotton stopper from a vial, force the flies to the bottom by tapping the vial on a table. When the flies have collected on the bottom of the vial, quickly remove the cotton stopper and invert the vial into the funnel. Holding the vial, funnel, and bottle firmly together, force the flies into the bottle by gently tapping the bottom of the bottle on a rubber pad. At least five pairs of the flies should be used as parents in making stock cultures.

Add a little yeast suspension to the stock vial and attach the vial to the side of the culture bottle with a rubber band. Eggs and larvae still in the vial will thus be saved to continue development and to provide more stock materials.

*Mutants.* The wild-type fly is the standard phenotype from which all mutant types are inherited departures. Each mutant type is given a descriptive adjective. Such names as "white" (for white eyes, a recessive) or "Bar" (for "barred" eyes, a dominant) are used.

For convenience a symbol is assigned to each mutant gene (see Figure 17 · 18). The symbol is sometimes the initial letter of the mutant name—for example, ebony body is represented by the symbol $e$. But the number of mutant genes is so large that they cannot all be represented by single letters; so additional letters are used, such as the one immediately following the initial letter ($ey$ for eyeless) or suggestive letters—especially consonants—from the rest of the name ($dp$ for dumpy). By convention the names and symbols of recessive mutant types begin with small letters, while names and symbols of dominants begin with capitals. *Drosophila* geneticists no longer use the alternative-sized letter for the alternative member of a pair of alleles. Instead they substitute a plus sign ($+$) as a superscript after the gene symbol to represent the wild-type allele. Example: the dominant wild-type allele of $b$ (black) is not $B$ but $b^+$; and the recessive wild-type allele of $B$ (Bar) is not $b$, but $B^+$.

The kinds of mutant you use with your classes should be ones that are easily distinguished by your students from the wild type. Ebony and dumpy mutants are good.

## Procedure

The experimental work should be preceded by at least one practice period in which students learn to etherize and handle flies properly and to distinguish between male and female flies. Begin by showing the BSCS Technique Film Loop *Handling Drosophila* (Thorne Films, Boulder, Colo.) two or three times.

*Etherizing.* After they are etherized, flies can be dumped onto the examination plates for observation. Care should be taken to avoid overheating the flies with a strong light. If the light source must be brought close to the flies, fluorescent lamps should be used. Or to filter out the heat, you can pass light from an incandescent lamp through a round flask filled with weak copper sulfate solution.

Do not leave flies in the etherizer more than one minute. Etherized flies recover in about five minutes. If the flies begin to recover before examination is completed, they may be returned to the etherizer for a second dose. Warn students that the flies are more easily killed by a second dose of ether than by the first; therefore, re-etherizing should not exceed thirty seconds. Take care that the students do not overetherize their flies and kill them—thus limiting the supply of flies for the use of subsequent classes. If flies are overetherized, their wings turn up vertically over their backs. If this happens, you might as well put them in the morgue (Figure 17·9).

*Making the cross.* After mating, female *Drosophila* store the sperms they receive and use them to fertilize a large number of eggs over a period of time. Therefore the females used in any experimental cross must be virgin. Flies used in maintaining stock cultures need not be virgin, since the females could only have been fertilized by males from the same genetic stock.

Females usually do not mate until twelve hours after emerging. If *all* the adult flies are shaken from a culture bottle, the females emerging in that bottle during the next twelve hours are likely to be virgin when collected. Some geneticists recommend collecting the females after a ten-hour period.

If a temperature of 20° to 22°C is maintained, mating, egg laying, and the development of larvae to a good size should take no more than a week. After seven or eight days the parent flies should be shaken out of the container. This will prevent confusion of the parent flies with the offspring when counts are made. Once flies begin to emerge, they may be classified and counted for ten days. Counting longer than this again runs into the danger of overlapping generations. The first $F_1$ flies may have mated before being counted and, hence, may have left some eggs in the same container.

*Records.* Adequate records are essential to the success of an experiment and an understanding of the results. Impress upon each student the importance of properly labeling culture containers and vials, and of keeping a daily record of all observations relating to the experiments.

Discussion

- (2): If no slipups have occurred, there should be only one phenotype.

- (3): The results of the $P_1$ mating illustrate the principle of dominance.

- (4): As long as a sex-linked trait is not used, the $F_1$ generation should not be affected by either parent carrying the mutant trait.

- (5): All the $F_1$ generation are genetically the same with respect to the trait being considered; therefore there is no need for precautions as to parentage. The flies of the $P_1$ generation have already been removed (p. 639, col. 1, ¶ 3).

- (6): *With respect to the trait being studied,* two phenotypes should occur among the $F_2$ flies. Students may notice other variations. If so, two points may be made: (a) the success of Mendel stemmed in part from his refusal to be distracted by variations other than the ones he was studying, and (b) variability among offspring is to be viewed later as an essential condition of evolution.

- (8): The combined data are more likely to approximate a 3:1 ratio of dominant to recessive than the data of a single team. This illustrates the first principle of Investigation 17.1.

- (10): If the data are *not* significantly different from the expected ratios, then the experiment indicates that the fruit-fly trait involved in the experiment was inherited according to the prediction of Mendelian theory.

- (11): If the difference is significant, then students should seek—as they have done several times before—to suggest factors in their procedure and technique that might account for this. Otherwise they must conclude that the fruit-fly trait involved in the experiment was not inherited according to Mendelian theory. Of course, such a conclusion should never be based on a single experiment.

## FURTHER DEVELOPMENTS IN MENDEL'S PRINCIPLES
### (pp. 641–651)

**p. 641, ¶ 2:** Like most textbook statements, this is an oversimplification. Sir Francis Galton, Darwin's cousin, fully appreciated the value of mathematics in biological studies. He was also a student of heredity but apparently did not know of Mendel's work.

**p. 641, ¶ 5:** We have deliberately avoided the mention of too many names, but, if you have a class with a keen interest in the history of science, you may want to introduce Hugo de Vries (Netherlands), Karl Correns (Germany), and Erich Tschermak von Seysenegg (Austria).

**p. 643, ¶'s 4–6:** This is another contribution to the student's concept of the scientific enterprise. It is, of course, applicable in many places, but this seems to be a good opportunity to discuss the nature of theory. It should be linked to the discussion of the theory of spontaneous generation in Investigation 6.4 and should be returned to when you are discussing the theories of evolution and natural selection in Chapter 18.

**p. 646, ¶ 2:** A review of meiosis may be needed at this point.

**p. 648, note 2:** The farther apart two genes are on a chromosome, the more potential breakage sites exist between them. This is essentially an intuitive matter. But suppose that breakage sites occur at 1-$\mu$ intervals; then two genes located 8 $\mu$ apart have more chances of separation by crossing over than two genes that are only 3 $\mu$ apart.

**p. 648, ¶ 3:** Even if the mathematics of recombination is not grasped, the idea that crossing-over produces new combinations of characteristics should be stressed. This becomes an important point in the discussion of evolution (pp. 687–688).

**p. 649, Fig. 17·19:** (45% **AB** + 5% **Ab** + 5% **aB** + 45% **ab**) × (45% **AB** + 5% **Ab** + 5% **aB** + 45% **ab**) = 20.25% **AABB** + 4.50% **AaBB** + 41.00% **AaBb** + 4.50% **AABb** + .25% **AAbb** + 4.50% **Aabb** + .25% **aaBB** + 4.50% **aaBb** + 20.25% **aabb**.

**p. 650, note 1:** This would occur if, in the formation of one parental gamete, nondisjunction had occurred in the chromosome bearing that locus. Thus a zygote containing three such chromosomes (trisomic) would be produced.

**p. 650, Fig. 17·20:** During the discussion of Investigation 17.3 you may want to point out a further complication in this situation. If hair is plucked from the back of a Himalayan rabbit and the animal is then placed in a low-temperature cage, the regenerated hair is dark; if the plucked rabbit is placed in a high-temperature cage, the regenerated hair is usually white.

## INVESTIGATION 17.3

### SEEDLING PHENOTYPES
### (pp. 651–652)

The nature-nurture argument in its various forms has had a long history. Biologists have recognized that as dialectic the argument gets nowhere. But, as a study of interaction between genetic constitution and environmental conditions, discussion of the matter has importance, particularly with respect to the survival of populations and to evolution. This investigation presents the problem in its modern context. Some students will see its relevance during future discussions, such as those on human skin color and human intelligence on p. 656.

### Materials

Seeds of corn or sorghum may be used, but tobacco has the advantage of requiring very little space for germinating large numbers of seeds. This is particularly important in providing for darkness; a single box on a window ledge will hold the petri dishes of several classes. Moreover, it has been found that the small size of the tobacco seeds arouses a great deal of interest. And at this stage of the course, many students have developed considerable pride in their laboratory dexterity—the small seeds challenge them.

## Procedure

The seeds should be counted out before the laboratory period and delivered to the teams in small vials.

Eight to ten days are normally required before counting begins. If the experiment is set up on a Monday, the first count usually can be made eight days later (on a Tuesday), and the last count then occurs on a Friday. If the experiment is set up on a Friday, the first count can be made on the tenth day (a Monday). Other schedules involve an inconvenient break for a weekend.

Teams of four are suggested. One pair of students can count the seedlings in Dish A and the other pair those in Dish B, each student checking the count of his partner. Exchanging dishes between pairs on alternate days provides a further check and emphasizes team responsibility.

While counting is in progress, you should check the counts of Dish B (on Day 1 especially). The distinction between the yellow and green cotyledons is sometimes rather difficult to make. And take care that the white radicles, which emerge from the seed coat first, are not counted.

## Discussion

- (1): If all goes well, there should be some green seedlings in Dish A and none in Dish B.
- (2): The only difference should be the presence of light in Dish A and its lack in Dish B.
- (3): Not unless all the seedlings in Dish A are green.

- (4): The percentage of green seedlings on Day 4 in Dish B should be greater than 0.
- (5): The change from dark to light environment.
- (6): Not unless 100 percent of the yellow seedlings became green.
- (7): Since all the seedlings were exposed to the same environmental conditions, it is reasonable to conclude that the differences are hereditary.
- (8): The data from Dish B on Day 2, taken in isolation, might be considered as supporting this hypothesis.
- (9): The data from Dish A, taken in isolation, might be considered as supporting this hypothesis.
- (10): Lack of chlorophyll in tobacco seedlings can result either from a genetic or from an environmental factor. Or, in language less likely to come from students: the environment may greatly alter or even entirely suppress a genetic potential; individual phenotypes may be unlike even though their genotypes are the same.

After conclusions have been reached by each team separately, data of all teams may be pooled on the chalkboard. A ratio of green:yellow can then be calculated, related to Mendel's results, and used to arrive at a decision on the kind of inheritance involved in cotyledon color.

Suggested questions for class discussion: What must have been the genotypes of the parent plants? What must have been their phenotypes? When investigating this trait, could you follow the Mendelian $P_1 - F_1 - F_2$ sequence of generations? (The last question brings up, somewhat prematurely, the matter of *lethal* genes. Actually, chlorophyll formation is inhibited in homozygous recessives only for a time. Some albino seedlings ultimately form chlorophyll and grow to maturity. Thus a $P_1$ cross is possible. And this, of course, brings up the relativity of the term "lethal.")

## HUMAN HEREDITY  (pp. 653–656)

**p. 653, Fig. 17·22:** In *A*, gene I appears to be a Mendelian dominant, but in *B* it appears to be nondominant (some black feathers on the heterozygote). You may have to point out to students that the figure illustrates p. 653, ¶ 2.

**p. 654, note 2:** (*a*) If either parent shows the trait, then at least half the offspring will have the dominant gene. (Of course, the statement does not apply to a single family with one or two children only.) (*b*) A gene for a sex-linked trait is on the X chromosome—and any offspring that gets that chromosome from the father must be a daughter. (*c*) Half of a carrier's X chromosomes have the recessive gene. If one of her gametes unites with a gamete containing a Y chromosome, the offspring will be a male and will show the trait; but a carrier's daughter has one X chromosome from the father, and this chromosome cannot have the gene for the trait unless the father shows the trait. (In early printings a sex-linked trait carried by a woman was said to go to "all of her sons" instead of to "one-half her sons.")

**p. 655, ¶ 2:** Human blood types are encountered again in Figure 18·18 and Investigation 19.3.

**p. 655, note 2:** Both I$^a$ and I$^b$ are dominant to i but are nondominant with respect to each other.

**p. 655, ¶ 3:** Some very recent research has cast doubt on this explanation of phenylketonuria as the result of a simple recessive gene.

**p. 655, Fig. 17·23:** This photomicrograph provides material for a good discussion. Note the X and Y chromosomes in the lower right-hand corner.

**p. 656, note 1:** Sex, p. 644; blood types (multiple alleles), pp. 649–650; phenylketonuria (Mendel's wrinkled peas), p. 631; mongolism (nondisjunction), pp. 646–647; eye color, skin color, and resistance to tuberculosis ("Combined effects of several loci"), pp. 650–651; and intelligence (related to the idea of Investigation 17.3), pp. 651–652.

## INVESTIGATION 17.4

### HUMAN INHERITANCE (pp. 656–658)

This investigation can be done as a homework assignment and checked in a class discussion. In some cases it may be best to discuss the first four questions in class before the students begin their independent study.

If charts for testing color blindness are available, you may have students make a study of this trait by testing their parents and siblings. But stress the tentative nature of results lest embarrassing matters of unknown adoptions be really or supposedly encountered.

- (1): One.
- (2): Two.
- (3): pX = 0.5, qY = 0.5.
- (4): pX = 1, qY = 0.
- (5): 50 percent.
- (6): 50 percent.
- (7): Assumption *b*.
- (8): Fewer male births than female must be expected.
- (9): Since the data are exactly opposite to the prediction, Assumption *a* is probably incorrect.
- (10): This gene must be recessive, because it does not appear in the $F_1$ of Pedigree A.
- (11): The trait appears to be sex-linked because of its transmission only to males in the $F_1$ of Pedigree B.
- (12): Victoria of England, Alice of Hesse, Irene, Alexandra, Alice, Beatrice, Victoria Eugenia. In the first printing the key incorrectly shows the symbol for the normal as colored.
- (13): 0 percent.

- (14): 0 percent.
- (15): 100 percent.
- (16): 50 percent. Note that in the case of Queen Victoria only one out of four were hemophiliac, but, of course, we do not know how many zygotes failed to survive.
- (17): 0 percent.
- (18): 50 percent.

---

## THE SOURCE OF NEW TRAITS
(pp. 659–664)

**p. 659, ¶ 2:** The term "mutation" is used somewhat ambivalently. Basically it refers to a phenotypic change. But it sometimes seems to refer to the postulated genetic change that is associated with the phenotypic change, the observable chromosomal change, or the inferred gene change. Normally, this does not seem to interfere with student comprehension, but you should keep it in mind when wording quiz or exam questions.

**pp. 660–662, "A Theory of Gene Mutations":** Before beginning this section, students should review pp. 425–426.

**p. 661, ¶ 2:** It is difficult to overemphasize the importance for biology of discoveries in molecular biology during the past fifteen years. But DNA has become a kind of status symbol, and the authors of the *Green Version* believe that the memorization of the "anatomy" of the DNA molecule is as inexcusable in high school biology today as was the memorization of crayfish appendages and grasshopper mouthparts yesterday. The important thing to emphasize is the way in which the structure of the molecule fits the function that hypothetical genes must perform.

**p. 662, note 1:** Probably not, at least for the scientists who have slipped into this easy way of wording their statements. But some of its use by journalists and popular writers almost certainly conveys impressions far removed from those intended by scientists. You as a teacher had best be as sparing as possible with anthropomorphic or even mechanistic terms and attempt constantly to separate observations from explanations.

**p. 662, ¶ 3:** Refer to Investigation 17.3 if the idea of lethal genes (not necessarily the term) came up during your discussion of chlorophyll-less tobacco seedlings.

**p. 663, ¶ 1:** This is a very difficult idea for students to grasp; it seems to contradict the idea of "random." But the idea is very important for understanding the mechanism of evolution in Chapter 18.

## MECHANISM OF GENE ACTION
(pp. 664–666)

**p. 666, ¶'s 2 and 3:** For the symbols, refer students to Figure 17·27. Note that uracil is the fifth base referred to on p. 425.

**p. 666, ¶ 4:** Stress the idea of *theory* here and revert to the earlier discussion concerning the nature of theory (p. 643). Students may find the concluding sentences more difficult to swallow than all the myths of Greece. But plausibility is not a necessary ingredient of a theory (many people still find heliocentricism implausible). A theory need only explain and integrate verifiable observations, and this the DNA-RNA-protein theory does—at least today.

---

## INVESTIGATION 17.5

### GENETIC DIFFERENCES IN PEAS
(pp. 667–669)

By associating a clear, macroscopically visible trait with a microscopically visible one and this, in turn, with a biochemical one, this investigation may make more real to the student the chemical basis of heredity.

### Materials

In the spring, when this investigation normally is done, pea seeds are easy to obtain. However, most varieties are wrinkled, and a little searching may be necessary to obtain a round variety; ask for "Alaska," the most widely planted round variety. Round and wrinkled varieties can also be obtained from biological supply houses, but more expensively.

Directions for preparing glucose agar: To 400 ml of distilled water add 8 g of agar (be sure it is plain agar) and 2 g of glucose-l-phosphate (the Cori ester). Boil vigorously until the foam becomes quite coarse. Pour into petri dishes. Cover and keep in refrigerator until one hour before use. The glucose-l-phosphate is expensive, so it is desirable to use small petri dishes and keep the agar layer thin. If these directions are followed, the amounts given here are sufficient to prepare forty dishes.

Be sure students use a separate medicine dropper — three altogether — for each of the two extracts and for the $I_2KI$.

For $I_2KI$ see p. T30.

## Procedure

As written, this exercise takes three days to complete. However, a two-day schedule can be used, as follows: *Day 1* — The initial weighing of peas and the observation of the starch grains. Have the preparation of the extract done out of class by a special team. *Day 2* — The observations of the glucose agar and (between observations) the weighing of the soaked peas.

On Day 1 the bottles are weighed wet because they will be wet when the final weighing is done.

Dried peas are very hard, and grinding them with mortar and pestle is difficult. It may be necessary to break the peas with a hammer and squeeze them in a pair of pliers before mortar and pestle are effective. Ideally a Waring Blender should be used (40 ml of water for each 10 g of peas). Be sure to clean the machine thoroughly between grindings.

The extract must be stored in the refrigerator, since the enzyme deteriorates rapidly at room temperature. But be sure to remove the extract from the refrigerator an hour before use, since action of the enzyme is very slow at low temperature.

When the test is made on the agar, the warmer the room, the better. In standing overnight, most of the solid materials will settle out of the extract, and the almost clear supernatant can then be decanted. However, clear extract entirely free of starch grains can be obtained quickly with a centrifuge.

## Discussion

- (1): If all goes well, the data should show that wrinkled peas absorb more water than do round peas.

- (2): If we assume that the peas that absorbed the most were able to do so because they had lost the most, the wrinkled peas lose more water than the round ones as they mature.

- (3): The grains of starch from round peas are simple ovals. The starch grains from wrinkled seeds are round in shape and compound, being subdivided into quadrants or possessing grooves. Whether or not students think they can make predictions depends on how consistent the various teams were in observing.

- (4) and • (5): Again, if all has gone well a consistently greater enzyme action should be obtained from the extract from wrinkled peas. The starch-forming enzyme involved in this investigation is starch phosphorylase. It combines glucose-1-phosphate molecules to form the amylose fraction of natural starch.

- (8) and • (9): Further breeding results would indeed be necessary to confirm that these three biochemical and structural characteristics are the result of single gene action. However, such an assumption is not unreasonable even with the students' limited data, since the enzyme is concerned with starch formation, there was an observed difference in the starch grains, and the ability of starch to hold water (as in puddings) is well known. Of course, students may be willing to make the assumption on the basis of the reading they have done in previous pages; this is not unreasonable, but give it second place to independent arguments.

---

PROBLEMS (pp. 670–671)

1. Bull = heterozygous for polled
   Cow A = homozygous for horned
   Cow B = homozygous for horned
   Cow C = heterozygous for polled

2. A herd of roan cattle only could not be independently maintained. If any breeding were allowed, both red and white offspring would soon occur. Of course, the rancher could maintain a herd by adding only the offspring of red and white cows (not considered a part of the herds) and preventing the roan animals from interbreeding.

3. The farmer should eliminate from his flock both parents and all offspring whenever a black sheep appears.

4. $F_1$ = all white
   $F_2$ = 3/4 white and 1/4 yellow
   A cross between an $F_1$ individual and a homozygous white individual would produce only white offspring.

5. The results of these breeding experiments can be explained on the basis of nondominance.

6. a. A or O children
   b. A or O children
   c. A, B, or AB children
   d. A, B, or AB children
   e. A, B, AB, or O children

7. a. The $F_1$ generation consists entirely of individuals that are tall and have red, round fruit.
   b. **P** = Round, **T** = Tall, **R** = Red: 1/64 **PPTTRR**, 1/32 **PPTtRR**, 1/32 **PpTTRR**, 1/16 **PpTtRR**, 1/32 **PPTTRr**, 1/16 **PPTtRr**, 1/16 **PpTTRr**, 1/8 **PpTtRr**, 1/64 **PPttRR**, 1/32 **PpttRR**, 1/32 **PPttRr**, 1/16 **PpttRr**, 1/64 **ppTTRR**, 1/32 **ppTtRR**, 1/32 **ppTTRr**, 1/64 **ppttRR**, 1/16 **ppTtRr**, 1/32 **ppttRr**, 1/64 **PPTTrr**, 1/32 **PPTtrr**, 1/32 **PpTTrr**, 1/16 **PpTtrr**, 1/64 **PPttrr**, 1/32 **Ppttrr**, 1/64 **ppTTrr**, 1/32 **ppTtrr**, 1/64 **ppttrr**.

c. Round, tall, red—27/64. Round, dwarf, red—9/64. Pear, tall, red—9/64. Pear, dwarf, red—3/64. Round, tall, yellow—9/64. Round, dwarf, yellow—3/64. Pear, tall, yellow—3/64. Pear, dwarf, yellow—1/64.

8. The mutant could be crossed with flies bearing traits produced by genes having known loci. Crossing-over with a known gene would produce breeding results from which the location of the mutant genes could be determined.

9. Since sexual reproduction is lacking, a new trait would depend upon a somatic mutation in a meristem cell, from which bud and shoot carrying the mutation might develop. The likelihood of this occurring is small. But this problem may lead a student to the topic of somatic mutations.

10. (a) XXX ("metafemale"): anatomical female with subnormal sexuality and subnormal mentality. (b) XXY (Klinefelter's syndrome): male with small testes that do not produce sperm and with some development of mammary glands. (c) XYY ("supermale"): many appear to be normal males of large stature, but some show excessively aggressive behavior.

    Also known are individuals with a single X chromosome (Turner's syndrome); these are sterile females. A case of an individual having a single Y chromosome was reported in 1968, but this requires confirmation.

11. Nondominance could be interpreted by a bloodline theory of inheritance. Also, phenotypic characteristics that are the result of the interaction of several genes could be so interpreted. However, Mendel's results, all of which fortuitously involved simple traits exhibiting the dominance phenomenon, were impossible to interpret by any kind of blending theory.

12. The problem involves the production of mutations, one of which, by chance, might be the wanted characteristic.

Anything, then, that might increase the mutation rate would be desirable (see pp. 663–664).

13. This problem concerns somatic mutations and mosaicism. See any good genetics text. But the student should be able to make a stab at the last question without a reference.

14. See the notes on Figure 17·20 (p. T266).

15. In mathematics, proof depends upon establishing the internal consistency of a system, beginning with postulates that are given or accepted as a base. In science, proof is dependent upon consistency with verifiable observations.

## SUPPLEMENTARY MATERIALS

### Additional Problems

Most of these are very simple, intended only to give practice in simple genetic thinking, not as extension for highly capable students.

1. In garden peas, tall vine is dominant and short vine is recessive. If a homozygous tall plant is crossed with a homozygous short plant, what genotypes are possible in the $F_1$ generation?

2. In garden peas, inflated pod is dominant and constricted pod is recessive. If a plant homozygous for inflated pod is crossed with a plant homozygous for constricted pod, what ratio of phenotypes would you expect to find in the $F_2$ generation? What ratio of genotypes would you expect?

3. In guinea pigs, short hair is dominant and long hair is recessive. A short-haired male and a short-haired female produced mostly short-haired offspring, but a few were long-haired. Show how you can determine the genotypes of the parents. [By considering all the possible genotypes and eliminating those that could not produce the observed results.]

4. In laboratory mice, the normal gray color is dominant over the albino (all-white) color. Starting with pure-bred albino and pure-bred gray as parents, what is the ratio of phenotypes in the $F_2$ generation?

5. A pea plant that was homozygous for axial flowers was crossed with a plant that was homozygous for terminal flowers (see Figure 17·4). What ratio of genotypes would you expect in the $F_2$ generation? What ratio of phenotypes would you expect?

6. In the following cases, Z stands for a certain dominant gene and z stands for a certain recessive gene. What ratios of genotypes would you expect from the following crosses: (a) ZZ × zz, (b) Zz × Zz, (c) Zz × zz, (d) Zz × ZZ?

7. In a certain species of plant, one purebred variety has hairy leaves and another purebred variety has smooth leaves. A cross of the two varieties produces offspring that all have smooth leaves. Predict the ratio of phenotypes in the next ($F_2$) generation.

8. In corn, yellow seed color is dominant and white is recessive. A certain ear of corn had a mixture of yellow seeds and white seeds. What color seeds could the parents have grown from? [Parents may have both been yellow (Yy × Yy) or one yellow and one white (Yy × yy).]

9. In a certain animal, a breed is known that always has a hairy tail; another breed is known that always has a naked tail. How would you determine which trait was dominant?

10. In garden peas, axial flower position is dominant and terminal flower position is recessive; tall vine is dominant and short vine is recessive. A plant that is known to be purebred for tall vine and axial flowers is crossed with a plant having short vines bearing terminal flowers. What is the phenotype of the offspring? What is the genotype of the offspring? Predict the kinds of offspring (phenotypes) that would appear in the $F_2$ generation and their ratios. [Offspring are tall, with axial flowers, genotype TtAa. In the $F_2$ generation we expect 9 tall with axial flowers to 3 tall with terminal flowers to 3 short with axial flowers to 1 short with terminal flowers.]

11. In snapdragons red flower color (**R**) is nondominant to white (**r**), the heterozygotes being pink; and normal (broad) leaves (**B**) are nondominant to narrow (grass-like) leaves (**b**), the heterozygotes having leaves of medium breadth. If a red-flowered, broad-leaved plant is crossed with a white-flowered, narrow-leaved one, what will be the phenotypes and their expected ratios in the $F_2$ generation?

12. Several different genetics situations are described below. In each case, you are to decide which of the following kinds of inheritance is involved:

   *a.* nondominance
   *b.* linkage with little or no crossing-over
   *c.* two genes on different chromosomes
   *d.* several to many genes on different chromosomes
   *e.* multiple alleles
   *f.* linkage with a high percentage of crossing-over

*Situation 1:* You have a number of plants belonging to an $F_2$ generation. About one-fourth have no thorns, about one-fourth have long thorns, and about one-half have short thorns, all about the same length. What kind of inheritance is involved? [*a*]

*Situation 2:* In another set of plants, also of an $F_2$ generation, you find the following phenotype ratios: 9 red flowers and broad leaves; 3 red flowers and narrow leaves; 3 white flowers and broad leaves; 1 white flower and narrow leaves. What kind of inheritance is involved? [*c*]

*Situation 3:* You discover a species of bird. In the population some have long crests on their heads, some have scarcely any crests, and many have crests showing all possible intermediate lengths. What kind of inheritance is involved? [*d*]

*Situation 4:* In a certain species of insect, three eye colors are known: red, orange, and yellow. If purebred red-eyed individuals are crossed with purebred orange-eyed, all the offspring are red-eyed. If purebred orange-eyed are crossed with purebred yellow-eyed, all the offspring are orange-eyed. If purebred red-eyed are crossed with purebred yellow-eyed, all the offspring are red-eyed. What is the most likely method of inheritance? [*e*]

*Situation 5:* In another case in which you study two traits of a plant at the same time, you find in the $F_2$ generation that three-quarters have hairy stems and green seeds while the other one-quarter have smooth stems and brown seeds. What kind of inheritance is involved? [*b*]

*Situation 6:* Among the many varieties of popcorn, one has an average ear length of 6 cm (ranges from 4 to 9) and another has an average ear length of 16 cm (ranges from 12 to 19). When the two varieties are crossed, the offspring have ears with an average length of 11 cm (ranges from 5 to 19). What is the most likely method of inheritance? [*d*]

*Situation 7:* The $F_2$ generation of a dihybrid cross in a plant showed the following ratio of phenotypes: 66% had hairy stems and round fruit; 9% had hairy stems and pear-shaped fruit; 9% had smooth stems and round fruit; 16% had smooth stems and pear-shaped fruit. What kind of inheritance is involved? [*f*]

## Audiovisual Materials

**Charts:** In teaching the basic ideas of progeny ratios to be expected from various crosses, repetition is valuable. A good way to secure this—in addition to the use of numerous problems—is through the prominent display of classroom charts that illustrate the ratios. Good charts are available from General Biological Supply House.

**Phonograph record:** "Genes—the Core of Our Being" (*The Scientists Speak: Biology*). Harcourt, Brace & Co., Inc. One of the greatest twentieth-century geneticists, the late H. J. Muller, speaks directly to the student, emphasizing mutations.

**Filmstrips:** *Introducing Genetics*, a set of six color filmstrips from Ward's Natural Science Establishment: *Dominance; Incomplete Dominance, Segregation, Punnett Square; Independent Assortment and Linkage; Genetics and the Cell; New Trait Combinations; Population Genetics.* A teaching manual is included.

This above-average filmstrip series presents the fundamental principles of genetics in a programed sequence.

*DNA: A Key to All Life.* Color. LIFE Filmstrips. A beautiful set of DNA illustrations based on an article that appeared in LIFE magazine.

**Motion-picture films:** *DNA: Molecule of Heredity.* Encyclopaedia Britannica Films. 16 mm. Color. 16 min. Biochemical mechanisms of inheritance are illustrated by animation. *Neurospora* experiments and human genetic disorders. A difficult but worthwhile film.

*Genetics: Improving Plants and Animals.* Coronet Films. 16 mm. Color. 13 min. A well-organized film that clearly shows some of the practical applications of genetics, thus adding a dimension to the student's study of Chapter 17. If you have time for but one film, this should probably be it.

*Biochemical Genetics* (AIBS Film Series). McGraw-Hill Book Co., Inc. 16 mm. Color. 28 min. Linkage, crossing-over, and gene-mapping are difficult ideas, and this film can help to clarify them.

## Teacher's References

Asimov, I. *The Genetic Code.* New York: New American Library of World Literature, Inc., 1963. (A short, popular, but clearly written expositon of the meaning of DNA.)

Demerec, M., and B. P. Kaufman. *Drosophila Guide.* Washington, D.C.: Carnegie Institute, 1962. (This pamphlet should be in the hands of every teacher who attempts to use fruit flies in his laboratory.)

Levine, R. P. *Genetics.* New York: Holt, Rinehart & Winston, Inc., 1962. (A good, succinct treatment for the teacher who needs a refresher.)

Moore, J. A. *Heredity and Development.* New York: Oxford University Press, 1963. (The relationship of heredity to embryology, with special attention to the role of DNA.)

Muller, H. J. *Studies in Genetics.* Bloomington: Indiana University Press, 1962. (Papers of the distinguished Nobel laureate, selected by him and organized around topics to which he contributed significantly.)

Stern, C. *Principles of Human Genetics.* 2nd ed. San Francisco: W. H. Freeman & Co., Publishers, 1960.

———, and E. R. Sherwood (eds.). *The Origin of Genetics: A Mendel Source Book.* San Francisco: W. H. Freeman & Co., Publishers, 1966. (Original background papers on the early history of the study of heredity.)

Strickberger, M. W. *Experiments in Genetics with Drosophila.* New York: John Wiley & Sons, Inc., 1962. (Excellent guide for the teacher unfamiliar with the handling of the fruit fly.)

———. *Genetics.* New York: The Macmillan Co., 1968. (An excellent recent textbook.)

Sturtevant, A. H. *A History of Genetics.* New York: Harper and Row, 1965. (A history by a man who played a large part in the development of genetics during the first half of the twentieth century.)

Winchester, A. M. *Genetics.* 3rd ed. Boston: Houghton Mifflin Co., 1966. (A standard college text that provides a balanced background.)

# 18

# Evolution

## MAJOR IDEAS

1. The idea of evolution, both of the earth itself (inorganic) and of its inhabitants (organic), is very old.

2. The life of Charles Darwin affords vivid evidence of the manifold forces that may mold a great biologist: reading, traveling, thinking, observing, collecting, conferring, experimenting, writing, conjecturing, documenting. . . .

3. In his theory of natural selection, Darwin provided a plausible explanation for the mechanism of organic evolution. After a partial eclipse early in this century, Darwin's theory now receives firm support through studies in many sophisticated areas of modern biology, including genetics, physiology, biochemistry, behavior, and population dynamics.

4. Evolution is a directed change in one or more characteristics of a population. Essentially it is a statistical concept involving a shift in the means of a series of frequency distributions such that a plot of the means has consistent direction.

5. The mechanisms of heredity maintain a basic stability in the characteristics of populations. If this were not so, it would be impossible to recognize change in species.

6. Mutations are the basic source of change, but where recombinations of genes are possible—as they are in sexual reproduction—the chance of genetic change is greatly multiplied.

7. The theory of natural selection provides an explanation for the directionality of evolution. Basically it rests upon differential reproduction among populations: Those that produce more offspring capable of living to maturity and of

reproducing themselves tend to survive; those that produce fewer offspring of lower viability and fecundity tend to die out.

8. The theory of natural selection is an adaptational explanation of evolution. It requires both a genetic constitution and an environment with which the genetic constitution interacts. Among species that live in highly stable environments, evolution proceeds slowly.

9. In a widespread species, distance — geographic isolation — prevents completely random mating throughout the population; speaking figuratively, we could say that eddies develop in the species' gene pool. As a result, recognizable discontinuities may occur, either through response to local environmental differences or, in small isolated populations, through random genetic drift. In such cases, the concept of subspecies is useful.

10. A new species originates when a population (whether originally recognizable as a subspecies or not) becomes reproductively isolated from other related populations. In most cases, reproductive isolation develops when genetic changes accumulate in populations that have become separated by a geographic barrier.

11. In some cases (mostly in angiosperms), new species are known to have originated suddenly through the mechanism of polyploidy. The continued existence of the necessarily small original population of such a new species is dependent upon reproductive success and upon interaction with the environment — natural selection.

## PLANNING AHEAD

Throughout the year major emphasis has been placed on planning ahead for laboratory work. In a course that places such stress on laboratory work and that makes such heavy demands on the teacher's time to implement a heavy laboratory program, this planning emphasis is justified. The need to plan ahead for laboratory work is now drawing to a close. Check on your needs for the investigations in Chapter 19, referring to p. T300 for a few special reminders. Then you may start to consider how best to store your materials and equipment so that they will be most readily available next year.

## GUIDELINES

If the idea of evolution seems to be new at this point, then the previous six hundred seventy-two pages have not been well understood. This is not *the* chapter on evolution; rather it is the chapter that deals with ideas concerning the mechanisms by which the biosphere has evolved. This is an outcome of reproduction and genetic mechanisms, and it is the logical culmination of Section Five. It might also be considered the climax of a biology course — if man did not exist.

The three major headings of the chapter provide a convenient partitioning for assignments: pp. 673–682 (guide questions 1–6), 682–694 (guide questions 7–14), and 694–710 (guide questions 15–21). The three investigations are firmly embedded in these assignments.

The first assignment is a narrative with no investigations, but it is of significance not only for an understanding of modern evolutionary thought but also for an appreciation of the making of a scientist. It is a variation on the historical motif that has been used to introduce a number of previous chapters. In the previous instances the intention has been to illustrate the dependence of scientific progress on technological advances, the piecemeal development of scientific concepts, and the international character of the scientific enterprise. Here, however, the intention is to illustrate the growth of an idea in the mind of a scientist and to depict him as a human being. Few biologists fit the purpose so well as Darwin. From his youth a man of many faults, leading (after his one great adventure) an outwardly dull and prosaic life, neither an amateur nor a professional by today's standards, ignorant of mathematics and remote from the universities, a turgid writer—what a wonderful antidote to the popular vision of the scientist as a superhuman figure in white laboratory coat! No matter that there can be no Darwin in the milieu of twentieth-century science; the uniqueness of every genius-environment complex provides a corollary.

The second assignment deals with the genetic aspects of evolution—the factors of stability and of change—and with natural selection—the factor of guidance. It includes two fairly difficult investigations, which can be done in class or can be assigned as homework. Since these investigations involve mathematics, the procedures as well as the results should certainly be discussed in class and misunderstandings cleared up. Unless this follow-up is made, the assignments may prove worthless as well as discouraging.

The third assignment delineates the process by which species presumably come into being—a combination of genetic action,

natural selection, and isolation. The accompanying Investigation 18.3 deals with a real evolutionary problem that was pursued by a contemporary biologist. It uses actual field data and should give students a "feel" for how research on evolution proceeds. Indeed, some of the questions are ones that arose during the original study, questions for which Dr. Stebbins' intensive fieldwork provided possible answers.

## TEACHING NOTES

### CHARLES DARWIN AND EVOLUTION (pp. 673–682)

**p. 673, ¶ 2:** Darwin was nearing his twenty-seventh birthday when he encountered the Galápagos. He was born February 12, 1809—a noteworthy day in both Shropshire and Kentucky.

**p. 674, Fig. 18·1:** The tree cacti pictured in the lower photograph are in the same genus (*Opuntia*) as the common prickly-pear cactus of the United States, but they certainly assume a very different life form.

**p. 675, Fig. 18·2:** Thirteen of the fourteen Galápagos finches are shown here. They differ mainly in bill shape and size and in associated feeding habits. The six dark species in the foreground feed on seeds of different sizes or on cacti. The ones above are tree species, feeding on insects of different sizes or on fruit and buds. The finch on the right, holding a cactus spine in its bill, belongs to the species that extracts insects from under the bark of the tree cacti pictured in Figure 18·1. About these various finches Darwin commented: ". . . one might really fancy that from an original paucity of birds in this Archipelago, one species had been taken and modified for different ends." There are several recent publications on these birds, including books by Lack and by Bowman (references: pp. T290–T291) and a *Scientific American* article, "Darwin's Finches," by David Lack (April, 1963), available as an offprint from W. H. Freeman Co.

**p. 675, ¶ 1:** For the term "niche," refer to p. 96. This chapter constantly harks back to the first three sections of the student's book.

**p. 675, ¶ 2:** It is fitting that today there is a Darwin Research Station in the Galápagos. Many interesting aspects of these islands have been written up in the September-October (1965) issue of *Pacific Discovery* magazine, which includes an account of the 1964 Galápagos International Scientific Project.

**p. 676, Fig. 18 · 3:** This photograph was taken in 1854, when Darwin was forty-five.

**p. 676, ¶ 1:** The phrase "study of nature" here does not mean merely bird watching or butterfly collecting. The study of nature is what is usually meant by the word "science" in America. British English still uses "nature" quite frequently in its basic sense; for example, the British counterpart of our journal *Science* is called *Nature*, published by the British Association for the Advancement of Science.

**p. 676, ¶ 3:** Here and in the next several pages an attempt is made to portray "Gas" Darwin as a real person, with faults as well as talents. Too seldom do we, as science teachers, attempt to bring distinguished scientists alive for our students. Perhaps this is why, in some respects, scientists have been separated in the minds of many from the rest of society. Chapter 15 also begins with biographical sidelights on Darwin, and in Chapter 13 (pp. 466–467) he is shown working with his son. Students who wish a further—and very provocative—acquaintance with Darwin might read his autobiography (*The Autobiography of Charles Darwin*, edited by Nora Barlow—London: Collins, 1958). Darwin's youth is described in his own words in "Chronicle of a Misspent Youth," *Natural History*, June-July, 1958, pp. 324–329.

**p. 677, ¶ 2:** A readable account of Charles Darwin's voyage on the *Beagle* is *Darwin of the Beagle*, 2nd ed., by Bern Dibner (New York: Blaisdell Publishing Co., 1964). Another is Darwin's own account, *Voyage of the Beagle* (reference: p. T290).

**p. 677, Fig. 18 · 4:** There is no certain answer to this question, of course. From the standpoint of general appearance, the leghorn breed would appear most similar to the red jungle fowl, though in other matters, such as coloration and behavior, other breeds may retain more genes from the wild ancestry. Among the most unusual of the breeds pictured here is the Yokohama, a long-tailed fowl whose tail-covert feathers, never molted, may exceed 20 feet in length. Such a character might appeal to chicken fanciers but would probably be an extreme handicap back in ancestral jungle country.

During the 1920's the *National Geographic Magazine* published excellently illustrated accounts of the various breeds of domestic fowl as well as of horses, cattle, and pigeons. Old issues are now difficult to obtain, but many libraries have bound volumes of the magazine. The U.S. Department of Agriculture publishes bulletins on the breeds of domestic animals, but these emphasize commercially important breeds rather than ones that illustrate the greatest diversity. Charles Darwin himself wrote a two-volume work on domesticated plants and animals: *The Variation of Animals and Plants under Domestication*.

**p. 678, Fig. 18 · 5:** Be sure the caption is considered; it should lead students back to pp. 65–69. This is very important recall before getting into "Speciation" later in the chapter.

**p. 681, Fig. 18 · 7:** Wallace became more famous for his later work on biogeographical distribution and in 1886 traveled throughout the United States on a lecturing junket. It is coincidental that he, like Darwin, was an avid beetle collector.

**p. 681, ¶ 2:** At the memorable July 1 Linnaean Society meeting, Darwin's paper was presented by Charles Lyell and Wallace's paper by Joseph Hooker. For some time Darwin had been corresponding with the American botanist Asa Gray about evolution. A short sketch embodying Darwin's evolutionary ideas had been sent to Gray in September of 1857, and this was presented at the Linnaean meeting to establish the priority of Darwin over Wallace. The July 1 meeting caused little stir. Amusingly enough, the president of the Linnaean Society at this time regretted in retrospect that no significant papers had been presented during his term of office. Yet a century later another Linnaean Society president looked back on the Darwin-Wallace presentation as "the most important event in the history of our Society. . . ." It was the publication of Darwin's book in 1859 that precipitated intellectual tumult.

**p. 682, ¶ 2:** In attempting to explain how hereditary variations occur, Darwin modified the ancient Greek idea of "pangenesis." According to his hypothesis, various parts of an organism's body produce tiny particles called "pangenes," which are carried to the gametes by the blood and thus affect the heredity of the next generation. This was really a kind of "acquired characteristics" theory, and it has long since been discarded.

## THE PROCESS OF EVOLVING
(in part — pp. 682–685)

**p. 682, ¶ 4:** You may want to use at this point the BSCS Inquiry Film Loop *The Peppered Moth: A Population Study.* It is most effective if you have students who can be counted upon not to have read ahead in their textbook, but it is good in any case.

**p. 683, note 1:** See ¶ 3, same page.

**p. 684, Fig. 18·9:** In order for the red form of screech owl to occur, the appropriate genetic material must be available in the population. Such genes do appear to be common in New England, less so elsewhere in the East, and rare or absent in the West. Geographic distance seems to prevent exchange of genetic material between New England owls and western owls. There is good evidence of selective ad-

vantage for the red form in New England. Tree squirrels also exhibit color-phase distributional patterns. Most of the tuft-eared squirrels in Colorado's mountains are gray, but in the Black Forest, somewhat isolated by high-plains grassland from the rest of the Colorado montane forest, the predominant form is black. Some middle-western towns have primarily white squirrels.

**pp. 685–688:** Review meiosis, mutation, the action of multiple alleles, and the role of genes in continuously varying traits before discussing "The Stability Factor" and "The Change Factor."

**p. 685, ¶ 3:** The rediscovery of Mendel's work on genetics at the turn of the present century seemed, indeed, to sound the death knell for Darwinian evolution, because the emphasis was on stability rather than on change. And De Vries' work on macromutations in evening primroses demonstrated great genetic changes, rather than the minor changes necessary for the process of Darwinian evolution. Only more recently (from the 1930's) has it been appreciated that most genetic changes *are* minor and do support Darwin's conception of evolution ("microevolution," as we call it today).

## INVESTIGATION 18.1

### THE HARDY-WEINBERG PRINCIPLE
(pp. 685–687)

This investigation demonstrates the application of mathematics to problems of genetics and evolution. By relating it to Investigation 18.2, you can emphasize the relationship between genes in populations and the action of natural selection. If a class has a good background in mathematical reasoning, the investigation may be assigned for home study and then discussed in class. In most cases, however, it is advisable to work with the class cooperatively.

### Procedure

• (1): Black ♂ × black ♀; black ♂ × speckled white ♀; speckled white ♂

× black ♀; speckled white ♂ × speckled white ♀.

- (2) and • (3): **BB** × **BB** → **BB**; **BB** × **bb** → **Bb**; **bb** × **BB** → **bB**; **bb** × **bb** → **bb**.

- (4): No.

- (5): 3 black to 1 speckled white.

- (6): No; it was then 1 black to 1 speckled white.

- (7): 0.5 **B** and 0.5 **b**.

- (8): Since the probabilities of the four kinds of matings are equal and each produces but one genotype (Items 1, 2, and 3), simply count the gene symbols in the four equally frequent offspring genotypes (**BB**, **Bb**, **bB**, **bb**). There are 4 **B**'s and 4 **b**'s; therefore the frequencies are 0.5 **B** and 0.5 **b**.

- (9): The gene frequencies (not the phenotype frequencies) are the same in both generations.

- (10): (0.5 **B** + 0.5 **b**) × (0.5 **B** + 0.5 **b**) = 0.25 **BB** + 0.50 **Bb** + 0.25 **bb**.

- (11): Suppose the third generation consists of 1000 individuals. Then 250 are **BB** (500 **B** genes) and 500 are **Bb** (500 **B** genes), totaling 1000 **B** genes. Also, 500 are **Bb** (500 **b** genes) and 250 are **bb** (500 **b** genes), totaling 1000 **b** genes. Therefore the frequencies are still 0.5 **B** and 0.5 **b**.

- (12): Yes.

- (13): Yes.

- (14): 200 male black beetles = 400 **B** genes; 300 male white beetles = 600 **b** genes; the frequencies are 0.4 **B** and 0.6 **b**.

- (15): The same as in the males.

- (16): (0.4 **B** + 0.6 **b**) × (0.4 **B** + 0.6 **b**) = 0.16 **BB** + 0.48 **Bb** + 0.36 **bb**.

- (17): Suppose the offspring generation consists of 1000 individuals. Then 160 are **BB** (320 **B** genes) and 480 are **Bb** (480 **B** genes), totaling 800 **B** genes. Also, 480 are **Bb** (480 **b** genes) and 360 are **bb** (720 **b** genes), total-ing 1200 **b** genes. Therefore the frequencies are 0.4 **B** and 0.6 **b**.

- (18): The calculations by the gene-pool method are the same as in • (16).

Conclusion

- (19): In a large, randomly mating population without selection pressure and without mutation, gene frequencies remain the same generation after generation. Your students are not likely to put in the qualifications, but these are very important: evolution involves a change in gene frequencies, and it is only the existence of mutations and of selection pressures that prevents the Hardy-Weinberg principle from stabilizing gene frequencies. At this point you can easily show the students that the calculations are based on random mating; further, students can easily see, when it is pointed out to them, that mutations at a given locus will change gene frequencies. However, the students may not yet be able to appreciate the effect of selection. When they have completed Investigation 18.2, come back to this point.

  The case of Hardy and Weinberg is like that of Darwin and Wallace and many others in the history of science—an example of nearly simultaneous discovery by two persons unknown to each other.

---

## THE PROCESS OF EVOLVING
(cont.—pp. 687–691)

**p. 687, "The Change Factor":** See note to p. 685, ¶ 3 (p. T279).

**p. 688, note 1:** A species of organism that reproduces only asexually is sometimes said to be "close to the end of the evolutionary road." While this is somewhat hyperbolic, the change factor for such species is indeed limited, because in such a species a mutation can pass only to the direct line of descendants from the individual in which it occurs. More importantly, however, such a species lacks the opportunity for increased variation by recombination that is available to species in which genes from two parents are necessary for the production of any offspring.

**p. 688, note 4:** All the evidence of modern genetics shows that traits of sexually reproducing organisms are passed on to offspring through gametes only and that the somatic (body) cells, which are involved in the "use or disuse" of structures, have no effect upon the genetic character of gametes. This is not to say, of course, that the environment in which DNA molecules in gametes find themselves may not have an influence on the expression of the particular DNA. Furthermore, the retention of nonfunctional, vestigial structures can be more readily explained through genetics and natural selection than through use and disuse.

**p. 689, Fig. 18·10:** There has been much argument over how valuable protective coloration really is. It would seem obvious that white hares are better camouflaged in snowy country than are brown cottontails. But no one survival factor can be considered in isolation from others. Brown cottontails do occur in snowy country as far north as Maine and southern Ontario; varying hares, however, do not reach Georgia, though they extend southward from Canada in mountains on both sides of the continent. This is the time to recall the discussion of Figure 8·11. The point of all this, of course, is the explanation for the origin and maintenance of these pelage and plumage characteristics.

**p. 690, note 1:** There is a brief but well-illustrated discussion of flightless birds in *The World of Birds*, by James Fisher and R. T. Peterson (Garden City, N.Y.: Doubleday & Co., 1964), pp. 26–27. See further *Birds of the World*, by O. L. Austin, Jr. (New York: Golden Press, 1961). Some flightless birds, such as ostriches, make up for flightlessness by a well-developed cursorial ability. Otherwise flightless birds have survived in situations where the ability to fly is not a significant talent and where conflict with other organisms (competition and predation) has been at a minimum.

**p. 690, Fig. 18·11:** The Irish elk, whose antlers resembled those of a moose, was actually more closely related to the modern European fallow deer. Our modern New World "elk" is also a type of deer rather than a true elk, its more appropriate name being "wapiti," whereas our American moose is equivalent to the present European elk.

## INVESTIGATION 18.2

### SICKLE CELLS AND EVOLUTION
(pp. 691–694)

Preface this investigation with a review of capillary circulation and the shape of normal human red blood cells. Sickling is associated with a simple biochemical defect: beta hemoglobin of sicklers contains, at the six-position, valine instead of the normal glutamic acid.

The investigation uses a Socratic technique and therefore involves some use of yes-and-no questions. In such a technique it is inevitable that the answers to some questions are given or implied at a later point in the development. Therefore, to obtain the most value from the investigation, it is necessary to work through it point by point. The aim is not to get correct, neatly written answers to all the questions; the aim is to see how the reasoning proceeds.

#### Procedure

If most of the students in the class have some facility in reasoning and can word their thoughts easily, they can be asked to work through the investigation independently. Class discussion can then center on points of controversy or confusion. In most cases, however, it is recommended that you work step by step with the class. If you do this, stop when you arrive at Item 13 and resume discussion the following day. This provides students with an opportunity to formulate hypotheses for Items 13–15. Even if they read on and find out which way the hypotheses should point, they will have some experience in wording hypotheses.

- (2): Note that the pedigree eliminates the possibility of sex linkage. Under conditions of the question, only nondominance is possible.

- (6): 25 percent.

- (7): If marriage is random with respect to this trait, 16 percent (0.16).

- (8): This is a repetition of Item 6.

- (9): Since offspring with sickle-cell anemia die in childhood, they can leave no descendants. Therefore parents who produce children with sickle-cell anemia have a reduced chance of descendants unless, on the average, they have more children than normal parents.

- (10): Two.

- (11): It should reduce the frequency of the sickling gene.

- (12): Darwin, of course, would have said nothing about gene frequencies but would have stated the matter in terms of the natural selection of individuals.

- (16): Any hypothesis for Item 13 must depend upon a mutation rate toward sickling that equals the rate of elimination by natural selection. Therefore the hypothesis is weakened by this information.

- (17): The information neither supports nor weakens a hypothesis based on differential fertility: It is negative evidence. But the tendency is to assume a "normal" situation in the absence of contrary evidence.

- (18): Since the malaria parasite lives within red blood cells at one point in its cycle (p. 223), it has a close association with them and with hemoglobin. Hookworms are not discussed spe-

cifically in the text (though illustrated in Figure 4·37). But from knowledge of the roundworm group, students should suspect that the connection of hookworms with hemoglobin is less intimate than that of *Plasmodium*. Nevertheless, hookworms are blood feeders, so this is merely a matter of differential probability.

- (19): The wording might be: The frequency of the sickling gene does not decline, because persons who carry it have a greater resistance to malaria (or hookworm) and therefore have greater survival than homozygous normal individuals.

- (20): "Sicklers" with malaria:

$$\frac{12}{43} = 27\%.$$

"Nonsicklers" with malaria:

$$\frac{113}{247} = 45\%.$$

- (21): When the chi-square test is applied, the expected frequencies of sicklers with malaria and without malaria are the frequencies in the sickler population that would correspond to the frequencies in the normal population.

Calculations of expected numbers per class: "Sicklers" with malaria: $\frac{125}{290} \times 43 = 18.5$. "Sicklers" without malaria: $\frac{165}{290} \times 43 = 24.5$. "Nonsicklers" with malaria: $\frac{125}{290} \times 247 = 106.5$. "Nonsicklers" without malaria: $\frac{165}{290} \times 247 = 140.5$.

Calculation of chi-square: "Sicklers" with malaria: $\frac{(12 - 18.5)^2}{18.5} = \frac{41.25}{18.5} = 2.23$. "Sicklers" without malaria: $\frac{(31 - 24.5)^2}{24.5} = \frac{41.25}{24.5} = 1.68$. "Nonsicklers" with malaria:

$$\frac{(113 - 106.5)^2}{106.5} = \frac{41.25}{106.5} = .39.$$

"Nonsicklers" without malaria:

$$\frac{(134 - 140.5)^2}{140.5} = \frac{41.25}{140.5} = .29.$$

$$\chi^2 = 4.59$$

The degrees of freedom equal (number of columns minus one) times (number of rows minus one). For the table on p. 693, this is $(2 - 1) \times (2 - 1) = 1 \times 1 = 1$. In the chi-square table on p. 641, the line "$\chi^2$ for two classes" gives the values for one degree of freedom.

- (22): The chi-square value indicated that the difference in the percentages of "sicklers" and "nonsicklers" with malaria (27 percent compared with 45 percent) could be expected to occur by chance between 1 and 5 times in 100 ($4.59 > 3.841$). This expectation is usually considered to indicate a "significant" difference. Therefore, we can reject the null hypothesis that there is no difference between sicklers and nonsicklers, and conclude that being a "sickler" reduces the likelihood of having malaria.

- (23): The difference is so great that a statistical test is not really needed, but the data give students another chance to go through the chi-square calculations with much simpler arithmetic than before.

    Calculations of expected numbers in each class: "Sicklers" with malaria: $\frac{16}{30} \times 15 = \frac{240}{30} = 8$. "Sicklers" without malaria: $\frac{14}{30} \times 15 = \frac{210}{30} = 7$. Because the two groups were of the same size, the calculations for the "nonsicklers" are the same.

    Calculations of chi-square: "Sicklers" with malaria: $\frac{(2 - 8)^2}{8} = \frac{36}{8} = 4.50$. "Sicklers" without malaria:

$$\frac{(13 - 7)^2}{7} = \frac{36}{7} = 5.14. \text{ "Nonsicklers"}$$

with malaria: $\frac{(14 - 8)^2}{8} = \frac{36}{8} = 4.50.$

"Nonsicklers" without malaria:

$$\frac{(1 - 7)^2}{7} = \frac{36}{7} = 5.14.$$

$$\chi^2 = 19.28$$

- (24): The chi-square value indicates that the difference between "sicklers" and "nonsicklers" with respect to malaria could be expected to occur by chance less than one time in a hundred ($19.28 > 6.635$). This expectation is termed "very significant." The null hypothesis is confidently rejected, and this constitutes support for the hypothesis in Item 19.

- (25): This is a somewhat ambiguous question. Students may have been impressed with the Hardy-Weinberg principle and answer No. But this situation is different from that in Investigation 18.1. There the original frequency was calculated on the basis of *both* original populations. Here the 22 percent applies to only one of the original populations. The frequency of the sickling gene in the American Indian and European populations was presumably close to zero, so combining the three populations reduces the *frequency* of the gene. It does not, however, decrease the *number* of such genes, which depends upon the number of individuals bearing them. This can be reduced only if there is some factor which reduces the number of individuals that bear the genes relative to the number that do not.

- (26): No.

- (27): Because of the selection pressure against the gene, we would expect its frequency in the total population to decrease.

- (28): The main point here is that natural selection operates to eliminate homo-

T 284

zygotes (through defective physiology) and to conserve heterozygotes (through protection against the debilitating effects of a parasite).

• (29): Lack of malarial parasites in the environment tends to change the frequency of the sickling gene from the frequency that can exist in an environment where the parasites are abundant.

• (30): With respect to oxygen supply, the sickling gene certainly is harmful. But when malaria is a factor in the environment, the sickling gene in the heterozygous state is an advantage to survival. When malaria is not a factor in the environment, the gene is a detriment to survival. Thus "harmful" and the other terms are relative (to the environment) rather than absolute terms. The terms also vary between homozygous and heterozygous states. The hybrid has an advantage that neither homozygote has.

SPECIATION (pp. 694–706)

**p. 694, ¶ 4:** The reference to the species concept is so important that you might well make it a class review assignment.

**p. 695, note 1:** Presumably a decrease in soot—hence in dark trees—would favor increased survival of the light-colored moths and a decline in number of dark-colored moths.

**p. 696, Fig. 18 · 15:** The fossil history of the Equidae is interestingly summarized in *Horses*, by G. G. Simpson (New York: Oxford University Press, 1951; also in paperback—New York: Doubleday & Co., Inc., 1951). Recall that students have themselves worked on another trait involved in horse evolution (Investigation 10.1).

**p. 697, Fig. 18 · 16:** Obviously, the horses in Figure 18 · 15 represent genera from different levels of geological time, whereas the honeycreepers are seven

contemporary species. Thus, no pictured honeycreeper could be ancestral to any of the others, but they might all have a common ancestor. In the case of the horses, of course, we are looking at variations through time, while with the honeycreepers we are viewing variations through space. As a reflective sidelight, it would seem likely that there is greater variability inherent in honeycreepers than in horses. There could be a number of reasons for this, including island distribution, more frequent breeding, and greater number of offspring per pair. Full-color pictures of the Drepanididae (honeycreepers) are to be found in *Field Guide to Western Birds*, 2nd ed., by R. T. Peterson (Boston: Houghton Mifflin Co., 1961). There is a concise discussion of speciation among these birds in E. O. Dodson's *Evolution: Process and Product*, 2nd ed. (New York: Reinhold Publishing Corp., 1960), pp. 310–311. A more comprehensive reference is "The Hawaiian Honeycreepers," by D. Amadon (*Bulletin of the American Museum of Natural History*, Vol. 95, 1950. Pp. 151–262).

**p. 700, Fig. 18 · 20:** This figure and also Figure 18 · 21 are derived from the work of Dr. Walter Auffenberg. When Figure 18 · 20 was constructed, the samples from Florida were analyzed according to the separate localities from which they were taken; all other samples were lumped by states.

**p. 700, ¶ 2:** The text is somewhat vague here concerning the nomenclature of subspecies—and the vagueness continues in Figures 18 · 21 and 18 · 23. Subspecies are represented by trinomials. Thus the black snake subspecies in the northeastern United States is called *Coluber constrictor constrictor*, that in the northern part of the Middle West *Coluber constrictor flaviventris*.

**p. 701, note 3:** By placing the two species of buntings in the same genus (*Passerina*), taxonomists have indicated that the two are closely related to each other.

**p. 702, Fig. 18 · 22:** Students should refer to ¶ 3 on p. 701. In presettlement days, trees lined the larger rivers, such as the Platte and the Arkansas, all the way to the Rocky Mountains. But apparently these were not sufficient to maintain populations of large woodpeckers, such as flickers. However, as trees were planted extensively throughout the Great Plains grassland in more recent decades, the two separated species of flickers, both of which depend upon fairly large trees for nesting sites, were able increasingly to come in contact with each other and interbreed, producing hybrids. Incidentally, the map in the early printings is out-of-date. It does not show the region of intergradation (orange) extending south into New Mexico, Oklahoma, and Texas.

**p. 703, notes 1 and 4:** If you agree that members of a single species cannot successfully breed with members of another species, then the fact that the two species of bunting can fairly successfully interbreed may suggest that they are really only one species. Even the biological definition of a species does not relieve taxonomists from the necessity of making subjective decisions! At present most taxonomists judge the amount of gene flow between the populations insufficient for recognition by a nomenclatural change. What the evidence suggests more emphatically, however, is that the isolation of the now-recognized two species has not existed long enough to produce *complete* reproductive isolation.

**p. 703, Fig. 18 · 23:** If a criterion for species separation involves nonbreeding between two somewhat similar groups in the same area, then one could argue that *fuscus* and *argentatus* are actually two separate species of gulls, since they occur together but do not interbreed — they are reproductively isolated. This figure is based on the work of Dr. Ernst Mayr (references: p. T291).

**p. 704, note 2:** From the practical standpoint of identification of specimens, there are few, if any, morphological differences that a taxonomist could use to distinguish separate species. This could be so because isolation has not existed long enough to produce discernible differences, or because all of the streams have exerted basically the same selective forces (i.e., the environments are all essentially the same). In similar cases, such fish populations are known to be capable of interbreeding under artificial conditions, suggesting that all the fish populations may best be regarded as a single species despite apparent reproductive isolation at present.

**p. 705, ¶ 4:** Although not discussed in this edition, there are instances in which man has succeeded in creating new species through artificial means. The best-known example is that of the Russian plant geneticist G. D. Karpechenko, who in 1928 crossed a radish with a cabbage (both species in the cabbage family) and eventually produced a self-reproducing new population — a new species. But, unfortunately for agriculturists, it had the root of a cabbage and the head of a radish. Even earlier, in 1925, Clausen and Goodspeed in the United States had crossed two species of *Nicotiana* (tobacco) and eventually produced a fertile hybrid — a new species.

## INVESTIGATION 18.3

### A STEP IN SPECIATION
(pp. 706 – 710)

In addition to illustrating the way in which speciation may proceed, this investigation should emphasize for students that a scientist's real work begins when he starts to organize and analyze data. Dr. Stebbins' research was published in the *University of California Publications in Zoology*, Vol. 48, 1949, pp. 377 – 526 – "Speciation in Salamanders of the Plethodontid Genus *Ensatina*." If you have this publication available, you can compare his interpretations with those of the students.

### Procedure

In preparing the map, students should be cautioned to use the correct colors and make accurate plottings; otherwise, correct interpretations are difficult to achieve.

- (1): The distribution in the state is not uniform. It seems likely that in those areas where the salamanders do not occur there are specific limiting factors—for example, arid or semiarid conditions.

- (2): When the distribution of salamanders is compared with the physiography of California, it is evident that the salamanders occur in the mountainous regions, except in the desert ranges.

- (3): The mere fact that subspecies are geographical variations within a species suggests that there should be order to the distribution of these subspecies. We are dealing here with clines, and it would be worth reminding the students of the discussion on *Coluber constrictor* (pp. 699–701). Because of ancestral relationships, adjacent subspecies should be more like each other than widely separated subspecies. There are exceptions, as part of this investigation will bear out; but the exceptions can be explained.

    Dr. Stebbins has postulated that subspecies 5, *picta*, is closest to the ancestral form and that subspeciation has taken place southward along the coastal and the inland mountains. This would explain the difference in pattern between coastal and inland mountain forms and similarity among coastal forms and among inland forms. If you have a sophisticated group of students, it might be worthwhile at the end of the investigation to discuss with them the most likely center of origin of the species, including a consideration of gene flow, clines, and isolating mechanisms.

- (4): The spotted forms tend to be in the inland Sierra Nevadas and the un- spotted forms along the coast, except in southern California, where both spotted and unspotted occur together.

- (5): Populations *eschscholtzii* and *klauberi* occur in the same area in southwestern California.

- (6): They represent genetic intergrades (hybrids) between subspecies.

- (7): The drawing should be an intergrade between *eschscholtzii* and *xanthoptica*. Making such a drawing is a difficult but challenging assignment, requiring a bit of imagination. There are clines from north to south between the two adjacent subspecies (*xanthoptica* in the north and *eschscholtzii* in the south). In general, from north to south the eyelids tend to become lighter and the dark pigmentation of body tends to disappear or become restricted to dots. To be more specific, toward the south:
    a. Lemon-yellow eye patch disappears.
    b. Orange coloration of ventral surface becomes restricted to underside of limbs and tail or is lost (sketches will not show this, of course).
    c. Yellow dots on back tend to disappear.
    d. Small black dots on sides of back appear.
    e. Tip of tail becomes lighter.
      This question should encourage students to look very carefully at the drawings, noticing things they might miss in a casual examination.

- (8): These two subspecies are geographically isolated by several hundred miles, with another subspecies occurring in between.

- (9): To see if there were any intergrade specimens and to see if the two subspecies populations occupied the same region.

- (10): As it turns out, the two subspecies are intermixed, with *no* intergrades.

- (11): This same type of situation, where two subspecies come in contact with each other but do not interbreed, is described on p. 703 in conjunction with the discussion of the herring gulls.

- (12): Population *klauberi*. This is the only form for which you have not located intergrades with other forms. The alert student might wonder if further collecting would turn up intergrades. A provocative discussion might involve what such intergrades, if found, would be between and why. Incidentally, many biologists formerly concluded that *klauberi* was a separate species.

- (13): Between *klauberi* and *croceator*. Note that the intergrade specimen has spots that tend to form bands. Individuals of *croceator* have definite spots, whereas those of *klauberi* are banded. Note also that the two spots on the head almost form a band. The line would be a clockwise arc from, roughly, 32/U to 35/Z (running from the most southerly *croceator* around the east side of *eschscholtzii* to the most northerly *klauberi*). These intergrades, incidentally, have been collected at 33/Y and 35/Y.

## Conclusion

- (14): The map shows intergrades between all the subspecies except for the two that exist together in southern California. It would seem likely, as mentioned earlier, that subspeciation has taken place from a common ancestor in the north (closely related to *picta*), down the two separated mountain chains. The two subspecies that exist together without intergrading must have become sufficiently different from each other so that they are reproductively isolated. You can see why these two were thought to be

separate species before all the information on the intergrades was available.

### For Further Investigation

Problem: What accounts for the one record of *xanthoptica* in the Sierras, whereas the rest of the subspecies occurs along the coast? [*There are several possible explanations. The specimen may have been introduced accidentally by man, or irrigation in this region may have made possible movement of the specimen across the broad valley. Indeed, more intensive collecting in the valley might show more specimens in the inland mountains, with perhaps a connection between the coastal and inland populations in the not too distant past. In actuality, more than just this one individual were located in the inland mountains, in this same general region. Also, more intensive collecting in the valley might demonstrate that the subspecies population actually extends all the way from the coast into the edge of the inland mountains. This possibility emphasizes the importance of complete collections of data upon which to base hypotheses.*]

---

## PROBLEMS (pp. 711–712)

1. Sexual reproduction, involving recombinations through (*a*) crossing-over in meiosis and (*b*) genes from two parents, increases the possible variability of offspring, thus affording more "choices" for changing selective forces to work on. Self-fertilization and parthenogenesis, on the other hand, tend to promote the genetic *status quo* (like mother, like daughter).

2. Man selects for a particular variety of traits in his domestic animals (and plants, too), traits that may or may not have survival value in the wild. Natural selection, on the contrary, selects only the set of traits best suited to survival in a particular environment; where environments differ within the geographical range of a species, some variation (subspecies) may, indeed, occur.

3. In the case of polydactyly, even dominant genes have to be "selected for." The possession of extra digits is of no present survival value. In the case of the Indian blood type, we are dealing with a relatively small, isolated population in which the recessive gene for Type O blood has attained a high frequency, perhaps by random genetic drift (see p. 734). However the i gene is frequent in the general population of the United States also. At present there is no evidence that any of the ABO blood types have survival advantage. Perhaps the main message of the problem is: Whether a gene is dominant or recessive has nothing to do with its survival value.

4. Presumably through natural selection working on available genes, the ptarmigan has evolved plumage changes which afford it protective coloration throughout the year.

5. It should be remembered that although sexual reproduction increases variety, there are other sources of change available to asexually reproducing organisms, such as gene and chromosomal mutations. If dominant, a gene mutation may show up much more rapidly in an asexually reproducing population than in a sexually reproducing one, which throws some doubt on the statement about the "end of the evolutionary road." But many such mutations are detrimental in an existing environment.

6. There is generally a relationship between clutch size and chances for survival. The important question is how many eggs survive to become reproductive adults. This number is undoubtedly lower as latitude becomes higher. Even if populations of adults at high latitudes were larger, this does not mean that these populations would replace the populations of lower latitudes. After all, the latter populations are probably already in balance with the carrying capacity of the land there.

7. If this problem is discussed with students in a class, it might be interesting to find out how many of the students are nearsighted or have diabetes. During frontier days, many people with such genetic traits undoubtedly did not survive to produce children, due to the action of natural selection. Now medical science countermands natural selection in many cases, allowing such genetic traits to become more widespread. But this is only the beginning of the discussion. . . .

8. With this one the student is pretty much on his own.

9. A good rule of thumb to keep in mind relative to the evolutionary process is that, in general, the more stable the environment, the less the evolutionary change. Oceans tend to afford a more stable environment than land and tend to have fewer isolating barriers. Thus, many marine organisms have shown little change through time. One would want, on the one hand, to review the sources and degree of variability within a particular species population and, on the other hand, to consider the stability of the species' environment. A changing environment associated with a variable species might result in rapid changes; static organisms in static environments ordinarily show little change. See G. G. Simpson, *Tempo and Mode in Evolution* (New York: Columbia University Press, 1944).

10. The canyon apparently represents a geographical barrier for the grasshopper populations. One might guess that at either end of the canyon, where the two color phases can fairly easily come together, there could be intergrades. Since the populations seem fairly separate in the main part of the canyon, it appears unlikely that they are flying across. This canyon actually exists as Black Canyon of the Gunnison in Colorado; intergrades *are* more common toward either end of the canyon;

and grasshoppers seldom are seen to jump toward the canyon, but rather fly back away from the rim.

11. There are various possible adaptations for a particular niche. In the case of a dark environment, one possibility is blindness, while another is bioluminescence combined with non-blindness. From the standpoint of natural selection, it makes little sense to have a population both blind and bioluminescent. Cave animals have evolved directly from organisms that lived outside of caves, in streams or on land. Although such organisms may have mutations resulting in blindness, few exhibit mutations resulting in bioluminescence. Once bioluminescence got started, mutations toward blindness might well have been subject to negative selection.

12. The more one considers this, the more consequences come to mind. Obviously, there would be an increase in mutation rate, thus affording greater variability for natural selection to work with. Also, changes in the environment induced by such a war might favor a new set of characteristics in organisms. Population size of certain organisms would be reduced, and populations might be isolated, leading to increased genetic drift. Many individuals might become sterile, which would have a serious effect on survival of certain species. If certain species are exterminated by such a war, it should be apparent that the "forward-direction-only" nature of evolution would insure that such species would never again show up on earth. On the other hand, elimination of some species might permit others, formerly unsuccessful, to flourish. A pertinent article is "The Biology of Nuclear War," by Bentley Glass, in *The American Biology Teacher*, Oct., 1962, pp. 407–425. Neal Hines has written a description of the aftereffects of radiation in *Proving Ground; An Account of the Radiobiological Studies in the Pacific, 1946–1961* (Seattle: University of Washington Press).

## SUPPLEMENTARY MATERIALS

### Invitations to Enquiry

*Invitation 13*, pp. 87–89 of the *Biology Teacher's Handbook*. (Reference: p. T35). Attempting to explain the development of resistance to DDT in a fly population provides practice in the making of hypotheses. This can arouse interest if it is used *before* the theory of natural selection has been encountered.

### Audiovisual Materials

**Phonograph record:** *The Scientists Speak: Biology.* Harcourt, Brace and Co., 1959. Julian Huxley speaks on his reasons for accepting the theory of natural selection. Huxley's voice is a link to Darwin; his grandfather was chief spokesman for the publicity-shunning Darwin.

**Filmstrips:** *Darwin Discovers Nature's Plan.* ("Darwin's World of Nature," Part 1). LIFE Filmstrips, 1959. Helps to vivify the story of Darwin's life.

*The Enchanted Isles: The Galapagos.* ("Darwin's World of Nature," Part 2). Color. LIFE Filmstrips, 1959. Excellent series of striking pictures that supplement the textbook description of the Galápagos; gives special attention to the finches and their influence on Darwin's thinking.

*Evolution Today.* ("Darwin's World of Nature," Part 9). Color. LIFE Filmstrips, 1960. Summarizes present views of the history of life, emphasizing the continuing discovery of fossil evidence.

**Motion-picture films:** *Darwin's Finches.* Film Associates of California. 16 mm. Color. 15 min. Motion adds considerably to the effect that can be obtained from the filmstrips listed above.

*The Peppered Moth: A Population Study.* A BSCS Inquiry Film Loop. Super-8. Color. (Rand McNally # 11–2969). Best used before the account of these moths is encountered in the textbook.

*Mimicry.* A BSCS Inquiry Film Loop. Super-8. Color. (Rand McNally # 11-2968). The student is led to hypothesize concerning the factors that might have given rise to selected examples of mimicry.

## Teacher's References

BARNETT, L. *The Wonders of Life on Earth.* New York: Time, Inc., Book Division, 1960. (A popularly written and beautifully illustrated consideration of evolution and life.)

BOWMAN, R. I. "Morphological Differentiation and Adaptation in the Galapagos Finches," *University of California Publications in Zoology,* Vol. 58, 1961. (This is a rather technical account of these birds.)

DARWIN, C. *The Voyage of the Beagle.* Annotated, with an introduction by L. Engle. New York: Doubleday & Co., Inc., 1962; also available in paperback as a Doubleday Anchor Book. (One of the best of the many editions of a book that would be a classic of scientific exploration even if it were not the foundation for the Darwinian theories.)

DE BEER, G. *Atlas of Evolution.* Camden, N.J.: Thomas Nelson & Sons, 1964. (An extremely well illustrated and somewhat popularized compendium on evolution.)
_____. *Charles Darwin.* New York: Doubleday & Co., Inc., 1964; also available in paperback as a Doubleday Anchor Book. (An excellent, illustrated biography of Darwin, with particular emphasis on his scientific achievements.)

DOBZHANSKY, T. *Genetics and the Origin of Species.* 3rd ed. New York: Columbia University Press, 1951. (A milestone in the application of genetics to evolution.)

DODSON, E. O. *Evolution: Process and Product.* New York: Reinhold Publishing Corp., 1960. (A very comprehensive and readable college textbook on all aspects of evolution, with many good examples.)

EHRLICH, P. R., and R. W. HOLM. *The Process of Evolution.* New York: McGraw-Hill Book Co., Inc., 1963. (An excellent college textbook on evolution, ranging in subject matter from the origin of life to the evolution of man.)

EISELEY, L. *Darwin's Century.* New York: Doubleday & Co., Inc., 1958; also available in paperback as a Doubleday Anchor Book. (Excellent history of the impact of Darwin on Western thought.)

FISHER, R. A. *The Genetical Theory of Natural Selection.* 2nd rev. ed. New York: Dover Publications, Inc., 1958. (Reprint of a book that had much to do with the revival of the natural-selection theory after its eclipse in the early years of the twentieth century.)

GLASS, B., and OTHERS (eds.). *Forerunners of Darwin: 1745–1859.* Baltimore: Johns Hopkins Press, 1959; also available in paperback. (An excellent contribution to intellectual history. Because pre-Darwinian evolution is neglected in the *Green Version*, the material in this book is important for your background.)

GRANT, V. *The Origin of Adaptations.* New York: Columbia University Press, 1963. (A recent survey by a plant geneticist of a topic central to understanding of the evolutionary process.)

GREEN, J. *The Death of Adam.* New York: The New American Library – Mentor, 1961. (A readable paperback concerned with the historical controversy over evolutionary thought.)

HAMILTON, T. H. *Process and Pattern in Evolution.* New York: The Macmillan Co., 1967. (A paperback introduction to natural selection as it operates in the reproducing individual, with consideration of the species as the unit of evolution.)

HUXLEY, SIR J., A. C. HARDY, and E. B. FORD (eds.). *Evolution as a Process.* 2nd ed. London: George Allen & Unwin, Ltd., 1958; also in paperback – New York: Collier Books, 1963. (Nineteen essays on evolutionary mechanisms by a wide array of specialists.)

IRVINE, W. *Apes, Angels & Victorians.* New York: McGraw-Hill Book Co., Inc., 1955. (The story of Darwin, Huxley, and evolution, written in a popular style.)

JUKES, T. H. *Molecules and Evolution*. New York: Columbia University Press, 1966. (A consideration of various aspects of biochemical evolution.)

LACK, D. *Darwin's Finches*. New York: Harper Torch Books, 1961. (A good account of the birds that aroused Darwin's interest in evolution.)

MAYR, E. *Animal Species and Evolution*. Cambridge, Mass.: Harvard University Press, 1963. (A basic reference for Chapter 18; a thorough and critical survey of the process of speciation in animals by a foremost authority.)

————. *Systematics and the Origin of Species*. New York: Dover Publications, Inc., 1964. (This classic deals with species formation from a zoological standpoint, with many examples.)

MERRELL, D. J. *Evolution and Genetics*. New York: Holt, Rinehart and Winston, 1962. (This is an excellent general textbook on all aspects of evolution, with much on mechanisms. Includes the evolution of man.)

PECKHAM, M. (ed.). *The Origin of Species by Charles Darwin — a Variorum Text*. Philadelphia: University of Pennsylvania Press, 1959.

SOLBRIG, O. T. *Evolution and Systematics*. New York: The Macmillan Co., 1966. (A concise paperback introduction to evolutionary principles, emphasizing the role of natural selection at the population level and pointing out evolutionary relationships between organisms.)

STEBBINS, G. L. *Variation and Evolution in Plants*. New York: Columbia University Press, 1950. (An excellent summary of speciation in plants, with emphasis on genetic mechanisms.)

TAX, S. (ed.). *Evolution After Darwin*. 3 vol. Chicago: University of Chicago Press, 1960. (Papers and discussions from an impressive meeting that celebrated the centennial of *The Origin of Species;* excellent material on all the phases of evolution.)

VOLPE, E. P. *Understanding Evolution*. Dubuque, Iowa: W. C. Brown Co., 1967. (A well-written and inclusive paperback for a student who would like to "explore" evolution in more depth.)

WALLACE, B. *Chromosomes, Giant Molecules, and Evolution*. New York: W. W. Norton & Co., 1966. (The contribution of genetics to the evolutionary process.)

# Section Six  MAN
# AND THE
# BIOSPHERE

Anyone who has followed this guide through the preceding sections should need no further orientation. It should be clear that Section Six is not an afterthought but the goal toward which the course has been moving from the start.

From the teaching viewpoint, it follows that Section Six must not be pushed aside in the year-end rush. Too many courses fizzle out in the June heat. If this is allowed to happen with the *Green Version*, much of the effort of preceding months will have been in vain. With a little forethought, such a debacle can be avoided.

Not more than three weeks are needed for Section Six, and much that is worthwhile can be accomplished in half that time. Only one investigation (19.3) involves extensive laboratory preparations; when it is completed, materials can be put away and equipment can be cleaned and stored for the summer. Then, viewing the course in retrospect (and their lives in prospect), students and teacher together can look at biology as a whole—and at its impact on the lives of men.

Section Illustration

Modern technology leveling this tropical forest may represent human progress or human disaster —or something between. A tremendous amount of knowledge is required to assess the situation. Section Six abounds in opportunities for quick and superficial judgments. Lead your students to recognize the need for deep biological understanding.

# 19

# The Human
# Animal

## MAJOR IDEAS

1. Anatomically, man is a vertebrate animal, a mammal of the order Primates; he is distinguishable from other primates by a number of structural features. These peculiarities lie not in unique structures but, rather, in the *degree* of development of basic primate structures.

2. Man's anatomical equipment allows him no single outstanding physical accomplishment, but it provides him with unparalleled versatility.

3. The physiological peculiarities of man are mostly temporal, centering upon his slow development to maturity. They are important primarily because they provide a foundation for the evolution of behavioral characteristics — on the basis of which man's unique culture has arisen.

4. During the past few decades paleontologists have uncovered an unlikely (but still meager) amount of fossil evidence for the evolution of hominids. Efforts to elucidate the pongid-hominid divergence have not been as successful; the great apes and man have apparently evolved along separate lines since the Miocene.

5. On the basis of the biological definition of species, all living hominids undoubtedly belong to one species. As in other wide-ranging species, partial geographic isolation has resulted in the development of varieties.

## PLANNING AHEAD

Chapter 19 contains the last laboratory investigations for the year; there are no investigations in Chapter 20. Consequently, the kind of planning ahead that has been principally discussed in the preceding chapters is now at an end.

There are other kinds of planning, however. One short-term kind was suggested in the "Planning Ahead" section of Chapter 18 (p. T276): planning for the most efficient storage of materials and equipment.

A second kind looks deep into next year. You probably found on many occasions during the past year that certain materials could have been much more easily procured if ordering had been done in the previous spring. You are now in next year's "previous spring." Review your experience from this year, list the materials or equipment that should be obtained now for next year, and send off your orders.

## GUIDELINES

"Man is an animal," is a statement of biological fact. Obviously this statement does not preclude other viewpoints. Science is not the whole of man's experience; remember the second BSCS objective (p. T3). A difference between man and other animals that is even sharper than the one discussed in the third paragraph of p. 716 is afforded by the idea of human spirit, or soul. But it is appropriate for biology teachers to recognize the limits of biological science—and of their own competency. Therefore, the discussion of man in Chapter 19 is confined to matters that are biological *sensu stricto* and is not allowed to transgress into the more remote parts of anthropology.

If there is such a thing as "pure" science, the search for human fossils is certainly such. Yet this is one form of science that captures the interest of almost everyone; the best indication is the space that newspapers are willing to devote to the subject. Not everything that is given space in newspapers is worthy of classroom use, but discussions of evidence for man's origin are almost always lively.

Considering that man is the most widely distributed macroscopic terrestrial organism, he shows remarkably little subspecific differentiation. Yet this little has been a matter of inordinate concern. It is, therefore, appropriate to conclude discussion of the human animal with this biologically trivial topic.

Work on the chapter can begin as appropriately with Investigation 19.1 as with study and discussion of pp. 716–722 (guide questions 1–8). Pp. 724–732 (guide questions 9–16) then form a second study assignment. Investigations 19.2 and 19.3, both of which are primarily concerned with variations in human populations, can be taken up at any convenient time. Investigation 19.3, with its fairly simple but self-motivating procedure, is an excellent concluding laboratory experience for the year.

## TEACHING NOTES

### THE UNIQUENESS OF MAN
(pp. 716–722)

**p. 716, ¶ 2:** It has probably been some time since students had occasion to refer to Appendix II. This is a good point at which to recall some ideas concerning classification. The order Primates is shown in some detail on p. 801.

**p. 718, ¶ 2:** Volumes of the brain cases of fossil hominids, as given in the 1963 edition and in various references that your students may find, are subject to a considerable amount of dispute because they are mostly based on fragmentary fossils.

**p. 718, Fig. 19·2:** In addition to the points made in ¶ 2, compare the relative sizes of brain case and face, the brow ridges, the sizes of the mouths, and the positions of the ears. In both species the size of the external ear varies greatly.

**p. 719, note 1:** Briefly, the Lamarckian argument might be that when canine teeth

MAN AND THE BIOSPHERE

no longer were much used, they gradually became smaller; the Darwinian, that individuals with shorter canine teeth, no longer being at a disadvantage with respect to fighting and perhaps being better able to chew without the rather clumsy big canines, had first no disadvantage and then a positive advantage in survival over individuals with large canines.

**p. 719, Fig. 19 · 3:** For an animation of the cheetah gait, see the BSCS Laboratory Block by A. G. Richards, *The Complementarity of Form and Function* (Boston: D. C. Heath & Co., 1963).

**p. 719, ¶ 4:** The figures given here are extremes—records of the best athletes. Your students may want to contribute other athletic records or perhaps some that supersede these.

**p. 720, ¶ 4:** The menstrual cycle of the female (pp. 615–617) is sometimes emphasized as a human peculiarity, but it seems to be only a slight extension of a primate variation on the mammalian pattern. To what degree it has contributed to the evolution of human societal organization is an interesting question, but one to be recommended for debate in the social-studies rather than the science classroom.

**p. 721, note 1:** A good place to begin is with A. Comfort, *Ageing: The Biology of Senescence* (New York: Holt, Rinehart, and Winston, 1964). This book has an excellent bibliography.

**p. 721, ¶ 4, last sentence:** Yet sociality is definitely a primate trend. A zoologist used to characterize primate behavior for his students as "social, dirty, noisy, and sexy." The last three characteristics seem to be derivable from the first.

**p. 722, ¶ 1:** Some of your more thoughtful students may not like the conservative implications of this paragraph. You might emphasize the fourth sentence: the discoveries of young innovators need not be lost; if useful, they become a part of that which is conserved—a kind of cultural natural selection.

## INVESTIGATION 19.1

### THE SKELETAL BASIS OF UPRIGHT POSTURE (pp. 722–724)

#### Materials

Skeletons of other quadruped mammals may be used in place of the cat skeleton. (Rat skeletons, however, are too small for good observation by groups.) Human skeletons are expensive, but full-size replicas difficult to distinguish from the real thing are now available. The small plastic models are not satisfactory for this investigation.

#### Procedure

If only one skeleton of each species is available—as is usually the case—the observational part of the investigation can be done in shifts. The skeletons are large enough to be seen easily, so an observing group may be rather large. At least two groups can make all the observations in a single period.

The items under "Discussion" and "Summary" can be worked out by students individually at home, but if time and materials permit, it is preferable to have this done cooperatively within each group before class discussion is begun.

- (3): Without terms for individual bones, this may be a little difficult to state; but in general the changes must bring the eye sockets to a forward orientation, and nasal and jaw bones must be shifted so that they lie under the eye sockets.

- (7): This may be a little difficult for students to determine. Both the position of the foramen and the musculature around it result in the human skull being balanced rather than braced on the top of the vertebral column. This makes us singularly liable to whiplash neck injuries in automobile accidents.

- (12): Students sometimes have difficulty interpreting this question, but even in Figure 19 · 1 the double curve of the human vertebral column is evident in comparison with the single curve of the gorilla's.

- (17): The rather firm pectoral girdles of hominids (as compared with those of cats) are usually associated with presumed former locomotion by brachiation. If this presumption is so, the shoulder architecture can be considered an example of *pre-adaptation;* that is, it was suited to the extensive use of the arms in wielding heavy tools and weapons when locomotion was shifted entirely to the posterior appendages.
- (23): A greater cranium volume implies a greater brain. This is the kind of inference that is the basis for much paleontological interpretation.
- (24): Binocular vision.
- (25): Many answers are possible. All should concern the kinds of skeletal adaptations that have been stressed in the preceding questions.
- (27): The weight of the "anterior"—actually, upper—part of man's body is primarily supported on the pelvic girdle.
- (29): A circus dog (which has a pectoral architecture similar to that of a cat —Figure 4·4) may be taught to walk short distances on its forelegs. Hand walking in man is not easy either, but the problems are more of equilibrium and cranial circulation than of weakness of support.
- (30) and • (31): See note to • (17) above.
- (33): It provides a springiness suited to leaping or a rapid getaway.
- (34): The tiring is merely a symptom of difficulty in balancing; it is remarkable enough that a man can balance himself on the full length of his feet.

## Discussion

Because much interpretation is left up to the teacher, the investigation should be concluded with a general class discussion. You may wish to refer to Investigations 4.1 and 14.1, in which man and other animals were compared with respect to various characteristics.

Any study of skeletons can become quite loaded with terminology. The terms used in the investigation are those that will be found useful for carrying on a discussion. You may add to them as you see fit.

## BECOMING HUMAN (pp. 724–732)

**p. 725, ¶ 2:** Actually, as stated on p. 728, ¶ 3, the first remains of "Neanderthal man" had been discovered in 1856, but the meaning of this find was then much disputed. You might ask students why human fossils are expected to be rare. Some points: populations of early hominids were apparently rather sparse (how far we have come in this respect!); most of the bones of hominids are rather fragile; in wet tropical conditions bone deteriorates rapidly unless buried under anaerobic conditions. It should be pointed out that the hominids —as contrasted with the early Hominoidea from which the family presumably evolved —are thought by many paleontologists to have belonged to savanna or grassland rather than forest ecosystems.

**p. 726, ¶ 1, last sentence:** Be sure students connect this with Item 6 of Investigation 19.1.

**p. 727, ¶ 3, first sentence:** This is probably an overstatement. Perhaps the only thing clear in human paleontology is that nothing is clear. You should emphasize the state of flux in this field—but try to keep as up-to-date as possible. Pp. 725–729 were written in a restrained way that, it was hoped, would be not too misleading on the day they were printed; nothing could be done about the days after.

**p. 727, note 4:** This indicates that the differences between the fossils are considered by some paleontologists to be of only specific rank. What *that* means is not clear, but some approximation of it can be made by considering the differences between the three examples of *Homo* and the one of *Australopithecus* in Figure 19 · 6. And some paleontologists *have* used other generic terms for the fossils here discussed as two species of *Australopithecus*.

**p. 727, ¶ 4:** Notice that the discussion is tracing the chronology of evolving man. Unfortunately, the chronology of the discoveries is almost the reverse. To use the latter chronology would improve the investigative character of the discussion, but it would require a length of exposition unavailable in this short, penultimate chapter.

**p. 727, Fig. 19 · 6:** The questions are primarily intended to elicit observations from students, not to establish technical criteria. Perhaps the most important point is the ratio of brain-case size to face size. The discussion on pp. 699–703 does not explicitly state that trinomials are used in nomenclature to designate subspecies, but this figure provides an example.

**p. 728, Fig. 19 · 7:** Much of the fossil evidence for *Australopithecus* and *Homo erectus* is fragmentary, and the skulls in Figure 19 · 6 are themselves to some extent reconstructions; but most of the musculature is based directly on skeletal evidence. Details of fleshy structures, such as external ear and nose, are less sure; and hairiness is quite uncertain. Even for modern man the artist has had to make compromises in the last respect, since different varieties of modern man (to say nothing of ages and sexes) vary markedly in the amount and character of hair.

**p. 728, Fig. 19 · 8:** Concerning the caption question see p. 674, ¶ 2. Also, for tool using in chimpanzees see J. G. Van Lawick, *My Friends the Wild Chimpanzees* (Washington, D.C.: National Geographic Society, 1966).

**p. 729, note 2:** Some anthropologists think that a good deal of hybridization occurred.

**p. 732, ¶ 2:** See W. C. Boyd (reference: p. 739).

## INVESTIGATION 19.2

### BIOLOGICAL DISTANCE
(pp. 732–735)

In some classes this investigation can be assigned as homework. Not all students, however, are able to work their way successfully through it; therefore some class discussion must follow the work at home. In classes where slow students predominate, the investigation is best done entirely in class, under step-by-step teacher direction.

Some of your students may want to read further on the subject of genetic criteria for distinguishing human populations. A later and smaller book than the one cited above is W. C. Boyd and I. Asimov, *Races and People* (New York: Abelard-Schuman, Ltd., 1955). It covers some of the same ground as the earlier book and is more readable for high school students.

Procedure

The data for British Columbia are derived from various tribal groups; those for New Mexico are confined to the Navahos. The data are obtained as blood types—A, B, AB, or O—and the gene frequencies are calculated from the phenotype frequencies.

- (1)–• (3): After working on Investigations 17.2 and 18.2, some students may argue that the slight differences between the British Columbia and Navaho populations represent nothing more than sampling errors. Without knowing the number of persons in the sample, it is not possible to test for the significance of the difference. But, in general, blood-type data are abundant, and in the source from which the data were derived, the difference was considered significant.

- (4) and • (5): Answers to these questions are likely to be as various as are the definitions of human races. Some students may react to these questions with, Why bother to distinguish racially between Eskimos and Indians? Or, phrased in the most likely form, Why bother? There is, of course, no rational answer to such questions. They are in the same category as, Why climb a mountain? With the course coming to an end, it is worthwhile to point out (again) that science is not *necessarily* concerned with "practical" questions. Yet, as stated in the Preface, it brings about improvements in the circumstances of human life more frequently than any other enterprise.

- (9): Later I$^b$-bearing populations would be most numerous nearest the point of origin—that is, closest to Asia.

- (10): The Eskimo population. This is supported by much other evidence.

- (11): On the basis of the I$^b$ gene *only*, the biological distance between central Asians and Basques equals that between central Asians and Navahos.

- (12): This ought to be a patent absurdity, but in matters of race there seems to be no criterion for absurdity. No racial, subspecific, or varietal status can be distinguished on the basis of one genetic locus. Moreover, all these terms denote a continuous interbreeding sub-population within a species population. Clearly Basques and Navahos seldom interbreed, though they undoubtedly are capable of doing so.

- (13): It is 0.57. If you wish to go into the practical consequences of Rh$^+$ and Rh$^-$ incompatibility, here is a good opportunity to do so. Often students bring the matter up, since it is now rather well known. But such a discussion is not necessary for the continued argument of the investigation.

- (14): It is 0.16.

- (15): 28 percent. This means that the amount of mixing is 28 percent of that required to make the difference between American and African Negroes with respect to Rh$^o$ indistinguishable from the difference between Europeans and Africans with respect to Rh$^o$. This method of calculation may seem faulty, since mixing must involve *both* populations. But under American conditions, most persons of mixed Negroid and Caucasoid ancestry are classified as Negroid, so that introgression of the Rh$^o$ gene into the "Caucasoid" population is undeterminable.

- (16): 13 generations.

- (17): About 2.2 percent. The answer to this question is a biological deduction from verifiable observations. If the class climate is suitable, you may wish to project the situation into the future—a suitable prelude to Chapter 20, which is entirely forward-looking. Such a projection is still a matter of science, but it is so obscured by sociological implications that you may not wish to pursue it. However, if the matter is gone into, it should be kept in mind that the answer to Item 17 assumes a constant rate of mixture—and this is highly unlikely. It is much more likely that the rate curve would show some of the characteristics of a growth curve. The Rh$^o$ gene would never disappear from a large population (in the absence of natural selection), but its frequency would become asymptotic to a level somewhat above that of the frequency in the European Caucasoid population. It should also be kept in mind that the point in time at which the Negroid and Caucasoid populations become indistinguishable with respect to frequency of the Rh$^o$ gene would not necessarily be a point at which the populations would be indistinguishable with respect to visible characteristics.

## INVESTIGATION 19.3

### HUMAN BLOOD GROUPS
(pp. 735–737)

This investigation is interesting to students and forms a fitting termination to the year's laboratory work. But it must be planned with particular care: First, written permission from parents of participating students is recommended; second, arrangements must be made to take care of cases of fainting that occasionally occur; third, only sterile, disposable lancets should be used, and each lancet must be discarded after *one* use. Some teachers arrange for the school nurse to carry out the procedure for obtaining blood. Under extremely unfavorable conditions, it might be well merely to demonstrate the blood-typing procedure and omit the consideration of blood-type percentages.

The "Background Information" should suffice for establishing the rationale of the procedure.

### Materials

Serums and supplies of alcohol can be shared by two or three teams.

If serums are old or have not been kept under refrigeration, many errors may occur. These are likely to be systematic rather than random errors, and of course they will affect the percentages.

### Procedure

Be sure that students understand the difference between *clumping* of red cells and *clotting* of blood.

### Discussion

When checking • (4) to • (9), you may be assisted by the following tables:

| GROUP | PLASMA | RED CELLS |
|:-----:|:------:|:---------:|
| O | anti-a and anti-b | neither |
| A | anti-b | A |
| B | anti-a | B |
| AB | neither | A and B |

Figure T–27

|  |  | RECIPIENT | | | |
|:--:|:--:|:--:|:--:|:--:|:--:|
|  |  | O | A | B | AB |
| DONOR | O | − | − | − | − |
|  | A | + | − | + | − |
|  | B | + | + | − | − |
|  | AB | + | + | + | − |

Figure T–28

- (10): This depends upon circumstances, of which you will have to be the judge.
- (11): The sample data have been chosen to represent populations from areas which have supplied ancestors to the present American population. Obviously they are not inclusive and must be used cautiously. American Indian populations, for example, vary greatly; the figures from Blackfeet in Montana are unreliable if applied to Cherokees in North Carolina. The data do serve, however, to emphasize the diverse biological roots of the present North American human population.

## PROBLEMS (pp. 738–739)

**1.** See note to p. 725, ¶ 2 (p. T297). Consider this comment of a paleontologist-archaeologist, born and educated in southern California, on transferring to an eastern university: "All that green stuff covers everything up!"

**4.** See note to p. 719, note 1 (pp. T295–T296.)

**6.** Advise students to begin with Howell (reference: p. 739) and proceed on the basis of its bibliography.

**7.** This is a highly speculative question. But the student needs to know something about the social organization of wolf packs as well as the organization of human tribes. A large order—and he had better plan to make the study a summer project. Advise a beginning with W. Etkin, *Social Behavior and Organization among Vertebrates*, and N. Tinbergen, *Social Behavior in Animals* (references: pp. T227 and T228).

## SUPPLEMENTARY MATERIALS

### Audiovisual Materials

**Filmstrip:** *Man Inherits the Earth* (Part 1A of the "Epic of Man"). Color. LIFE Filmstrips. Rather glib but colorful portrayal of early man.

**Motion-picture films:** *Blood Groups, Skin Color, and Gene Pools.* (AIBS Film Series). McGraw-Hill Text-Film Division. 16 mm. Color. 28 min. Will serve as a review of some genetic principles important in human racial differentiation and as background to Investigation 19.2.

*Evolution of Man.* (AIBS Film Series). McGraw-Hill Text-Film Division. 16 mm. Color. 28 min. Dr. Marshall Newman, eminent anthropologist of the Smithsonian Institution, discusses the evidence for man's existence during the Pleistocene.

### Teacher's References

COON, C. S. *The Origin of Races.* New York: Alfred A. Knopf, Inc., 1962. (Has been a center of controversy because of its interpretations of evidence, but Coon's grasp of his material is undoubted.)

———. *The Story of Man.* 2nd ed. New York: Alfred A. Knopf, Inc., 1962. (Narrative account of human origins and prehistory.)

DART, R. A. *Adventures with the Missing Link.* New York: Harper & Brothers, 1959. ("Popular" account of the australopithecines.)

DOBZHANSKY, T. *Mankind Evolving.* New Haven, Conn.: Yale University Press, 1962. (A distinguished geneticist looks at the history of the hominids.)

HARRISON, G. A., U. S. WEINER, U. M. TANNER, and N. A. BARNICOT. *Human Biology.* New York: Oxford University Press, 1964. (A survey of physical anthropology.)

HULSE, F. S. *The Human Species.* New York: Random House, Inc., 1963. (Introduction to physical anthropology, placing emphasis on genetics. Strong on the developments of the last twenty years and weak on the historical development of anthropology.)

LA BARRE, W. *The Human Animal.* Chicago: University of Chicago Press, 1954. (The evolution of man and of his culture from the viewpoints of anthropology and psychology.)

LeGros Clark, Sir W. E. *History of the Primates.* 4th ed. Chicago: University of Chicago Press, 1963. (A good summary by an authority.)

———. *Man-Apes or Ape-Men?* New York: Holt, Rinehart, and Winston, 1967. (Chiefly concerned with the australopithecines; this is a rather technical discussion of controversial interpretations of the fossils.)

Morris, D. *The Naked Ape.* New York: McGraw-Hill Book Co., Inc., 1967. (An entertaining account of the peculiarities of *Homo sapiens.*)

Tax, S. (ed.). *The Evolution of Man: Man, Culture and Society.* Vol. 2 of "Evolution after Darwin." Chicago: University of Chicago Press, 1960. (Addresses delivered at a convocation honoring the centennial of *The Origin of Species.*)

Turnbull, C. M. *The Forest People.* New York: Doubleday & Co., Inc., 1962. (An excellent account of primitive man in modern times—the pygmies of the Congo—and of their close ecological relationships with their environment.)

Washburn, S. L. (ed.). *Social Life of Early Man.* Chicago: Aldine Publishing Co., 1961.

# 20

# Man in the
# Web of Life

---

## MAJOR IDEAS

1. Gradually, as his technology has improved, man's position in the biosphere has shifted. Primitive man was a member of a biotic community, important but not dominant; modern man overrides all natural community boundaries, fabricates new communities, and overbalances meteorological and geological forces in reshaping the earth.

2. Throughout his history, improvement of man's understanding has resulted in improvement in his technology, and improvement in his technology has resulted in improvement of his understanding. The problems of modern man lie as much in the proper application of understanding and technology as they do in the further improvement of either. And most of these problems are basically biological.

3. The roots of most major biological problems—from malnutrition to floods, from traffic to smog—lie in the rapidly increasing world density of human population. As in all other populations, this density involves the four determiners natality, mortality, immigration, and emigration, of which the last two have (at present) zero values. It is clear that solutions to human overpopulation must be through a reduction of natality.

4. For man the living world is not only an entity that demands study, yielding understanding; it is also an experience that demands appreciation, yielding aesthetic pleasure. But scientific study is itself fraught with aesthetic qualities. Thus biology is doubly a humanistic enterprise.

## PLANNING AHEAD

Is there anything more to be said about planning ahead? Yes.

If you have decided not to use this course next year, then you certainly need to plan ahead.

If you *do* expect to use the course again, you undoubtedly have ideas for modifying it. These ideas should be worked out. As in all public performances, spontaneity in teaching is most effective when it springs from solid preparation.

The emphasis throughout this year on planning for laboratory work is justified —but it is not sufficient. Planning should involve more than logistics; it also should involve tactics and strategy—and, further, a philosophical consideration that (to extend the image) might be called polity. It is clear that no science teacher can ever rest from this kind of planning. Plan ahead. If you have not done so, join your fellows in The National Science Teacher's Association and the National Association of Biology Teachers. Plan ahead: Discover by courses or reading what is currently happening on the research frontiers of some branch of biology with which you have had little acquaintance. Plan ahead: Read and ponder some work of biological humanism or biological philosophy. (A subversive suggestion: A. Koestler's *The Ghost in the Machine.* New York: The Macmillan Co., 1967. Or, more constructive, J. M. Reiner's *The Organism as an Adaptive Control System.* Englewood Cliffs, N.J.: Prentice-Hall, Inc., 1968.)

## GUIDELINES

Field and laboratory equipment has been inventoried and stored. But—hopefully—student impressions of a year's contact with living things remain. These impressions are the materials for work on Chapter 20.

The first thing to do is to return to pp. 32–33. The problems posed at the beginning of the student's biology course constitute the foundation for discussion in Chapter 20. They are not taken up seriatim,

nor is explicit reference to each to be found in Chapter 20. The present plight of man in the biosphere is much too complex for such a simplistic approach to be valid. But the problems of Chapter 1 are all implicit in Chapter 20. And having been exposed to eighteen intervening chapters, most students should be in a position to bring some further biological maturity to a few year-end periods of reading, thought, and discussion.

The form that such discussion takes will depend upon your sagacity and the students' insight. The areas considered in the chapter should by no means limit the discussion. And wherever possible, the information and insights gained during the year's study of biology should be woven into the prospect of the future. Above all, endeavor to make each student feel his personal responsibility for applying whatever knowledge of science he possesses to the decisions that will need to be made by his generation.

## TEACHING NOTES

### MAN AND THE BIOLOGICAL COMMUNITY (pp. 741–745)

**p. 742, Fig. 20·1:** Just as extant species that have retained primitive characteristics help us to visualize organisms of the past, so primitive human cultures surviving in remote parts of the modern world suggest to us the conditions of life in ancient human cultures. But study of such surviving primitive cultures must proceed rapidly, for modern culture is penetrating everywhere.

**p. 744, Fig. 20·3:** The contrast between this figure and Figure 20·2 is self-evident, but the implications of the contrast require some thinking. For example, Figure 20·3 represents the industrial America of today better than a panorama of Gary's steel mills does. Concentrations of industrial population are possible only because such wholesale production of food is possible. On the other hand, Figure 20·3 implies a great industrial complex, for only that can produce and keep running such a fleet of machines.

**p. 746, ¶ 1:** Sharks remain a rather serious danger, as man has turned in recent years toward increasing exploitation of the seas. An active program of research on protection from sharks has been carried on in recent years, mostly under the sponsorship of the Office of Naval Research.

**p. 746, Fig. 20 · 5:** The figures in this table are derived primarily from *Statistical Abstract of the United States.*

**p. 747, ¶ 5:** DDT is dichlorodiphenyl-trichloroethane, or more precisely 1, 1, 1,-trichloro-2, 2,-di(*p*-chlorophenyl)-ethane. Biology is not the only science that makes use of long terms! See further, p. 768.

**p. 748, note 3:** On the basis of the 1960 prediction and an increase rate of 1.7 percent, the predictions (in billions) are 1960, 2.900; 1961, 2.949; 1962, 2.999; 1963, 3.050; 1964, 3.102; 1965, 3.155; 1966, 3.209; 1967, 3.264; 1968, 3.320; 1969, 3.376; 1970, 3.433; 1971, 3.491; 1972, 3.550; 1973, 4.154. Consult a recent almanac to get actual world population figures.

**p. 749, Fig. 20 · 6:** The graph bears a striking resemblance to the one drawn in Investigation 2.1, but students should be cautioned concerning the dangers of extrapolation. In early printings the curve was printed just about one block too low on the grid, making the absolute figures wrong but not, of course, affecting the shape of the curve.

**p. 750, ¶ 5:** But birth rate tells only part of the story; an important factor in population increase is the great number of people in the fecund age group (ages fifteen to forty-five). Population increases in proportion to (1) the rate of increase (similar to the interest rate in financial matters), and (2) the number of people doing the reproducing (equivalent to the amount of money drawing interest). Therefore, although the *rate of increase* is declining, there is an ever-expanding population doing the reproducing. Even if our rate of increase were reduced to 0.1 percent, the population would continue to grow.

**p. 750, note 1:** On the basis of the 1965 birth and death rates of 19.4 and 9.4 and on the assumption that emigration equals immigration, the rate of population increase is 10 per thousand population, or 1 percent.

**p. 751, ¶ 3:** Concerning the possibility of emigration from the world, there are three major problems: (1) no planet is yet known that would support man, (2) the energy cost to lift any sizable part of our population to another planet is beyond all present consideration — to say nothing of the energy required to deliver support systems to the population in space, and (3) the by-product of missile blast in the world atmospheric pollution would be great and probably would result in major changes in climate. Even present measurements of the increase of atmospheric aerosols and their effects in increasing the reflection of solar radiation indicate a decrease in world temperature. (See p. 765, ¶ 3.)

**p. 753, Fig. 20 · 8:** Why should the land required to feed one person in the United States increase from 0.4 to 0.8 hectares? A major reason is that an increasing number of the calories produced go to feed animals that in turn manufacture costly, higher-protein diets. It might also reflect to some extent a decrease in soil fertility.

**p. 754, ¶ 3:** There are important programs to supplement the protein-deficient diets of peoples who live in countries where they cannot afford the luxury of feeding plants to animals in order to get high-quality proteins. One program involves adding to the carbohydrate diet low-cost proteins — for example, fish meal, egg powder, yeast, and soybeans. Another high-protein food (used in Latin America) is called Incaparina; it includes 1 part of oilseed meal (residue after oils have been extracted from cottonseeds or soybeans) and 2 parts of grain, with additions of yeast and vitamin A. Look back at Figure 1 · 12 on p. 22 to recall why it takes so many calories to produce animal protein.

**p. 754, Fig. 20 · 9:** The development of hybrid corn, perhaps the first "practical" result from the science of genetics, is discussed in most genetics textbooks (see "Teacher's References" for Chapter 17, p. T274).

**p. 758, ¶ 2:** Early concepts of forest conservation included the idea that water is conserved by the presence of forests in a watershed. Many now believe that if water supply is the *major* concern, a watershed with grass or low-shrub cover is superior to one with trees. This is true because much rainfall is intercepted by the trees and evaporates before joining the groundwater. Secondly, the trees remove much of the groundwater through transpiration. As always in resource management, all purposes must be considered before a management program for a particular watershed is planned.

**p. 761, ¶ 2:** Wildlife and forests seem to have an intrinsic appeal for fifteen- or sixteen-year-old males. This is as pronounced in urban as in rural areas. A majority of students majoring in forestry and wildlife management now come from urban and suburban areas; and agricultural research, if not agricultural practice, increasingly draws its recruits from these sources.

**p. 761, note 1:** The question is primarily rhetorical, but it could arouse some discussion.

**p. 762, Fig. 20·19:** See J. C. Greenway, *Extinct and Vanishing Birds of the World* (1958); G. M. Allen, *Extinct and Vanishing Mammals of the Western Hemisphere with the Marine Species of All the Oceans* (1942); and F. Harper, *Extinct and Vanishing Mammals of the Old World* (1945)—all published by the American Committee for International Wildlife Protection, New York.

**p. 762, ¶ 2:** "For one species to mourn the death of another is a new thing under the sun. The Cro-Magnon who slew the last mammoth thought only of steaks. The sportsman who shot the last pigeon thought only of his prowess. The sailor who shot the last auk thought of nothing at all. But we, who have lost our pigeons, mourn the loss. Had the funeral been ours, the pigeons

would hardly have mourned us. In this fact, rather than in . . . nylons or . . . bombs, lies objective evidence of our superiority over the beasts."

Aldo Leopold, *Sand County Almanac and Sketches Here and There* (New York: Oxford University Press, Copyright © 1948)

**p. 764, Fig. 20·22:** The scene is Manhattan, but at times smog conditions develop over almost every large city.

## VALUES (pp. 769–772)

**p. 772:** A summary for Chapter 20—a chapter that looks both backward and forward—seems inappropriate. Instead, the authors feel that a fitting close to the book is found in the words with which Charles Darwin, rising above his customary pedestrian style, grandly concluded *The Origin of Species*.

## GUIDE QUESTIONS (pp. 772–773)

4. Complexity reduces population fluctuations because it provides more competing, predatory, or parasitic species to control surges in populations of any one species. Moreover, complexity makes it more difficult for a species to find a readily available or abundant food supply. For example, contrast the condition of an insect species that feeds only on pine needles in a community where only 1 out of every 25 trees is pine and in a plantation where every tree is a pine.

## PROBLEMS (pp. 773–774)

1. There is no single, good definition for "life," but this should stimulate discussion of some of its major attributes.

2. Biological control involves the manipulation of either organism or environment or both to utilize inherent limiting factors for control purposes. For example, if in one developmental stage an insect injurious to a field crop is particularly vulnerable to flooding, fields might be flooded at the proper time. Biological control requires detailed

knowledge of life cycles, behavior, and ecological relationships. Biological control usually has minimal effects upon other species in a community. Reference material on this topic is scattered, but students might begin with recent volumes of *Audubon Magazine*.

3. This is primarily a thought problem for your more sophisticated students. Facts are difficult to come by, but there is evidence that food-import programs may have actually decreased the food production of some countries while stimulating an increased rate of population growth.

5. The quotation simply shows that the Pygmies, like the American Indians before invasion by Europeans, recognized that they were a *part* of the ecosystem rather than *apart* from it.

7. (a) Ceylon has higher birth and death rates; therefore there is a great preponderance of young, and the life expectancy of an individual is low. (b) The young and the old age groups have increased relative to the "middle-age" group in the U.S.A. as a result of better control of childhood infectious diseases and of the diseases of old age. The increase in the young also results from a high natality rate. This distribution of age groups in the population places an increasing economic burden on the "middle-age" class, which is the principal supporting one. (c) The birth rate for the population as a whole will decline, since the number of reproducing individuals declines. (d) The rate of population increase will be greater in Nation A, since the earlier age of delivery of the first child reduces the length of a generation. Therefore, more progeny will be produced per unit time—an increased rate. If you knew the proportions of the population that were of childbearing age in both nations, the hypothesis would be on firmer ground.

8. If wastes are quickly picked up and utilized by organisms so that they do not accumulate sufficiently to harm the ecosystem, they are not pollutants.

## SUPPLEMENTARY MATERIALS

### Audiovisual Materials

**Filmstrip:** *Competitive Land Use.* McGraw-Hill Filmstrips. Color. A good visualization of some problems of planning for multiple land use.

**Motion-picture films:** *Biology in Today's World.* Coronet Films. 16 mm. Color. 11 min. May be used to stimulate some thinking about the role of biology in maintaining our present civilization.

*Poisons, Pests, and People.* National Film Board of Canada. 16 mm. Black-and-white. 30 min. An old film, but it presents the pesticide problem in an unusually rational manner.

### Teacher's References

BROWN, H. *The Challenge of Man's Future.* New York: The Viking Press, Inc., 1954. (More recent surveys of the problems of human populations and resources exist, but this is still one of the most scholarly, balanced, and inclusive.)

CLEPPER, H. (ed.). *Careers in Conservation.* New York: The Ronald Press Co., 1963. (Useful information for counseling students with an interest in natural resources.)

DUBOS, R. *Mirage of Health.* New York: Harper & Brothers, 1959. (A thoughtful essay on the world health problem by a distinguished professor of the Rockefeller University.)

GOODMAN, F. T., R. W. EDWARDS, and J. M. LAMBERT (eds.). *Ecology and the Industrial Society.* New York: John Wiley and Sons, 1965. (Reports from a symposium that explored the impacts of industrialization on the ecology of Britain, where industrialization was earliest.)

LANDSBERG, H. H., L. L. FISCHMAN, and J. L. FISHER. *Resources in America's Future.* Baltimore: Johns Hopkins Press, 1963. (A recent authoritative survey.)

LORD, R. *The Care of the Earth: A History of Husbandry.* Camden, N.J.: Thomas Nelson & Sons, 1962. Also in paperback — New York: The New American Library of World Literature, Inc., 1963. (Although this book begins with prehistory and ranges throughout the world, the main theme is the relatively brief career of Anglo-American agriculture and the ecological basis for any continuing cultivation of the soil.)

MAY, J. M. (ed.). *Studies in Disease Ecology.* New York: Hafner Publishing Co., Inc., 1961. (Emphasizes infectious diseases that are still serious morbidity and mortality factors, especially in tropical countries.)

MOOREHEAD, A. *No Room in the Ark.* New York: Harper & Brothers, 1959. (Not science, but the work of an intelligent and perspicacious journalist; a survey of conditions in an area — Africa — where human populations are pressing dramatically upon a wildlife still reminiscent of the great Age of Mammals.)

SAUER, C. O. *Land and Life: A Selection from His Writings.* Berkeley: University of California Press, 1963. (The fourth part of this volume, "The Farther Reaches of Human Time," contains materials from Sauer's contributions to the human ecology of the past.)

THOMAS, W. L. (ed.). *Man's Role in Changing the Face of the Earth.* Chicago: University of Chicago Press, 1956. (A survey by many experts of the activities of man — past and present — in modifying ecosystems.)

UDALL, S. L. *The Quiet Crisis.* New York: Holt, Rinehart & Winston, Inc., 1963. ("An attempt to outline the land-and-people story of our continent," this book adopts a historical approach to resource conservation and proceeds to view the future with a great deal of ecological understanding.)

WINSLOW, C. E. A. *The Conquest of Epidemic Disease.* Princeton, N.J.: Princeton University Press, 1953. (A historical treatment.)

# A

## A SUGGESTED TIME SCHEDULE

## INTRODUCTION

Many teachers have requested a time schedule for the *Green Version* course. In view of the multiple variables involved, the authors have hesitated to fulfill this request. Length of periods; number of periods per week; length of school year; students' previous science experiences; teachers' interests, competencies, and teaching styles; availability of facilities and equipment; local biological resources—these are among the factors that must be considered.

Nevertheless, excellence in teaching is predicated upon careful and thorough organization. It is always wise to lay out a master plan—one that serves as a measuring stick as the school year progresses. And a weekly layout is as essential as a detailed daily plan if you are to utilize student time most efficiently. Therefore, the authors finally decided to provide some assistance in these tasks through the following schedule.

It is suggested that before you embark upon your planning, you review carefully "Organization," pp. T7–T10, and "Organizational Alternatives," pp. T10–T11.

### Cautions

In studying this schedule, there are three important things to remember. First, the amount of time allocated is not a direct indication of the importance of the topic or concepts included, but merely an estimate of the time required for their more or less adequate consideration. Second, the laboratory work is essential to the course and must not be sacrificed merely to maintain a time schedule. Third, each teacher will need to modify the time schedule to meet the needs and interests of his students.

### The Schedule

The allocation of time suggested in the table on pp. T311–T312 is based upon a school year of thirty-six weeks.

## Section One:   THE WORLD OF LIFE: THE BIOSPHERE

### 7 1/2 weeks

As stated on p. T11, Sections One and Six are indispensable to the philosophy of the *Green Version*. Four weeks have been assigned to Chapter 1. The whole course lies ahead, and its success or failure depends upon getting off to a good start. This chapter lays the groundwork and establishes the direction of the course. It is here that you develop with students your basic procedures for laboratory work, for classroom discussions, for home assignments—in effect, your *modus operandi*. All this takes time.

Chapter 1: The Web of Life
*4 weeks*

Chapter 2: Individuals and Populations
*2 weeks*

Chapter 3: Communities and Ecosystems
*1 1/2 weeks*

## Section Two:   DIVERSITY AMONG LIVING THINGS

### 3 1/2 weeks

Only three and a half weeks have been allocated to Section Two. Remember, the emphasis here is upon diversity of organisms and the concepts of classification and nomenclature. Beware of getting in a *cul-de-sac* by attempting a "type study" of living things.

Chapter 4: Animals
*1 1/2 weeks*

Chapter 5: Plants
*1 week*

Chapter 6: Protists
*1 week*

## Section Three:   PATTERNS IN THE BIOSPHERE

### 5 weeks

Section Three has been given five weeks, but if you have dropped behind in your schedule, Chapter 9 may be considered expendable. (See p. T11.)

Chapter 7: Patterns of Life in the Microscopic World
*1 1/2 weeks*

Chapter 8: Patterns of Life on Land
*1 1/2 weeks*

Chapter 9: Patterns of Life in the Water
*1 week*

Chapter 10: Patterns of Life in the Past
*1 week*

# Section Four: WITHIN THE INDIVIDUAL ORGANISM

### 11 weeks

Section Four includes some topics that may have been learned in previous science courses. You should be sensitive to needless repetition, especially in Chapters 11, 13, and 14. Many courses in general science or intermediate science treat cellular structure and physiology in some depth. Also, some health courses contain much on human anatomy; therefore, parts of Chapter 14 may be omitted or used only for review. If all this gains you some time, spend it on Chapter 12 or 15, depending upon your students' interests.

Chapter 11: The Cell
*2 weeks*

Chapter 12: Bioenergetics
*3 weeks*

Chapter 13: The Functioning Plant
*1 1/2 weeks*

Chapter 14: The Functioning Animal
*2 1/2 weeks*

Chapter 15: Behavior
*2 weeks*

# Section Five: CONTINUITY OF THE BIOSPHERE

### 7 weeks

Though seven weeks have been allotted to Section Five, the chapter "Reproduction" may take less than the three-week period indicated. Reproduction is being taught increasingly in the lower grades, where it is frequently a part of family-life education. Any time gained can profitably be expended on Chapter 18.

Chapter 16: Reproduction
*3 weeks*

Chapter 17: Heredity
*3 weeks*

Chapter 18: Evolution
*1 week*

# Section Six: MAN AND THE BIOSPHERE

### 2 weeks

As previously indicated, Section Six is essential, and to meaningfully complete the course, you must allow time for these last two chapters. Not the amount of time, however, but your earnestness and commitment, together with the use of current articles from newspapers and magazines, are your keys to success with "Man and the Biosphere."

Chapter 19: The Human Animal
*1 week*

Chapter 20: Man in the Web of Life
*1 week*

# B

# SUMMARY OF MATERIALS
# AND EQUIPMENT

The consolidated lists of materials and equipment on the following pages may prove helpful for teachers or supervisors who are planning to use the *Green Version* for the first time. This appendix may also serve as a yearly checklist in school systems that must order supplies six months to a year in advance. An experienced teacher and a science supervisor have cooperated in making the lists. In using the lists, keep these points in mind:

1. A few items are omitted. These are items easily obtained from students (e.g., cardboard boxes, food samples) and organisms that are a matter of choice (e.g., those in Investigations 1.1, 1.4, and 5.2).

2. Substitutes are feasible for some of the listed items. For suggestions, check the notes on each investigation.

3. Quantities for one class are specified on the basis of 30 pupils, usually working as six teams. In calculating the quantities needed for four classes, the authors have allowed for the possibility of reusing equipment. This is not always a simple matter; it often depends upon the opportunities for cleanup between periods or the possibilities of staggering investigations among classes.

4. If a school has more than one biology teacher, the quantities needed are not necessarily obtained by multiplying the quantities required for one teacher by the number of teachers. Again, this is not simple; each school must consider the feasibility of sharing equipment, the possibilities of staggering topics and investigations—even temperaments of teachers involved.

5. For the most part, estimates are close to minimal, with only small allowances for loss and breakage. However, customary dealers' units have been used; therefore, 4 ounces of a chemical may be listed for one class even though 4 ounces is sufficient for four classes.

## MATERIALS

| Item | 1 Class | 4 Classes |
|---|---|---|
| Acetic acid, glacial | 1 lb | 1 lb |
| Acetone | 1 lb | 3 lb |
| Aceto-orcein solution | 4 oz | 8 oz |
| Agar | 1 lb | 1 lb |
| Alcohol | | |
| ethyl, 95% | 1 gal | 1 gal |
| isopropyl, 70% | 1 gal | 1 gal |
| Aluminum foil | 2 rolls | 4 rolls |
| Ascarite | 1 lb | 1 lb |
| Bacteria | | |
| *Agrobacterium tumefaciens* | 1 culture | 4 cultures |
| *Sarcina lutea* | 1 culture | 4 cultures |
| *Serratia marcescens* | 1 culture | 4 cultures |
| Beans, dried | 1 lb | 2 lb |
| Beef extract | 4 oz | 8 oz |
| Benedict's solution | | |
| (or Fehling's solution, A and B) | 1 lb | 3 lb |
| Benzine | 1 lb | 1 lb |
| Bouillon cubes | 1 jar | 2 jars |
| Brine shrimp | 1 box | 2 boxes |
| Bromthymol blue solution, aqueous | 1 oz | 2 oz |
| Carnoy's fluid, with chloroform | 150 ml | 500 ml |
| Cellophane sheets, 2 colors | | |
| red | 5 sheets | 10 sheets |
| blue | 5 sheets | 10 sheets |
| Cellulose tubing | 50 ft | 50 ft |
| Chalk, 3 colors | 2 sticks per color | 8 sticks per color |
| Cheesecloth | 1 square yd | 4 square yd |
| Chloroform | 1 lb | 2 lb |
| Chromatography paper | 1 roll | 2 rolls |
| Cleansing tissue | 1 box | 2 boxes |
| Clinitest tablets (*See* Tes-tape) | | |
| Copper sulfate, anhydrous | 1 lb | 1 lb |
| Cornmeal | 1 lb | 3 lb |
| Cornstarch | 1 lb | 1 lb |
| Cotton | | |
| absorbent | 1 lb | 3 lb |
| nonabsorbent | 1 lb | 4 lb |
| Crayfish | | |
| living | 1 doz | 2 doz |
| preserved | 1 doz | 2 doz |

| Item | 1 Class | 4 Classes |
|---|---|---|
| Crayons, glass-marking | 3 doz | 6 doz |
| Crystal-violet solution | 1 oz | 2 oz |
| *Daphnia*, living | 1 culture | 3 cultures |
| Dextrose, C.P. (glucose) | 5 lb | 5 lb |
| Distilled water | 10 gal | 40 gal |
| Drinking straws | 1 box | 2 boxes |
| *Drosophila* (*See* Fruit flies) | | |
| Earthworms, living | 1 doz | 4 doz |
| Eggs, chicken, fertilized, unincubated | 36 | 144 |
| Elodea (*Anacharis*) | 2 bunches | 8 bunches |
| Eosin | 1 oz | 4 oz |
| Ether | | |
|     ethyl | 1 lb | 2 lb |
|     petroleum | 1 lb | 2 lb |
| Fehling's solution (*See* Benedict's solution) | | |
| Filter paper, 100-ml diameter | 5 pkg | 10 pkg |
| Formalin | 4 pt | 2 gal |
| Frogs, living | 12 | 48 |
| Fruit flies, living | | |
|     mutant (e.g., "ebony") | 1 culture | 1 culture |
|     wild type | 1 culture | 1 culture |
| Fungicide (sodium hypochlorite or commercial bleach) | 1 qt | 1 qt |
| Gauze bandage | 1 box | 3 boxes |
| Glucose (*See* Dextrose) | | |
| Glycerin | 1 lb | 1 lb |
| Graph paper | | |
|     semilogarithmic | 60 sheets | 250 sheets |
|     square coordinate | 600 sheets | 2400 sheets |
| Gravel, small aquarium | 10 lb | 20 lb |
| *Hydra*, living | 1 1/2 doz | 6 doz |
| Hydrochloric acid | 1 lb | 5 lb |
| Hydrogen peroxide | 1 lb | 3 lb |
| Iodine—potassium-iodide solution ($I_2KI$) | 8 oz | 24 oz |
| Lens paper | 4 books | 10 books |
| Limewater | 2 qt | 4 qt |
| Manganese dioxide, powder | 1 lb | 2 lb |
| Markers, felt-tip | 6 | 12 |
| Methylene blue solution | 1 oz | 3 oz |
| Methyl red solution | 2 oz | 4 oz |
| Microorganisms, mixed | 1 culture | 3 cultures |
| Molasses | 1 pt | 1 pt |

| Item | 1 Class | 4 Classes |
|---|---|---|
| Oats, rolled | 1 box | 3 boxes |
| Onion bulbs | 6 | 12 |
| Paper, heavy blotting | 3 sheets | 10 sheets |
| Paper clips | 1 box | 1 box |
| Paper cups, small | 200 | 600 |
| Paper toweling | 12 rolls | 48 rolls |
| Paraffin | 1 lb | 1 lb |
| Paste | 1 jar | 3 jars |
| Pencils, red | 1 doz | 4 doz |
| Peppercorns | 1 oz | 1 oz |
| Peptone | 4 oz | 8 oz |
| Petroleum jelly | 1 jar | 2 jars |
| Phenolphthalein solution | 100 ml | 400 ml |
| pH test paper, wide-range | 1 roll | 2 rolls |
| Pins, "bank" or "florist" | 2 boxes | 3 boxes |
| Pipe cleaners | 4 doz | 16 doz |
| Planarians, living | 24 | 100 |
| Plants, potted (bean, tomato, sunflower, coleus, *Zebrina*, etc.) | 10 | 20 |
| Plastic bags, sandwich-size | 250 | 800 |
| Potassium phosphate, monobasic | 1 lb | 1 lb |
| Potassium sodium tartrate | 1 lb | 1 lb |
| Potatoes, white | 6 | 18 |
| Pot labels, wooden | 100 | 200 |
| Propionic acid | 4 oz | 4 oz |
| Quinine sulfate | 4 oz | 4 oz |
| Rubber bands, assorted | 1 box | 2 boxes |
| Rubber tubing | | |
| 3/16″ inside diameter, to fit 6- or 7-mm glass tubing | 24 ft | 65 ft |
| 1/4″ inside diameter, for Bunsen burner | 18 ft | 30 ft |
| Sand | | |
| coarse | 25 lb | 50 lb |
| fine, washed | 25 lb | 50 lb |
| Seeds | | |
| bean | 1 lb | 2 lb |
| corn, field-type | 1 lb | 2 lb |
| lettuce | 1 pkg | 2 pkg |
| pea | | |
| genetic strain "round" | 1/2 lb | 1 lb |
| genetic strain "wrinkled" | 1/2 lb | 1 lb |
| sunflower | 2 pkg | 4 pkg |
| tobacco | 1 pkg | 4 pkg |

| Item | 1 Class | 4 Classes |
|---|---|---|
| tomato | 2 pkg | 4 pkg |
| vetch | 4 oz | 1 lb |
| Serums, blood-testing, anti-A and anti-B | 1 set | 2 sets |
| Snails, living, small | 12 | 48 |
| Sodium bicarbonate | 1 lb | 1 lb |
| Sodium carbonate | 1 lb | 1 lb |
| Sodium chloride | 1 lb | 5 lb |
| Sodium citrate | 1/2 lb | 1/2 lb |
| Sodium hydroxide | 1 lb | 1 lb |
| Sodium hypochlorite (*See* Fungicide) | | |
| Soil, garden | 1 bu | 4 bu |
| Sow bugs (or pill bugs), living | 60 | 200 |
| Spinach | 1 lb | 4 lb |
| Sponge, synthetic | 3 | 12 |
| Stakes, wooden | 48 | 48 |
| Starch, soluble | 4 oz | 1 lb |
| String, cotton cord | 1 ball | 2 balls |
| Sucrose | 1 lb | 5 lb |
| Tape, pressure-sensitive | | |
| masking | 1 roll | 2 rolls |
| transparent | 1 roll | 2 rolls |
| Tes-tape (or Clinitest tablets) | 1 roll | 2 rolls |
| Toothpicks | | |
| flat | 1 box | 1 box |
| round | 1 box | 1 box |
| Vermiculite | 25 lb | 50 lb |
| Wrapping paper | 1 roll | 1 roll |
| Yeast | | |
| brewer's | 4 oz | 8 oz |
| dried | 3 pkg | 12 pkg |

## EQUIPMENT

| Item | 1 Class | 4 Classes |
|---|---|---|
| Aquariums | 3 | 3 |
| Autoclave (or pressure cooker) | 1 | 1 |
| Balance, 0.1-g sensitivity | 2 | 3 |
| Battery jars, large | 4 | 8 |
| Beads, glass, pea-size | 2 lb | 4 lb |
| Beads, poppit, 2 colors | 360 per color | 360 per color |

| Item | 1 Class | 4 Classes |
|---|---|---|
| Beakers, Griffin low-form: | | |
| 50-ml | 36 | 100 |
| 100-ml | 36 | 36 |
| 250-ml | 36 | 100 |
| 600-ml | 12 | 12 |
| 1000-ml | 10 | 10 |
| Berlese apparatus | 5 | 10 |
| Bottles, dropping, 10-ml | 12 | 12 |
| Bottles, small, with plastic lids | 48 | 48 |
| Bottles, wide-mouth, screw-cap | | |
| 2-oz round | 30 | 120 |
| 4-oz round | 24 | 96 |
| 4-oz square | 30 | 60 |
| 8-oz round | 18 | 64 |
| Brushes, camel-hair | 18 | 24 |
| Brushes, small, water-color type | 12 | 12 |
| Bunsen burners | 6 | 12 |
| Cans, 1-lb coffee type, with plastic lid | 10 | 10 |
| Clamps | | |
| burette | 12 | 24 |
| pinch or spring | 3 | 3 |
| Clothesline, plastic (50-ft lengths) | 6 | 6 |
| Corks | | |
| assorted sizes | 1 pkg | 1 pkg |
| No. 6 size | 1 pkg | 2 pkg |
| Cover slips | 3 oz | 6 oz |
| Culture bottles (glass vials), | | |
| $25 \times 95$ mm | 48 | 172 |
| Culture tubes, screw-cap, | | |
| $20 \times 150$ mm | 36 | 144 |
| Dissecting needles, straight | 60 | 60 |
| Dissecting pans | 10 | 24 |
| Etherizers (funnels and shot glasses) | 6 | 6 |
| File, triangular | 6 | 6 |
| Finger bowls, glass or clear plastic, | | |
| 250-ml (4-in diameter) | 60 | 240 |
| Flasks, Erlenmeyer | | |
| 250-ml | 24 | 36 |
| 500-ml | 6 | 24 |
| Flowerpots | | |
| 4-in diameter | 24 | 60 |
| 6-in diameter | 24 | 60 |
| 6-in diameter (shallow form) | 24 | 144 |
| Flowerpot saucers, to fit 6-in pots | 24 | 144 |

| Item | 1 Class | 4 Classes |
|---|---|---|
| Forceps | | |
|     fine-pointed | 30 | 36 |
|     student-grade | 30 | 36 |
| Funnels, glass, long-stem | 6 | 6 |
| Funnels, glass, 75-mm diameter | 6 | 6 |
| Funnel supports | 6 | 6 |
| Glass covers, 5-in squares | 48 | 144 |
| Glass rods | 1/2 lb | 1/2 lb |
| Glass slides | | |
|     "micro-culture" (with center | | |
|         depression) | 12 | 12 |
|     ordinary microscope | 1/2 gross | 1 gross |
| Glass tubing, 6- to 7-mm diameter | 5 lb | 10 lb |
| Graduated cylinders | | |
|     10-ml | 10 | 24 |
|     25-ml | 10 | 12 |
|     100-ml | 12 | 12 |
|     500-ml | 2 | 2 |
| Hammers (or small mallets) | 3 | 3 |
| Hand lenses | 36 | 48 |
| Hot plate, electric 2-plate | 1 | 1 |
| Incubator, 50-egg capacity | 1 | 3 |
| Inoculating loops | 12 | 24 |
| Jars, glass | | |
|     1-liter | 15 | 60 |
|     4-liter | 6 | 12 |
| Jars, waste, crockery | 6 | 6 |
| Lamps, gooseneck (with 60- to | | |
|     150-w bulbs) | 6 | 12 |
| Lancets, sterile, disposable | 36 | 144 |
| Medicine droppers | 48 | 96 |
| Metersticks | 9 | 9 |
| Microscopes | | |
|     monocular | 15–20 | 15–20 |
|     stereo | 8–12 | 8–12 |
| Mortar and pestle | 6 | 6 |
| Nails, 8-penny | 24 | 36 |
| Petri dishes, Pyrex, 100 × 15 mm | 36 | 144 |
| Pipettes | | |
|     1-ml or 5-ml | 6 | 12 |
|     10-ml | 6 | 12 |
| Razor blades | 12 | 24 |
| Refrigerator, 9 to 11 cubic ft | 1 | 1 |
| Ring stands | 6 | 12 |

| Item | 1 Class | 4 Classes |
|---|---|---|
| Rulers, metric, transparent | 18 | 36 |
| Scalpels | 12 | 24 |
| Scissors | | |
|     dissecting | 12 | 12 |
|     fine-pointed | 12 | 24 |
| Seed flats | 6 | 12 |
| Skeletons, mounted | | |
|     cat | 1 | 1 |
|     frog | 2 | 2 |
|     human | 1 | 1 |
| Slides, prepared | | |
|     hydras, longitudinal sections | 9 | 12 |
|     planarians | | |
|         cross sections | 9 | 12 |
|         whole mounts | 9 | 12 |
|     earthworms, cross sections | 9 | 12 |
|     onion-root tips, longitudinal | | |
|         sections | 9 | 12 |
| Spatulas | | |
|     porcelain | 6 | 6 |
|     stainless-steel, 4-in blade | 6 | 6 |
| Stoppers, rubber | | |
|     No. 5, solid | 12 | 48 |
|     No. 6, solid | 24 | 48 |
|     No. 6, 1-hole | 24 | 96 |
|     No. 6, 2-hole | 12 | 48 |
|     No. 7, 2-hole | 12 | 24 |
| Test tubes | | |
|     $13 \times 100$ mm | 60 | 240 |
|     $16 \times 125$ mm | 120 | 280 |
|     $18 \times 150$ mm | 60 | 144 |
|     $25 \times 200$ mm | 24 | 48 |
| Test-tube holders | 12 | 12 |
| Test-tube racks | 12 | 24 |
| Thermometers, $-10°C$ to $+110°C$ | 18 | 24 |
| Tile, plastic, white | 10 squares | 12 squares |
| Trowels, garden | 6 | 6 |
| Vacuum bottles | 6 | 6 |
| Volumeter | 6 | 6 |
| Watches, with second hands | 10 | 10 |
| Watch glasses, Syracuse form | 24 | 36 |
| Wire baskets, 50-tube capacity | 1 | 4 |

# C

# INDEX TO FORMULATIONS

## SOME SUPPLIERS

The following list consists primarily of suppliers of materials to which reference has been made in the preceding pages. In addition, addresses of some general laboratory suppliers are listed. The list is provided as a service and implies no recommendation by the Biological Sciences Curriculum Study. For the more routine kinds of laboratory equipment, you would do well to deal with local companies if you can find any.

CAMBOSCO SCIENTIFIC CO. Boston, Mass. 02135

CAROLINA BIOLOGICAL SUPPLY CO. Burlington, N.C. 27216 (*See also* Powell Laboratories)

CCM: GENERAL BIOLOGICAL, INC. 8200 S. Hoyne Ave., Chicago, Ill. 60620

CENTRAL SCIENTIFIC CO. 1700 N. Irving Park Rd., Chicago, Ill. 60613

CLINTON MISCO CORP. P. O. Box 1005, Ann Arbor, Mich. 48106

COLUMBIA RECORDS. Educational Department, 799 Seventh Ave., New York, N.Y. 10019

CORONET FILMS. Coronet Bldg., Chicago, Ill. 60601

EALING FILM LOOPS. 2225 Massachusetts Ave., Cambridge, Mass. 02140

ENCYCLOPAEDIA BRITANNICA FILMS, INC. 1150 Wilmette Ave., Wilmette, Ill. 60091

FAUST SCIENTIFIC SUPPLY CO. 2801 Industrial Dr., Madison, Wis. 53713

FILM ASSOCIATES OF CALIFORNIA. 11014 Santa Monica Blvd., Los Angeles, Calif. 90025

FOLKWAYS RECORD & SERVICE CORP. 165 W. 46th St., New York, N.Y. 10036

W. H. FREEMAN AND CO. 660 Market St., San Francisco, Calif. 94104

GENERAL BIOLOGICAL SUPPLY HOUSE, INC. (*See* CCM: General Biological, Inc.)

HARCOURT, BRACE & WORLD. 757 Third Ave., New York, N.Y. 10017

HARLOW, WILLIAM. Syracuse University, Syracuse, N.Y. 13210

HEIDENKAMP NATURE PICTURES. (*See* Ealing Film Loops)

HOUGHTON MIFFLIN CO. Boston, Mass. 02107

INDIANA UNIVERSITY FILMS. Indiana University Audiovisual Center, Bloomington, Ind.

INTERNATIONAL COMMUNICATIONS FILMS, INC. Division of Doubleday and Co., Garden City, N.Y. 11530

INTERNATIONAL FILM BUREAU, INC. 332 S. Michigan Ave., Chicago, Ill. 60604

IOWA STATE UNIVERSITY. (*See* Ealing Film Loops)

LIFE FILMSTRIPS. Time & Life Bldg., 9 Rockefeller Plaza, New York, N.Y. 10020

MACALESTER SCIENTIFIC CORP. Waltham, Mass. 02154

McGRAW-HILL PUBLISHING CO. Text-Film Division, 327 West 41st St., New York, N.Y. 10036

NASCO. Fort Atkinson, Wis. 53538

NATIONAL AERONAUTICS & SPACE AGENCY. Washington, D.C. 20025

NATIONAL FILM BOARD OF CANADA. Canada House, 680 Fifth Ave., New York, N.Y. 10019

A. J. NYSTROM AND CO. 3333 Elston Ave , Chicago, Ill. 60618

OXFORD BIOLOGICAL FILMS. (*See* Ealing Film Loops)

POPULAR SCIENCE PUBLISHING Co. Audiovisual Division, 355 Lexington Ave., New York, N.Y. 10017

POWELL LABORATORIES (CAROLINA BIOLOGICAL). Gladstone, Ore. 97027

RAND MCNALLY & Co., P. O. Box 7600, Chicago, Ill. 60680

SARGENT-WELCH SCIENTIFIC Co. 7300 N. Linder Ave., Skokie, Ill. 60076

SCHETTLE BIOLOGICALS. P. O. Box 184, Stillwater, Minn. 55082

SHELL OIL Co. 149–07 Northern Blvd., Flushing, N.Y. 11354 – *also:* 430 Peninsular Ave., San Mateo, Calif. 94401

SOCIETY FOR VISUAL EDUCATION, INC. 1345 W. Diversey Pkwy., Chicago, Ill. 60614

STANSI SCIENTIFIC DIVISION. Fisher Scientific Co., 1231 North Honore St., Chicago, Ill. 60622

THORNE FILMS, INC. 1229 University Ave., Boulder, Colo. 80302

UNITED WORLD FILMS, INC. 1445 Park Ave., New York, N.Y. 10029

UNIVERSITY OF CALIFORNIA. Department of Visual Education, Berkeley, Calif. 94720

WALT DISNEY NATURE FILMS. (*See* Ealing Film Loops)

WARD'S NATURAL SCIENCES ESTABLISHMENT. P. O. Box 1712, Rochester, N.Y. 14603 – *also:* P. O. Box 1749, Monterey, Calif. 93940

WELCH SCIENTIFIC Co. (*See* Sargent-Welch Scientific Co.)

**DATE DUE**

| | | | |
|---|---|---|---|
| OCT 2 | NOV 3 | | |
| NOV 2 | DEC 16 '85 | | |
| NOV 27 | MAY 8 86 | | |
| DEC 13 | MAY 8 '86 | | |
| FEB 2 | MAY 20 '87 | | |
| OCT 20 | FEB 07 1998 | | |
| OCT 12 | | | |
| DEC 15 | | | |
| NOV 9 | | | |
| OCT 22 | | | |
| | | | |
| | | | |

IGHSMITH 45-227